BASIC READINGS IN NEUROPSYCHOLOGY

UNDER THE EDITORSHIP

OF GARDNER MURPHY

BASIC READINGS IN
NEUROPSYCHOLOGY

EDITED BY **ROBERT L. ISAACSON,**

DEPARTMENT OF PSYCHOLOGY,

THE UNIVERSITY OF MICHIGAN

HARPER & ROW, PUBLISHERS

NEW YORK, EVANSTON, AND LONDON

C-2

LIBRARY OF CONGRESS CATALOG CARD NUMBER: 64–10949

❧ CONTENTS

v

✻ PREFACE

THIS COLLECTION OF PAPERS includes many articles that represent a significant segment of the classic literature of neuropsychology. The word *neuropsychology* is used to describe the relationship between behavior and the activities of the nervous system, and it is found in ever-increasing frequency in current literature in the field of physiological psychology. Of course, not all psychologists, nor all physiological psychologists, are primarily interested in the interaction between the nervous system and behavior, but since the work of Lashley, neuropsychology has become a major branch of physiological psychology. Today there is an increase both in the number of publications in the area of neuropsychology and in the number of psychologists on research teams containing neuroanatomists, neurosurgeons, neurologists, biochemists, and other professional students of neural *and* behavioral phenomena.

The student beginning his study of neuropsychology is confronted with a vast number of original articles and a not inconsiderable number of review articles. Too often, I believe, the student fails to return to the original reports and relies on discussions of them appearing in reviews. Many of the early articles that represent milestones in psycho-physiological research go unread. These original contributions are important for more than historical reasons; the student should learn why classics are classics through critical study and evaluation. Often, however, this is not easy for the student to accomplish, for even where library facilities are excellent, the articles may not be available in numbers sufficient for assignment as readings to groups of students. Unfortunately, many universities do not have complete sets of journals, which makes the problem more acute. By making these original articles more readily available to the student, this volume can serve as a supplement to library facilities.

One can see the profound and continuing effects of research

conducted in the 1930s and 1940s upon present research by examining the references in recent experimental reports. I have attempted to bring together certain studies which seem to be most often cited as turning points in the study of the relation between neural activity and behavior.

Of course, almost everyone interested in neuropsychology has his own approach to the field, and the selections found in this book represent my own areas of greatest interest. Many readers may feel that many important contributions were overlooked, but not all the classic papers could be included in one book and many difficult decisions had to be made among well-known papers. I attempted to choose the ones that would be most useful to the beginning student.

Although each of these papers has received considerable recognition through subsequent research, a few additional comments may be in order.

At the beginning of the collection there are three papers dealing with the neural basis of sensory processes. First is a paper by Hamilton K. Hartline on his analysis of the activity found in single fibers of the vertebrate visual system. The activity in single units of the nervous system had been recorded earlier, but the extension of recordings to fibers in the vertebrate eye represented a distinct advance. Next there is a more recent contribution by David H. Hubel and Torsten N. Wiesel describing research on the "receptive fields" in the visual system. Even though the study of receptor fields using the techniques of Hubel and Wiesel is of recent vintage, this research has been of great significance for undestanding the sensory mechanisms. Third in this group is a paper by Irving T. Diamond and W. D. Neff. Before the publication of this paper, the auditory projection areas presented a strange problem because ablation of the auditory areas of neocortex failed to produce the dramatic effects that might have been expected: auditory discriminations of frequency and loudness seemed as efficient as before the operation. In the paper reprinted in this collection, Diamond and Neff reported the loss of complex pattern discrimination which follows ablation of the auditory areas of neocortex.

Neural correlates of emotion have long been investigated, but one of the greatest single theoretical stimulants for research appeared in a paper by James W. Papez in 1937. He proposed a circuit of emotionality that included those structures known today as the limbic system or rhinencephalon. This book includes both this theoretical paper and Paul D. MacLean's provocative work on the limbic system, which emphasizes its relation to the autonomic nervous system.

The next group of papers deals with effects of lesions of the forebrain. The history of research in these areas is interesting in itself, although an extended discussion of it is inappropriate here. The works of Philip Bard and Vernon B. Mountcastle and of Heinrich Klüver and Paul C. Bucy were dramatic stimulants to work involving both the neocortical mantle and the subcortical structures of the brain. The extensive lesions of the temporal lobes made by Klüver and Bucy produced what may be the best-known composite of symptoms in the experimental study of the relations between behavior and neural mechanisms, the Klüver-Bucy Syndrome.

A large body of subsequent research has attempted to fractionate the temporal lobe syndrome. Largely, the purpose has been to associate one or more of the symptoms of the Klüver-Bucy Syndrome with damage to a particular area destroyed in the more complete temporal lobe lesion. One of the favorite targets for such investigations has been the amygdaloid nucleus, which lies deep in the temporal lobes. The contribution of Leon H. Schreiner and Arthur Kling, the next study in this collection, was a definitive study of effects of amygdalectomy on emotional behavior.

Karl H. Pribram and Lawrence Kruger made an analysis of the organization of the anatomical structures that constitute the limbic system. On the basis of several kinds of evidence three systems of phyletically old cortex were delineated. Their divisions of what had been called the "olfactory brain" has received wide acceptance and provides a firm ground for future research.

Appearing next is the paper by Giuseppe Moruzzi and Horace W. Magoun in which they demonstrated the function of the reticular formation of the brain stem in modifying the electrical activity of the neocortex. Besides providing important data about the physiological activities of the reticular formation, this report has prompted many further investigations and provided support for theories of physiological function, behavior, and mental experiences. Almost every recent article, whether experimental or theoretical, that discusses the functions of the brain makes note of the singular contribution of these two investigators.

Albert W. Hetherington and S. W. Ranson's paper was one of the first studies to report consistent effects of hypothalamic lesions on food intake. Before their contribution, the results of lesions in the hypothalamus had not been reproducible. Following their lead, later researchers have been able to pinpoint the anatomical locus of hyperphagia and approach a more complete understanding of the behavioral effects produced by the lesions.

Many readers will be acquainted with the article by Eliot Stellar which originally appeared in 1954. This is one of the most commonly cited articles in the current literature and represents an integrative summary of the findings concerning the role of the hypothalamus in motivated behavior.

Fourteen years after the work by Hetherington and Ranson, James Olds and Peter M. Milner launched an entirely new realm of physiological and behavorial research through electrical stimulation of the septal area of the rat forebrain. Their remarkable finding was that the animals behaved as though the stimulation were pleasurable. Whether or not these effects produced by electrical stimulation can be best understood in terms of hedonic quality is not known, but the results reported by Olds and Milner have often been replicated in many regions of the brain by many investigators.

The next two papers report somewhat similar attempts to understand the processes underlying the formation of "temporary connections" in the brain. Frank Morrell and Herbert H. Jasper describe the changes in the electrical activities of the brain of unanesthetized monkeys as conditioning is established to a variety of stimuli. In the paper by E. Roy John and Keith F. Killam the reader will discover how these investigators attempted to localize the formation of temporary connections by tracing over various stages of conditioning the electrical responses in many brain areas produced by a flickering light.

The paper by Roger W. Sperry is widely known, and psychologists and others who have read this paper often become intense advocates of his position. Sperry proposes that we can understand mental activities and behavior only if we view them in terms of their contribution to preparations for motor adjustments to the environment. In addition, the article provides a perspective for the many different divergent types of approaches used by investigators interested in the nervous system and behavior.

At this point, something should be said about the omission of the works of two scientists: Karl S. Lashley and Donald O. Hebb. The many works of Lashley have long been recognized as representing important contributions to our knowledge of the relationship between the nervous system and behavior. Fortunately a selection of his most important contributions has recently been published.[1] This makes papers readily available to students, and inclusion of them in this volume is therefore unnecessary.

There is little doubt that Hebb has provided a most provocative approach to understanding the neural mechanisms underlying behavior. His book, *The Organization of Behavior*,[2] is a landmark in theoretical accounts of neural organization. His basic proposals have been modified in subsequent publications,[3] but I believe that his most significant contribution was made in *The Organization of Behavior*, and it should be read before the later modifications. In addition, most of Hebb's contributions are generally available through modern library facilities.

I would like to express my appreciation to all of the authors in this collection who were kind enough to allow me to reprint their papers in this volume. I would also like to express gratitude to the current editors of the journals in which these articles were published and various scientific societies, associations, and publishers that have granted permission to reprint the articles.

Finally, I would like formally to acknowledge the help of Mrs. Ruth Frankena, administrative assistant in the Department of Psychology of the University of Michigan, who was indispensible in organizing the papers and illustrations, and in keeping track of all the correspondence involved in this undertaking. My thanks to her for this wonderful help.

ROBERT L. ISAACSON

Ann Arbor, Michigan
October, 1963

---

[1] Beach, F. A., Hebb, D. O., Morgan, C. T., & Nissen, H. W. (eds.), *The Neuropsychology of Lashley, Selected Papers of K. S. Lashley,* New York, McGraw-Hill, 1960.

[2] Hebb, D. O., *The Organization of Behavior,* New York, John Wiley, 1949.

[3] For example: Hebb, D. O., Drives and the C.N.S. (conceptual nervous system). *Psychol. Rev.,* 1955, **62**, 243-254; Hebb, D. O., *A Textbook of Psychology,* Philadelphia, W. B. Saunders, 1958; and see also Milner, P. M., The Cell assembly: Mark II. *Psychol. Rev.,* 1957, **64**, 242-252.

BASIC READINGS IN NEUROPSYCHOLOGY

THE RESPONSE OF SINGLE OPTIC NERVE FIBERS OF THE VERTEBRATE EYE TO ILLUMINATION OF THE RETINA ❖ *H. K. Hartline*

IN A SERIES OF THREE PAPERS Adrian and Matthews (1927, 1928) presented a study of the discharge of impulses in the optic nerve of the eel's eye, and so opened a new approach to problems of visual physiology. In those papers the simultaneous activity of large numbers of optic nerve fibers was recorded. The possibility of extending that work to an analysis of the activity in single optic nerve fibers was suggested by the subsequent investigation of Hartline and Graham (1932) on the optic nerve fibers of a primitive arthropod eye (*Limulus*). The present paper describes the discharge of impulses in single optic nerve fibers of the cold-blooded vertebrate eye, in response to illumination of the retina.

METHOD. The usual methods for obtaining action potentials from only one fiber in a nerve trunk have not succeeded when applied to the vertebrate optic nerve. It is therefore necessary

REPRINTED FROM *The American Journal of Physiology*, **121**:400-415. COPYRIGHT © 1938 BY THE AMERICAN PHYSIOLOGICAL SOCIETY.

1

to utilize the intra-ocular portion of the optic nerve fibers, by exposing the fundus of the eye and dissecting small bundles of fibers from the anterior (*vitreous*) surface of the retina, where they converge to the head of the optic nerve.

From a freshly pithed animal [in most of these experiments large bullfrogs (*Rana catesbiana*) were used] an eye is excised, pinned fundus down in a moist chamber, and its anterior half (cornea, lens, choroid body) removed. A wide V-shaped cut extending almost to the nerve head gives access to the fundus and permits the vitreous humor to be drained away. It is then possible to dissect free small bundles of nerve fibers for a length of 1–2 mm., and these may be further dissected until only one fiber remains active. A bundle is severed where it enters the nerve head and the cut end lifted up onto one of the electrode wicks; the second electrode is diffuse, touching the surface of the retina. The action potentials from such bundles of nerve fibers are amplified and recorded by means of an oscillograph. The preparation is mounted in a light-tight, electrically shielded box, in the hollow walls of which water at constant temperature (*ca.* 20°C.) is circulated.

Prepared in this manner the retinas of most cold-blooded vertebrate eyes survive for 4–8 hours, as evidenced both by the normal type of retinal action potentials which can be obtained from them (*cf.* Chaffee, Bovie & Hampson, 1923) and by the normal responses and lack of spontaneous activity in nerve fiber bundles freshly dissected from the retina. Fine bundles themselves, after having been lifted away from the retina, rarely remain conducting for more than an hour or two, and usually fail to show action potentials in a much shorter time. Attempts to obtain single fibers are successful in only a very small percentage of trials.

Light from a concentrated tungsten filament lamp is focussed by a condensing lens 12 mm. in diameter upon an objective lens, which in turn forms an image (⅛ size) of the illuminated condensing lens upon the retina. A 45° prism close to the objective lens reflects the light downward onto the retina; it can be rotated so as to project the rays at approximately normal incidence onto that portion of the retina from which the nerve fibers in any particular bundle come. At the condensing lens can be placed a suitable diaphragm to limit the size and shape of the illuminated area; this diaphragm is carried on crossed micrometers controlling its position to within 0.01 mm., and its image is accurately focussed on the retina by micrometer movements carrying the preparation itself. The intensity of illumination upon the retina can be reduced by known amounts with Wratten Neutral Tint filters; the full intensity (no filters in the beam) is $2 \cdot 10^4$ meter candles.

RESULTS. The discharge of impulses in any moderately large bundle of intra-ocular optic nerve fibers of the vertebrate eye is similar to that previously described for the whole optic nerve. Beginning several hundredths of a second after the light is turned on, there is a strong, brief outburst of impulses. Impulses continue to be discharged at a low rate as long as light continues to shine, and when it is turned off there is a renewed vigorous outburst which subsides gradually. Such responses were initially described by Adrian and Matthews (1927) in the eel's optic nerve and subsequently recorded by Granit (1933) from the mammalian optic nerve. It is not until the bundles have been dissected down until only one, or at most only a few, fibers remain active that a new and striking property of the vertebrate optic response is revealed. For such experiments show conclusively that not all of the optic nerve fibers give the same kind of response to light. This diversity of response among fibers from closely adjacent regions of the same retina is extreme and unmistakable; it does not depend upon local conditions of stimulation or adaptation, but appears to be an inherent property of the individual ganglion cells themselves.

Types of response. In Figure 1 are records of the action potentials in single optic nerve fibers of the frog's retina. Figure 1A shows a response in which the initial burst of impulses, at high frequency, is followed by a steady discharge at much lower frequency which lasts throughout the duration of illumination. When the light is turned off this discharge stops. Such a response is similar to that from a simple photoreceptor, observed in *Limulus* optic nerve fibers, even to the short pause following the initial burst. But while *Limulus* optic nerve fibers invariably show this type of response, in the frog's retina it is obtained in less than 20 per cent of the fibers. The other fibers show strikingly different types of response. At least 50 per cent respond (Fig. 1B) with a short burst of impulses at high frequency when the light is turned on, but show no impulses as long as it continues to shine steadily; when the light is turned off there is another

Fig. 1. Oscillographic records of the action potentials in three single intra-ocular optic nerve fibers of the frog's eye, showing three characteristic response types. *A.* Response to illumination of the retina consisting of an initial burst of impulses, followed by a maintained discharge lasting throughout illumination. There is no response to cessation of illumination in this fiber (the "off" response in this record is partly due to retinal potential, partly to another fiber which discharged several small impulses). See also Fig. 6. *B.* Response only to onset and cessation of light. See also Fig. 2, Fig. 5A and C. *C.* Response only to cessation of illumination. See also Fig. 5B, D and E. In this and subsequent records, the time is marked in ⅕ sec., and the signal marking the period of illumination fills the white line immediately above the time marker.

brief outburst of impulses. Such responses constitute the most prominent feature of the vertebrate optic response—bursts of impulses occurring only when the conditions of illumination on the retina are changed abruptly. In a third type of response, occurring in about 30 per cent of the fibers, no impulses appear at all during illumination, but there is a vigorous discharge of impulses when the light is turned off (Fig. 1C). This discharge may last many seconds, and usually subsides gradually. It is undoubtedly responsible for most of the "off" response obtained from the whole optic nerve.

Most of the optic nerve fibers in the vertebrate eye give responses similar to one or another of the above described types. These categories, however, are not absolutely rigid, and it would be a mistake to ignore the occasional fiber whose response is intermediate in character. Thus it is not infrequently found that a fiber whose response is of the first type has a maintained level of discharge of a low and irregular frequency, which tends to adapt out after several seconds. No clear-cut cases have been found in which a fiber giving an initial burst followed by a maintained discharge has shown an "off" response; the doubtful cases which have been recorded could have been due to a second fiber, as is the case in Figure 1A (see Fig. 6A for a clear-cut case, where there is no additional fiber giving an "off" effect). Fibers have been found, however, whose response lacks the initial burst; in these rare cases the discharge builds up slowly (in 2–3 secs.) to a steady level of *ca.* 20–30 per second. When the light is turned off these fibers do show an "off" effect—a distinct increase in frequency for several tenths of a second before the discharge subsides. It is true that fibers which respond predominantly to a change in intensity with "on" and "off" bursts may occasionally show very irregularly scattered impulses or bursts of two or three impulses every few seconds during steady illumination. This, however, is quite different from the regular discharge of Figure 1A, and may be regarded as an atypical, intermediate variety of response. Furthermore, fibers showing predominantly an "off" response are occasionally found in which a few scattered impulses "escape" during prolonged illumination.

From these observations it follows that the responses of the entire optic nerve are complex, containing different contributions from different fibers. An analysis of the optic response must therefore take up the properties of the different types of single fiber response separately.

Effect of intensity. Chief among the factors governing the response in any single fiber is the intensity of illumination with which the retina is stimulated. In Figure 2 is shown a series of records of the responses to lights of different intensity of a single fiber of the "on-off" response type. With higher intensities of light the responses show shorter latent periods, higher maximum frequencies of discharge and greater numbers of impulses in both the "on" and the "off" bursts. This holds from threshold to intensities 4–5 logarithmic units above it. In Figure 3 are plotted, on the left, the reciprocals of the latent periods and, on the right, the frequencies of the discharges (measured from the first six impulses) for both the "on" and the "off" bursts in this same fiber. In this fiber the threshold intensity was the same for both the "on" and the "off" bursts; frequently, however, one or the other of the bursts may have a somewhat lower threshold (usually within 1 logarithmic unit). It is to be noted that the curves rise abruptly from threshold—frequently the weakest response obtainable has a fairly large number of impulses, at a fairly high

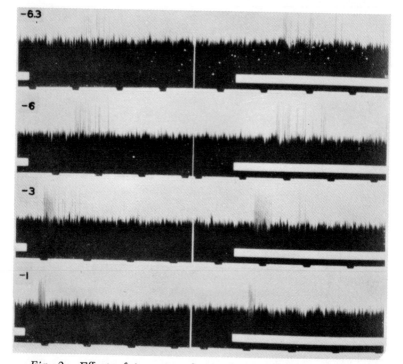

Fig. 2. Effect of intensity of retinal illumination upon the discharge of impulses in a single optic nerve fiber of the frog's eye. Logarithm of the intensity indicated on each record (unit intensity $= 2 \cdot 10^4$ meter candles, in this and subsequent figures). Diameter of the spot of light $= 0.10$ mm. Portions of the records, representing 2–3 secs. in each case, have been removed. They contained no impulses, except for the −6 record, which showed four impulses scattered over 2.5 secs.

frequency. While the threshold is sharp, it is not always reliable, and may fluctuate in spite of carefully controlled conditions.

The experiment of Figure 2 and Figure 3 shows the very considerable range over which intensity is effective in speeding up the discharge. This might be expected in view of the wide range which is covered by single visual sense cells in the *Limulus* eye (Hartline & Graham, 1932). This experiment also shows the characteristic effect of very high intensity in reducing the number of impulses and often the frequency of discharge in the bursts. This is especially pronounced for the "off" burst, which may be entirely missing at the highest intensities available.

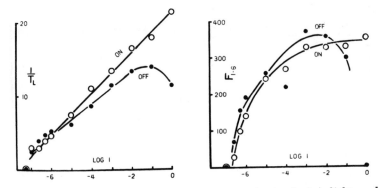

Fig. 3. The relation between intensity of stimulating light and response in a single optic nerve fiber of the frog's eye. Data from experiment of Fig. 2. On left the ordinates give reciprocal latent period (T_L, secs.); circles give values for "on" burst, dots for "off" burst. On right, ordinates give frequency (impulses per sec.) for the first six impulses of the bursts; circles give values for "on" burst, dots for "off" burst. Abscissae, in both graphs, give the logarithms (base 10) of the stimulating intensity. When no response appears, $1/T_L$ is assigned a value of zero; if fewer than 6 impulses are discharged, F_{1-6} is given a value of zero.

Similar effects of intensity can be shown for the other types of response. In Figure 4A are plotted the frequencies of various parts of the discharge in a fiber giving an initial burst followed by a maintained discharge. The initial frequency (first three impulses) and maximum frequency (usually between the fifth and eighth impulses) of the initial burst are given, together with the final level of frequency attained after four seconds of steady illumination. This graph may be compared with a similar plot for the *Limulus* single optic nerve fiber (Hartline & Graham, 1932, Fig. 6). At low intensities, near threshold, the maintained discharge usually adapts out completely after a second or two, and often only the initial burst can be obtained.

The degree of activity in a fiber giving only an "off" response is also dependent upon the intensity of the light. In Figure 4B are plotted the initial frequencies of the discharge from such a fiber, in response to cessation of lights of different intensities. The sharp threshold and the diminished values at high intensities are similar to the corresponding plot of the "off" burst of Figure 3. This particular fiber gave a rather short, sharply de-

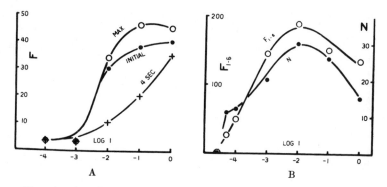

Fig. 4. A. The relation between the logarithm of intensity of retinal illumination (abscissae) and frequency of response (ordinates) in a single optic nerve fiber of the frog's eye. This fiber gave a response consisting of an initial burst followed by a discharge which was maintained throughout illumination. Dots and circles give, respectively, initial and maximum frequencies (three impulses) of initial burst; crosses give the frequency attained after 4 secs. of steady illumination. *B.* The relation between intensity and response of a single optic nerve fiber in the frog's eye. This fiber gave a response only upon cessation of illumination. Abscissae give the logarithms of the intensity of light. Ordinates (F_{1-6}, on the left) for the circles give the frequency (impulses per sec.) for the first six impulses; ordinates (N, on the right) for the dots give the total number of impulses in the burst.

fined burst not unlike the "off" response in a typical "on-off" fiber. This enabled a reliable count to be made of the total numbers of impulses in the bursts, also plotted in Figure 4B. Usually, however, as has been said, the discharge in a fiber giving only an "off" response is prolonged, and dies down very gradually. (Compare Fig. 1B with C; Fig. 5A and C with B, D and E.) The higher the intensity the longer does the discharge last; at very high intensities the initial part of it may be reduced to a few impulses, but after several seconds it is gradually resumed, and may persist for many minutes at a frequency which may be as high as twenty or thirty impulses per second. Several instances have been observed where such a discharge broke up into rhythmic bursts, coming at about 3–5 per second.

Change in intensity. The amount of change in intensity also affects the magnitude of the responses. Fibers which discharge a brief burst of impulses in response to the onset and cessation of illumination also respond to a sudden increase or decrease in its intensity (Fig. 5A); the bursts, however, have fewer impulses at a lower frequency. Likewise the "off" fibers will respond, though less strongly, if the illumination is partially reduced (Fig. 5B) but not if it is increased in intensity. The frequency of the maintained discharge in those fibers which show such a response is of course determined only by the level of the steady illumination—an increase or decrease in intensity results in a corresponding rise or fall in frequency (Fig. 7C).

Light and dark adaptation. A given intensity of light is effectively weaker in the light-adapted retina than after dark adaptation. As dark adaptation proceeds the response to a given intensity increases, and correspondingly the threshold falls, rapidly at first and then more gradually. After one-half hour in the dark a fiber may respond to light 1/100–1/1000 the intensity of that necessary to elicit a response in the light-adapted condition. The essential character of the response in any given fiber, however, is unchanged by adaptation. Reliable quantitative measurements of the effect of adaptation in these experiments are difficult to obtain, owing to the comparatively short time fibers stay alive in a dissected bundle.

Duration of exposure. The strength of an "off" response at a given intensity depends on the length of time the preceding light has been allowed to shine. It is entirely absent following short flashes, and in general is stronger the longer the exposure. This is true for the fibers giving both "on" and "off" bursts (Fig. 5C) as well as for fibers giving only "off" responses (Fig. 5D). Similarly the "on" burst will be absent or weak unless there has been a sufficiently long period of darkness preceding (Fig. 7B). The exact time requirements for the development of the "on" and "off" bursts vary widely with different fibers.

Inhibition of the "off" response. The presence, in the vertebrate eye, of a fair percentage of fibers responding only when the light is turned off or reduced in intensity is one of the somewhat surprising findings of the present study. Although no impulses appear in such fibers during illumination, it is to be emphasized that the "off" discharge depends upon the preceding period of illumination for its excitation. The effect of this excitation does not appear until after the stimulating agent has been re-

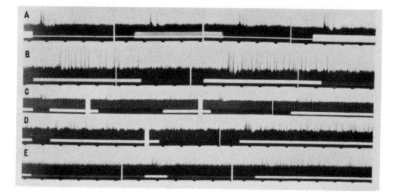

Fig. 5. Records of the impulse discharge in single optic nerve fibers of vertebrate eyes. Record B is from an alligator, the rest are from frogs. Recording as in Fig. 1. *A.* Response to a partial reduction and to an increase in intensity of an "on-off" fiber. Left to right: Onset of light (log I = −2.0); intensity reduced by 0.5 log unit; intensity increased to original value; light turned off. *B.* Response to partial reduction in intensity in a fiber giving only "off" responses. Left to right: light of an intensity log I = −2.0 reduced in intensity by 0.7 log unit; (a length of record equivalent to ½ sec., showing a gradually decreasing discharge, has been removed) light increased to original intensity; (a length of record equivalent to 1 sec., showing no impulses, has been removed) light turned off; (a length of record equivalent to 1 sec., showing a steadily decreasing discharge, has been removed) light turned on again. *C.* (Time scale same as in the other records.) Effect of exposure in producing an "off" burst in an "on-off" fiber. Left to right: exposures, to a constant intensity, of 0.18 sec., 0.70 sec., 3.0 secs. Exposures made successively within about 10 secs. of each other, hence the "on" bursts in last two records are somewhat weaker than in first record, taken in the completely dark-adapted condition. *D.* Same as C for a fiber giving only an "off" response. Left to right: exposure to a constant intensity of 0.20 sec. and of 2.2 secs. *E.* Inhibition of "off" discharge by re-illumination. (See also B of this figure.) After an interruption of 0.23 sec. light is turned on again (middle section of record); full "off" response shown in last section of record.

moved. Indeed, if the retina be re-illuminated before an "off" response has subsided, the discharge is abruptly suppressed. This may be seen in Figure 5E, by comparing the effect of the brief interruption of the illumination with the fully developed "off" response following permanent cessation of the light. A very brief interruption (shorter than the latent period of the "off" response) will still give rise to a burst of impulses, but one which is very short and with considerably reduced impulse frequency. The prolonged "off" discharge following intense and prolonged illumination can always be stopped by re-illumination, even at considerably lower intensity. Following such a period of low illumination the discharge re-appears, augmented by the "off" response caused by cessation of the weak light.

This inhibitory action of light on the "off" discharge is one of the most striking features of the vertebrate optic response. Most of its effects which have been noted here have already been described in responses from the whole optic nerve (Granit & Therman, 1935; Granit & Riddell, 1934). The present results clarify the analysis considerably, by showing the roles played by different fibers. Thus the latency of the suppression of the "off" discharge is usually very short—shorter than the latency of the "on" bursts in other fibers, especially under the conditions of light adaptation which necessarily exist. Hence in bundles containing many active fibers a brief pause occurs, shortly following re-illumination, during which no impulses are discharged (Fig. 7B). This interval between the time when the activity in the "off" response fibers has been suppressed and the moment of appearance of the "on" bursts in other fibers probably corresponds to the "A" wave of the retinal action potential. As shown by Granit and Therman (1935), the principal effect of the "A" wave is to remove what "off" effect may be present; it is large when there is still a strong discharge in the "off" response fibers. When the discharge has subsided in most of these fibers, after dark adaptation, and the "on" bursts in other fibers are stronger and have a shorter latency, the "A" wave is correspondingly small.

Stability of Response Types. a. *Conditions of stimulation.* It is to be seen from the preceding sections that the various types of response which are obtained in different fibers are characteristic of the particular fibers in question, rather than being due to the conditions of stimulation. Thus fibers giving "on" and "off" bursts, or only "off" responses, do so over the entire range of intensities to which they respond; and fibers in which a discharge is maintained during steady illumination show this response for all intensities except near threshold. Likewise during light and dark adaptation of the eye, the type of response in any given fiber does not change. Frogs kept in bright sunlight for as long as 4–6 hours show no essential differences in the types of responses from those which have been kept in complete darkness for 48 hours, have had their eyes removed and prepared in red light, and the nerve bundles rapidly dissected in the weakest possible white light.

b. *External factors.* In order to test the possible influence of some of the more obvious external factors which might affect the retina, the following experiments were done. While not extensive, they do indicate a considerable stability in the essential features of the various response types. *Asphyxia:* if hydrogen is passed through the moist chamber, responses quickly become feeble and soon fail; they return to their former strength if oxygen is promptly readmitted. But at no time do they change their essential character during asphyxia. *pH and CO_2:* changing the pH of the Ringer's solution between 6.8 and 8.5 (phosphate buffers) with which the retina was then bathed for a few minutes produced no very apparent change in the responses, in one experiment. Two per cent CO_2 mixed with the air passed into the moist chamber causes reversible failure, with no change in the character of the responses. *Ion unbalance:* bathing the retina for a few minutes with Ringer's solution containing no calcium brings about a great increase in spontaneous activity, and tends to prolong the bursts of both the "on-off" and "off" types, with possibly some tendency to show "escape" of scattered impulses during illumination. Ringer's solution containing no potassium, on the other hand, abolishes even that spontaneous activity which may be present normally, and reduces the number of impulses in the bursts caused by change in illumination. In fibers which normally show a maintained discharge the response is not abolished, although its frequency may be reduced. These changes with unbalanced Ringer's solution are all reversible. *Temperature:* between 18° and 24°C. there is a marked speeding up of the responses with higher temperature, but there is no essential change in their character. *Season:* over a period of three years these experiments have shown no differences that could be correlated with the season of the year, or whether the animals were freshly caught or had been kept in the laboratory.

Thus external agents which definitely affect the degree of response do not, however, change its essential character. That seems to be a fixed attribute of each particular ganglion cell.

Responses in other vertebrates. Responses in optic nerve fibers have been recorded in a variety of cold-blooded vertebrates other than the frog. These experiments include one shark, one *Necturus,* a number of turtles and alligators, one iguana and several varieties of snakes. While not extensive, they show unmistakably the same general result that is found in the experiments on frogs. In the eyes of all these animals there are fibers which maintain a discharge as long as the retina is illuminated (or at least for the first several minutes), other fibers which give bursts of impulses only in response to changing the intensity of light, and still others which respond only when the illumination is reduced. Minor differences have, however, been found, and a more exhaustive comparative study might even reveal significant variation in optic function among different vertebrates. Thus in the experiment on *Necturus* the maintained discharge disappeared completely after a half minute exposure to light, and the "off" responses were feeble and required at least ten or more seconds' exposure before they could be elicited. And in both the turtle and alligator eyes fibers are not infrequently found giving only a brief burst when light is turned on, with neither maintained discharge nor "off" response. On the other hand, where one might expect to find striking differences, as in the pure cone retina of the snake, neither the actual types of response nor the relative frequency with which they were obtained differed notably from those in the mixed, though predominantly rod retina of the frog. (Only four satisfactory experiments have been done on the snake eye, since it is a difficult preparation.)

Spatial effects. No description of the optic responses in single fibers would be complete without a description of the region of the retina which must be illuminated in order to obtain a response in any given fiber. This region will be termed the receptive field of the fiber. The location of the receptive field of a given fiber is fixed; its extent, however, depends upon the intensity and size of the spot of light used to explore it, and upon the condition of adaptation; these factors must therefore be specified in describing it. For moderate intensities (less than *ca.* 4 logarithmic units above threshold) and small spots (of the order of 0.1 mm.) the receptive fields of most of the fibers of the frog's retina are roughly circular, with a diameter of the order of 1 mm. in the dark-adapted condition. Even at threshold a small spot of light 0.05 mm. in diameter will usually elicit a response in most fibers anywhere within an area of *ca.* 0.5 mm. diameter. At higher intensities the size of this region from which a response can be

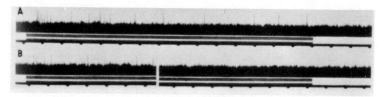

Fig. 6. Records of the impulse discharge in a single optic nerve fiber of the frog's eye, showing stronger response upon illumination in center of receptive field of the fiber than that obtained near margin. A. Spot of light (log I = −2.0) 0.05 mm. in diameter carefully centered on most sensitive portion of the retina for this fiber. B. Spot placed 0.22 mm. from this position (a portion of this record corresponding to 0.66 sec., and containing one impulse 0.45 sec. from the last one in the record, has been removed). Responses to this spot could be obtained anywhere within a radius of *ca.* 0.4 mm. of the position giving record A; the discharge was maintained throughout the entire period of illumination, however, only for positions very close to the central one (within *ca.* 0.05 mm.).

obtained is larger, but the strongest response is always obtained from the central portion of the receptive field; from the margins the response is usually of the threshold type (Fig. 6). Thus the results of illumination of different points within a restricted region of the retina converge upon a given ganglion cell, and cause responses in its axone. This convergence extends over greater distances the stronger the stimulus; and for a given intensity the effects are strongest in the center of the region of convergence. Of particular importance to the present discussion is that, no matter what part of the receptive field is stimulated, the response in any given fiber is always essentially of the same type. This holds true for all types of response, and applies to stimulation anywhere within the receptive field. A few apparent exceptions have been observed, in which the type of response was different for different positions on the retina of the stimulating spot of light. In those cases where opportunity permitted a closer investigation, however, they proved to be either anomalous effects near threshold, or else due to two active fibers whose action potentials were so nearly similar as to be confused.[1] If true exceptions do exist, they must be quite rare; nevertheless they would

[1] Such confusion does not arise very often, and when it does there is usually adequate opportunity to recognize the impulses due to separate fibers when the bundle begins to die, since it is very unlikely that different fibers will fail to conduct at the same time and show the same changes in the form and magnitude of their action potentials.

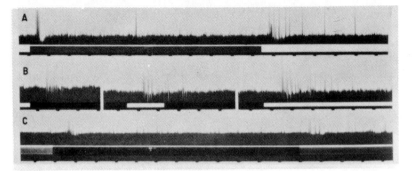

Fig. 7. Records of the discharge of impulses in bundles of optic nerve fibers of vertebrate eyes, each showing different types of responses in different fibers from the same region of the retina. *A.* Bundle from turtle's eye, showing one fiber giving "on" and "off" bursts (large impulses); another discharging impulses throughout whole period of illumination (small impulses); and a third giving only a brief "off" response (medium-sized impulses). *B.* Bundle from frog's eye, showing two active fibers, one giving typical "on" and "off" bursts (large impulses), the other responding only to turning light off. Re-illumination after 0.36 sec. (middle part of record) stopped the discharge in fiber giving only the "off" response (compare with last part of record, where light was left off) and produced a very weak "on" response in the "on-off" fiber. *C.* Bundle from frog's eye, showing a fiber (small impulses) which maintained its discharge at a low frequency during period of illumination at beginning of record. Intensity doubled, this fiber gave an initial burst and then maintained its discharge at a higher level of frequency. Intensity reduced to its former value; frequency in this fiber dropped, and another fiber responded with a vigorous "off" response (large, thin impulses). A third fiber (medium-sized, thin impulses) gave a short burst in response to the increase, and very few impulses (difficult to distinguish) in response to the decrease.

be of considerable significance in explaining the diversity of the response types.

No correlation has been noted between the type of response given by a fiber and the location in the retina of its receptive field; all response types can be obtained from any part of the retina. (Whether this holds true for the foveal region in animals possessing a well-defined rod-free area needs to be determined.) Indeed, the receptive fields of different fibers picked up in the same bundle frequently overlap considerably, and in fortunate preparations, where impulses in different fibers can be clearly distinguished by differences in the form and magnitude of their action potentials, it is easy to show that fibers with different types of response are usually present and are stimulated simultaneously by a small spot of light (Fig. 7). Such observations constitute good evidence for the distinctness of the response types, for they are obtained under identical conditions of adaptation, stimulation and external environment.

DISCUSSION. From this experimental study it is apparent that each individual ganglion cell has a relatively fixed character of response, which, with few exceptions, falls under one of three distinct types. Concerning the explanation of this rather unexpected result one can only speculate. The retina, of course, does not possess a homogeneous population of end-organs, and it is possible that the different types of response originate in different types of visual sense cells, merely being relayed through the ganglion cells unaltered. Thus the rods and cones might give rise to responses of different types. Ignoring for the moment the presence of all three types of response in the pure cone retina of the snake, it is still difficult to fit three response types into a duplicity theory, and evidence is still lacking that would associate any of the response types with either rod or cone function. But different forms of both rods and cones are present in most cold-blooded vertebrate retinas, and different sense cells show adaptation of their responses in different degrees. It is not unreasonable to assume that certain of either the rods or cones, or both, might adapt completely following their initial discharge of impulses. Even pure "off" responses might be supposed to originate in certain cells excited by a shift in their equilibrium in the sense opposite to that which usually gives rise to the discharge of impulses.

The diversity of response might, on the other hand, originate in the layers of the retina between the rod and cone layer and the ganglion cells. Thus a given ganglion cell may be subject to diverse and rival influences, and its response determined by the relative amounts of each. This, in turn, may be fixed in large measure by the anatomical connections between the ganglion cell and its underlying neurones. This study in fact has shown clearly that the excitation produced by light may be subject to modification by an influence which may justifiably be termed inhibitory. Thus the relative amounts, and rates of rise and fall, of excitatory and inhibitory influences upon a ganglion cell might determine its response. The "off" effect may then be due to a post-inhibitory release of the effects of an excitation which are all the greater for having been suppressed during the actual period of illumination. Granit and his co-workers have urged the use of these concepts in the interpretation of optic response.

Still another explanation to be considered is the possibility that functional differences may exist among the ganglion cells. While subject to essentially the same influences from the underlying retinal layers, different ganglion cells may respond differently to shifts in their equilibrium. The further consideration of these and other possibilities must wait upon the results of further experiments.

SUMMARY

1. Action potentials in single optic nerve fibers of cold-blooded vertebrate eyes may be obtained from small intra-ocular bundles dissected off the interior surface of the retina of excised, opened bulbs.

2. Responses in different single fibers from the same retina show different types of response. In about 20 per cent of the fibers response to illumination of the retina begins with a burst of impulses at high frequency, followed by a steady discharge at lower frequency which is maintained throughout illumination, and stops when the light is turned off. About 50 per cent of the fibers show only a burst of impulses in response to the onset of illumination, and another in response to its cessation; no impulses are discharged during steady illumination of the retina. The third type of response, obtained from about 30 per cent of the fibers, shows no discharge either at the onset of illumination, or throughout its duration, but gives a vigorous and prolonged discharge when the light is turned off.

3. In general the higher the intensity of retinal illumination the shorter is the latent period of the response, the higher its frequency of discharge, and the greater the number of impulses in a burst.

4. Fibers which give a response to the onset and cessation of light also respond, though less strongly, to an increase or a reduction in its intensity. Fibers giving only an "off" response respond, though less strongly, to a reduction in intensity; they give no response to an increase.

5. As dark-adaptation of the eye progresses, the discharge

which can be obtained from any fiber in response to a given intensity increases; the threshold of response correspondingly falls, rapidly at first and then more gradually, for half an hour or more.

6. "Off" responses are weak or absent following short periods of illumination; similarly "on" responses require a sufficiently long preceding period of darkness for their full development.

7. The discharge in fibers giving only an "off" response is promptly suppressed by re-illumination of the retina.

8. The type of response in any given fiber does not depend upon conditions of stimulation or adaptation of the eye. Even certain external agents (asphyxia, CO_2, ion unbalance, temperature), while affecting the responses, do not alter their essential character.

9. Experiments on fish, amphibian and reptilian eyes give essentially the same results as regards the types of response found.

10. Responses can be obtained in a given optic nerve fiber only upon illumination of a certain restricted region of the retina, termed the receptive field of the fiber.

11. The location on the retina of the receptive field of a fiber is fixed. Its extent depends upon the size and intensity of the spot of light used to explore it, and upon the state of adaptation of the eye.

12. With possible rare exceptions the type of response in any fiber does not depend upon the portion of its receptive field which is illuminated.

13. The type of response in a fiber is not correlated with the location of its receptive field in the retina.

14. The question is discussed as to whether the diversity in types of response is due to different types of sensory cells, whether it arises in the intermediate layers of the retina or whether it is the result of functional differences among the ganglion cells.

REFERENCES

Adrian, E. D., & Matthews, R. *J. Physiol.*, 1927, **63**, 378.
Adrian, E. D., & Matthews, R. *J. Physiol.*, 1927, **64**, 279.
Adrian, E. D., & Matthews, R. *J. Physiol.*, 1928, **65**, 273.
Chaffee, E. L., Bovie, W. T., & Hampson, A. *J. opt. Soc. Amer.*, 1923,
    7, 1.

Hartline, H. K., & Graham, C. H. *J. cell. comp. Physiol.*, 1932, **1**, 277.
Granit, R. *J. Physiol.*, 1933, **77**, 207.
Granit, R., & Riddell, L. A. *J. Physiol.*, 1934, **81**, 1.
Granit, R., & Therman, P. O. *J. Physiol.*, 1935, **83**, 359.

[ADDENDA FROM THE ORIGINAL PRINTING OF THIS ARTICLE: *From the Eldridge Reeves Johnson Foundation for Medical Physics, University of Pennsylvania. Received for publication August 9, 1937.*]

RECEPTIVE FIELDS OF
SINGLE NEURONS IN THE CAT'S
STRIATE CORTEX ❉ *D. H. Hubel*
and T. N. Wiesel

IN THE CENTRAL NERVOUS SYSTEM the visual pathway from retina to striate cortex provides an opportunity to observe and compare single-unit responses at several distinct levels. Patterns of light stimuli most effective in influencing units at one level may no longer be the most effective at the next. From differences in responses at successive stages in the pathway one may hope to gain some understanding of the part each stage plays in visual perception.

By shining small spots of light on the light-adapted cat retina Kuffler (1953) showed that ganglion cells have concentric receptive fields, with an 'on' centre and an 'off' periphery, or vice versa. The 'on' and 'off' areas within a receptive field were found to be mutually antagonistic, and a spot restricted to the centre of the field was more effective than one covering the whole receptive field (Barlow, FitzHugh & Kuffler, 1957). In the freely moving light-adapted cat it was found that the great majority

REPRINTED FROM *The Journal of Physiology*, **148**:574-591. COPYRIGHT © 1959 BY *The Journal of Physiology*.

of cortical cells studied gave little or no response to light stimuli covering most of the animal's visual field, whereas small spots shone in a restricted retinal region often evoked brisk responses (Hubel, 1959). A moving spot of light often produced stronger responses than a stationary one, and sometimes a moving spot gave more activation for one direction than for the opposite.

The present investigation, made in acute preparations, includes a study of receptive fields of cells in the cat's striate cortex. Receptive fields of the cells considered in this paper were divided into separate excitatory and inhibitory ('on' and 'off') areas. In this respect they resembled retinal ganglion-cell receptive fields. However, the shape and arrangement of excitatory and inhibitory areas differed strikingly from the concentric pattern found in retinal ganglion cells. An attempt was made to correlate responses to moving stimuli with receptive field arrangements. Some cells could be activated from either eye, and in these binocular interaction was studied.

METHODS

In this series of experiments twenty-four cats were used. Animals were anaesthetized with intraperitoneal thiopental sodium (40 mg/kg) and light anaesthesia was maintained throughout the experiment by additional intraperitoneal injections. The eyes were immobilized by continuous intravenous injection of succinylcholine; the employment of this muscle relaxant made it necessary to use artificial respiration. Pupils of both eyes were dilated and accommodation was relaxed by means of 1% atropine. Contact lenses used with a suitably buffered solution prevented the corneal surfaces from drying and becoming cloudy. The lids were held apart by simple wire clips.

A multibeam ophthalmoscope designed by Talbot & Kuffler (1952) was used for stimulation and viewing the retina of the left eye. Background illumination was usually about 0.17 log. metre candles (m.c.), and the strongest available stimulus was 1.65 log. m.c. Many sizes and shapes of spots of light could be produced, and these were well focused on the retina. Stimulus durations were of the order of 1 sec.

For binocular studies a different method of light stimulation was used. The animal faced a large screen covering most of the visual field. On this screen light spots of various sizes and shapes were projected. The light source was a tungsten filament projector mounted on an adjustable tripod. Stimuli could be moved across the screen in various directions and with different speeds. Spots subtending an angle as small as 12 min. of arc at the cat's eyes could be obtained, but generally 0.5–1° spots were used for mapping receptive fields. (Dimensions of stimuli are given in terms of equivalent external angles; in the cat 1 mm. on the retina subtends about 4°.) Spots were focused on the two retinas with lenses mounted in front of the cat's eyes. Lenses for focusing were selected by using a retinoscope. Spot intensities ranged from −0.76 to 0.69 log. cd/m². A background illuminance of −1.9 log. cd/m² was given by a tungsten bulb which illuminated the whole screen diffusely. Intensities were measured by a Macbeth Illuminometer. Values of retinal illumination corresponding to these intensities (Talbot & Kuffler, 1952, Fig. 4) were within the photopic range but were lower than those employed with the ophthalmoscope. Whenever the two methods of stimulation were checked against each other while recording from the same unit they were found to give similar results. This principle of projecting light spots on a screen was described by Talbot & Marshall (1941). Areas responsive to light were marked on sheets of paper fixed on the screen, in such a way as to indicate whether the responses were excitatory or inhibitory. The sheets of paper then provided permanent records of these responses, and showed the shape, size and orientation of the regions.

Single-unit activity was recorded extracellularly by techniques described previously (Hubel, 1959). A hydraulic micro-electrode positioner was attached to the animal's skull by a rigidly implanted plastic peg. The cortical surface was closed off from the atmosphere to minimize respiratory and vascular movements of the cortex (Davies, 1956). This method gave the stability needed for thorough exploration of each receptive field, which often took many hours. Electrodes were electrolytically sharpened tungsten wires insulated with a vinyl lacquer (Hubel, 1957). Cathode follower input and a condenser-coupled pre-amplifier were used in a conventional recording system.

Recordings were made from parts of the lateral gyrus extending from its posterior limit to about Horsley-Clarke frontal plane 10. At the end of each penetration an electrolytic lesion was made (Hubel, 1959) and at the end of the experiment the animal was perfused, first with normal saline and then with 10% formalin. The borders of the trephine hole were marked with India ink dots and the brain was removed from the skull and photographed. Paraffin serial sections were made in the region of penetration and stained with cresyl violet. These sections showed that all units described were located in the grey matter of the striate cortex. Correlation between location of units in the striate cortex and physiological findings will not be dealt with in this paper.

There is evidence that cortical cells and afferent fibres differ in their firing patterns and in their responses to diffuse light (Hubel, 1960). The assumption that the spikes recorded were from cell bodies is based on these differences, as well as on electrophysiologic criteria for distinguishing cell-body and fibre spikes (Frank & Fuortes, 1955; Hubel, 1960).

RESULTS

Several hundred units were recorded in the cat's striate cortex. The findings to be described are based on thorough studies of forty-five of these, each of which was observed for a period of from 2 to 9 hr. Times of this order were usually required for adequate analysis of these units.

In agreement with previous findings in the freely moving light-adapted cat (Hubel, 1959) single cortical units showed impulse activity in the absence of changes in retinal illumination. Maintained activity was generally less than in freely moving animals, and ranged from about 0.1–10 impulses/sec. The low rate was possibly due to light barbiturate anaesthesia, since on a number of occasions deepening the anaesthesia resulted in a decrease of maintained activity. This need not mean that all cortical cells are active in the absence of light stimuli, since many quiescent units may have gone unnoticed.

In most units it was possible to find a restricted area in the retina from which firing could be influenced by light. This area was called the receptive field of the cortical unit, applying the concept introduced by Hartline (1938) for retinal ganglion cells. The procedure for mapping out a receptive field is illustrated in Figure 1. Shining a 1° spot (250 μ on the retina) in some areas of the contralateral eye produced a decrease in the maintained activity, with a burst of impulses when the light was turned off (Fig. 1a, b, d). Other areas when illuminated produced an increase in firing (Fig. 1c, e). The complete map, illustrated to the right of the figure, consisted of a long, narrow, vertically oriented region from which 'off' responses were obtained (triangles), flanked on either side by areas which gave 'on' responses (crosses). The entire field covered an area subtending about 4°. The elongated 'off' region had a width of 1° and was 4° long.

Most receptive fields could be subdivided into excitatory and inhibitory regions. An area was termed excitatory if illumination produced an increase in frequency of firing. It was termed inhibitory if light stimulation suppressed maintained activity and was followed by an 'off' discharge, or if either suppression of firing or an 'off' discharge occurred alone. In many units the rate of maintained activity was too slow or irregular to demonstrate inhibition during illumination, and only an 'off' discharge was seen. It was, however, always possible to demonstrate inhibitory

24

D. H. HUBEL AND T. N. WIESEL

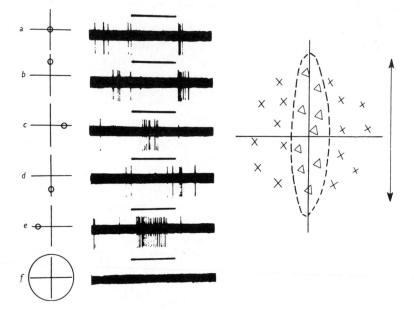

Fig. 1. Responses of a cell in the cat's striate cortex to a 1° spot of light. Receptive field located in the eye contralateral to the hemisphere from which the unit was recorded, close to and below the area centralis, just nasal to the horizontal meridian. No response evoked from the ipsilateral eye. The complete map of the receptive field is shown to the right. ✕, areas giving excitation; △, areas giving inhibitory effects. Scale, 4°. Axes of this diagram are reproduced on left of each record. *a,* 1° (0.25 mm.) spot shone in the center of the field; *b–e,* 1° spot shone on four points equidistant from center; *f,* 5° spot covering the entire field. Background illumination 0.17 log m.c. Stimulus intensity 1.65 log m.c. Duration of each stimulus, 1 sec. Positive deflexions upward.

effects if the firing rate was first increased by stimulation of excitatory regions.

As used here, 'excitatory' and 'inhibitory' are arbitrary terms, since both inhibition and excitation could generally be demonstrated from both regions, either during the light stimulus or following it. We have chosen to denote receptive field regions according to effects seen during the stimulus. Furthermore, the word 'inhibition' is used descriptively, and need not imply a direct inhibitory effect of synaptic endings on the cell observed, since the suppression of firing observed could also be due to a decrease in maintained synaptic excitation.

131 Io.1

c.1

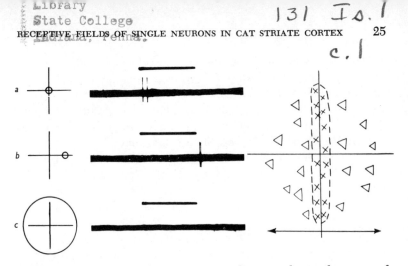

Fig. 2.   Responses of a unit to stimulation with circular spots of light. Receptive field located in area centralis of contralateral eye. (This unit could also be acrivated by the ipsilateral eye.) *a*, 1° spot in the centre region; *b*, same spot displaced 3° to the right; *c*, 8° spot covering entire receptive field. Stimulus and background intensities and conventions as in Fig. 1. Scale, 6.

When excitatory and inhibitory regions (used in the sense defined) were stimulated simultaneously they interacted in a mutually antagonistic manner, giving a weaker response than when either region was illuminated alone. In most fields a stationary spot large enough to include the whole receptive field was entirely without effect (Fig. 1*f*). Whenever a large spot failed to evoke responses, diffuse light stimulation of the entire retina at these intensities and stimulus durations was also ineffective.

In the unit of Figure 1 the strongest inhibitory responses were obtained with a vertical slit-shaped spot of light covering the central area. The greatest 'on' responses accompanied a stimulus confined to the two flanking regions. Summation always occurred within an area of the same type, and the strongest response was obtained with a stimulus having the approximate shape of this area.

In the unit of Figures 2 and 3 there was weak excitation in response to a circular 1° spot in the central region. A weak 'off' response followed stimulation in one of the flanking areas (Fig. 2*a, b*). There was no response to an 8° spot covering the entire receptive field (Fig. 2*c*). The same unit was strongly activated by a narrow slit-shaped stimulus, measuring 1° by

8°, oriented vertically over the excitatory region (Fig. 3A). In contrast, a horizontal slit of light was completely ineffective, despite the fact that the central area was capable of evoking a response when stimulated alone (Fig. 2a). As the optimum (vertical) orientation of the slit was approached responses appeared and rapidly increased to a maximum.

These findings can be readily understood in terms of inter-acting excitatory and inhibitory areas. The strength of the response to a vertically oriented slit is explained by summation over the excitatory region and by the exclusion of inhibitory regions. When parts of the inhibitory flanking areas were included by rotating the slit, responses were reduced or abolished. Thus a horizontal slit was ineffective because it stimulated a small portion of the central excitatory area, and large portions of the antagonistic regions.

Some units were not responsive enough to permit mapping of receptive fields with small light spots. In these the effective stimulus pattern could be found by changing the size, shape and orientation of the stimulus until a clear response was evoked. Often when a region with excitatory or inhibitory responses was established the neighbouring opposing areas in the receptive field could only be demonstrated indirectly. Such an indirect method is illustrated in Figure 3B, where two flanking areas are indicated by using a short slit in various positions like the hand of a clock, always including the very centre of the field. The findings thus agree qualitatively with those obtained with a small spot (Fig. 2a).

Receptive fields having a central area and opposing flanks represented a common pattern, but several variations were seen. Some fields had long narrow central regions with extensive flanking areas (Figs. 1–3): others had a large central area and concentrated slit-shaped flanks (Figs. 6, 9, 10). In many fields the two flanking regions were asymmetrical, differing in size and shape; in these a given spot gave unequal responses in sym-metrically corresponding regions. In some units only two regions could be found, one excitatory and the other inhibitory, lying side by side. In these cases of extreme asymmetry it is possible that there was a second weak flanking area which could not be demonstrated under the present experimental conditions.

An interesting example of a field with only two opposing regions is shown in Figure 4. The concentrated inhibitory region

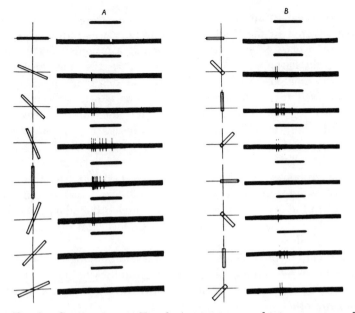

Fig. 3. Same unit as in Fig. 2. A, responses to shining a rectangular light spot, 1° × 8°; centre of slit superimposed on centre of receptive field; successive stimuli rotated clockwise, as shown to left of figure. B, responses to 1° × 5° slit oriented in various directions, with one end always covering the centre of the receptive field: note that this central region evoked responses when stimulated alone (Fig. 2a). Stimulus and background intensities as in Fig. 1; stimulus duration 1 sec.

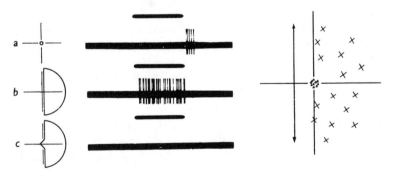

Fig. 4. Responses evoked only from contralateral eye. Receptive field just outside nasal border of area centralis. a, 1° spot covering the inhibitory region; b, right half of a circle 12° in diameter; c, light spot covering regions illuminated in a and b. Background and stimulus intensities and conventions as in Fig. 1. Scale, 12°.

was confined to an area of about 1° (Fig. 4a). The excitatory
area situated to the right of the inhibitory was much larger: a
spot of at least 4° was required to evoke a response, and a very
strong discharge was seen when the entire 12° excitatory area
was illuminated (Fig. 4b). Despite the difference in size between excitatory and inhibitory areas, the effects of stimulating
the two together cancelled each other and no response was
evoked (Fig. 4c). The semicircular stimulus in Figure 4b was
of special interest because the exact position of the vertical
borderline between light and darkness was very critical for a
strong response. A slight shift of the boundary to the left,
allowing light to infringe on the inhibitory area, completely
cancelled the response to illumination. Such a boundary between
light and darkness, when properly positioned and oriented, was
often an effective type of stimulus.

Cortical receptive fields with central and flanking regions may
have either excitatory (Fig. 2) or inhibitory (Fig. 1, 6, 7)
centres. So far we have no indication that one is more common
than the other.

The axis of a field was defined as a line through its centre,
parallel to an optimally oriented elongated stimulus. For each
of the field types described examples were found with axes
oriented vertically, horizonally or obliquely. Orientations were
determined with respect to the animal's skull. Exact field
orientations with respect to the horizontal meridians of the
retinas were not known, since relaxation of eye muscles may
have caused slight rotation of the eyeballs. Within these limitations the two fields illustrated in Figures 1–3 were vertically
arranged: a horizontal field is shown in Figures 6, 9 and 10, and
oblique fields in Figures 7 and 8.

All units have had their receptive fields entirely within the
half-field of vision contralateral to the hemisphere in which they
were located. Some receptive fields were located in or near the
area centralis, while others were in peripheral retinal regions. All
receptive fields were located in the highly reflecting part of the
cat's retina containing the tapetum. So far, retinal ganglion-cell
studies have also been confined to the tapetal region (Kuffler,
1953).

It was sometimes difficult to establish the total size of receptive fields, since the outer borders were often poorly defined.

Furthermore, field size may depend on intensity and size of the stimulus spot and on background illumination, as has been shown for the retina by Hartline (1938) and Kuffler (1953). Within these limitations, and under the stimulus conditions specified, fields ranged in total size from about 4° to 10°. Although in the present investigation no systematic studies have been made of changes in receptive fields under different conditions of stimulation, fields obtained in the same unit with the ophthalmoscope and with projection techniques were always found to be similar in size and structure, despite a difference of several logarithmic units in intensity of illumination. This would suggest that within this photopic range there was little change in size or organization of receptive fields. No units have been studied in states of dark-adaptation.

Responses to Movement

Moving a light stimulus in the visual field was generally an effective way of activating units. As was previously found in the freely moving animal (Hubel, 1959), these stimuli were sometimes the only means by which the firing of a unit could be influenced. By moving spots of light across the retina in various directions and at different speeds patterns of response to movement could be outlined in a qualitative way.

Slit-shaped spots of light were very effective and useful for studies of movement. Here also the orientation of the slit was critical for evoking responses. For example, in the unit of Figure 3 moving a vertical slit back and forth across the field evoked a definite response at each crossing (Fig. 5a), whereas moving a horizontal slit up and down was without effect (Fig. 5b). The vertical slit crossed excitatory and inhibitory areas one at a time and each area could exert its effect unopposed, but a horizontal slit at all times covered the antagonistic regions simultaneously, and was therefore ineffective. The response to a vertical slit moved horizontally was about the same for the two directions of movement.

In some units a double response could be observed at each crossing of the receptive field. The receptive field in Figure 6 had an extensive inhibitory centre flanked by elongated, horizontally oriented, concentrated flanking regions. A horizontal slit moved slowly up or down over the receptive field evoked a

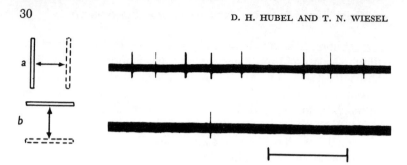

Fig. 5. Same unit as in Figs. 2 and 3. Receptive field shown in Fig. 2. Responses to a slit ($1° \times 8°$) moved transversely back and forth across the receptive field. *a*, slit moved horizontally. *b*, slit moved vertically. Background and stimulus intensities as in Fig. 1; time, 1 sec.

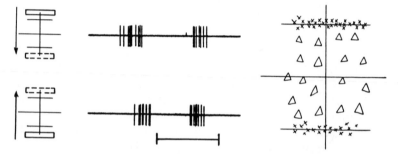

Fig. 6. Slow up-and-down movements of horizontal slit ($1° \times 8°$) across receptive field of left eye. Burst of impulses at each crossing of an excitatory region. For details see Fig. 9. $\times$, excitatory; $\triangle$, inhibitory. Background illumination -1.9 cd/m²; stimulus intensity 0.69 cd/m²; time, 1 sec.

discharge as each excitatory region was crossed. A further description of this unit is given in the binocular section of this paper (p. 31).

Many units showed directional selectivity of a different type in their responses to movement. In these a slit oriented optimally produced responses that were consistently different for the two directions of transverse movement. In the example of Figure 7, the receptive field consisted of a strong inhibitory area flanked by two excitatory areas, of which the right was weaker than the left. Each region was elongated and obliquely oriented. As usual, a large spot was ineffective (Fig. 7c). A narrow slit, with its long axis parallel to that of the field, produced a strong response when moved transversely in a direction down and to the left, but only a feeble response when moved up and to the

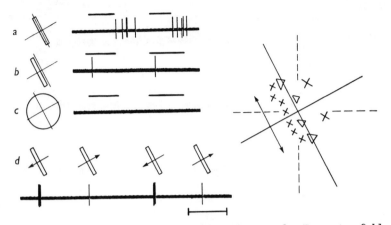

Fig. 7.   Unit activated from ipsilateral eye only. Receptive field just temporal to area centralis. Field elongated and obliquely oriented. Left excitatory flanking region stronger than right. *a,* 1° × 10° slit covering central region; *b,* 1° × 10° slit covering left flanking region; *c,* 12° spot covering entire receptive field; *d,* transverse movement of slit (1° × 10°) oriented parallel to axis of field—note difference in response for the two directions of movement. Background and stimulus intensities and conventions as in Fig. 6. Scale, 10°; time, 1 sec.

right (Fig. 7*d*). A tentative interpretation of these findings on the basis of asymmetry within the receptive field will be given in the Discussion.

A number of units responded well to some directions of movement, but not at all to the reverse directions. An example of this is the unit of Figure 8. Again a slit was moved back and forth transversely in a number of different directions. Only movements up and to the right evoked responses. As with many units, this one could not be activated by stationary stimuli; nevertheless, by using moving stimuli it was possible to get some idea of the receptive field organization—for example, in this unit, the oblique orientation.

Binocular Interaction

Thirty-six units in this study could be driven only from one eye, fifteen from the eye ipsilateral to the hemisphere in which the unit was situated, and twenty-one from the contralateral. Nine, however, could be driven from the two eyes independently. Some of these cells could be activated just as well from either eye, but often the two eyes were not equally effective, and

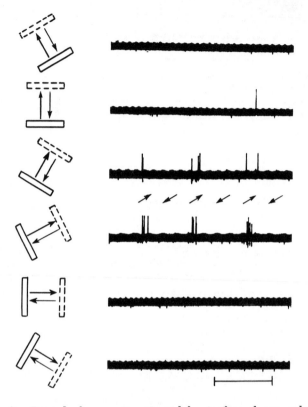

Fig. 8. Records from unit activated by ipsilateral eye only; un-responsive to stationary spots, influenced by movement in an area temporal to area centralis. A slit (0.5° × 8°) moved back and forth transversely with different orientations, as shown to the left. For slit orientations evoking responses only one direction was effective—up and to the right. Stimulus background intensities as in Fig. 6; time, 1 sec.

different degrees of dominance of one eye over the other were seen. In these binocular units the receptive fields were always in roughly homologous parts of the two retinas. For example, a unit with a receptive field in the nasal part of the area centralis of one eye had a corresponding field in the temporal part of the area centralis of the other eye.

Receptive fields were mapped out on a screen in front of the cat. With the eye muscles relaxed with succinylcholine the eyes diverged slightly, so that receptive fields as charted were usually side by side, instead of being superimposed. Whenever the receptive fields of a single unit could be mapped out in the two eyes separately, they were similar in shape, in orientation of their axes, and in arrangements of excitatory and inhibitory regions within the field.

The receptive fields shown in Figure 9 were obtained from a binocularly activated unit in which each field was composed of an inhibitory centre flanked by narrow horizontal excitatory areas. Responses of the same unit to a horizontal slit moved across the field have already been shown in Figure 6, for the left eye.

Summation occurred between corresponding regions in the receptive fields of the two eyes (Fig. 9). Thus simultaneous stimulation of two corresponding excitatory areas produced a response which was clearly stronger than when either area was stimulated alone (Fig. 9A). As the excitatory flanks within one receptive field summed, the most powerful response was obtained with a stimulus covering the four excitatory areas in the two eyes (Fig. 9B). Similarly, summation of 'off' responses occurred when inhibitory areas in the two eyes were stimulated together (Fig. 9C).

Antagonism could also be shown between receptive fields of the two eyes (Fig. 10A). Stimulated alone the central area of the left eye gave an 'off' response, and one flanking area of the right eye gave an 'on' response. When stimulated simultaneously the two regions gave no response. The principles of summation and antagonism could thus be demonstrated between receptive fields of the two eyes, and were not limited to single eyes.

Finally, in this unit it was possible with a moving stimulus to show that opposite-type areas need not always inhibit each other (Fig. 10A), but may under certain circumstances be mutually reinforcing (Fig. 10B). The right eye was covered, and a spot was projected on the screen, over the centre (inhibitory) area of the left eye. Moving the spot as illustrated, away from the centre region of the left eye, produced an 'off' response (Fig. 10B, 1). When the left eye was covered and the right eye uncovered, making the same movement again evoked a response as the flanking excitatory region of the right eye was illuminated (Fig. 10B, 2). The procedure was now repeated with both eyes uncovered, and a greatly increased response was produced (Fig. 10B, 3). Here the movement was made in such a way that the 'off' response from the left eye apparently added

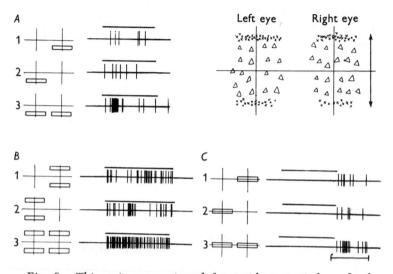

Fig. 9. This unit was activated from either eye independently. The illustration shows summation between corresponding parts of the two receptive fields. Receptive field in the contralateral eye was located just above and nasal to area centralis; in the ipsilateral eye, above and temporal. Receptive fields of the two eyes were similar in form and orientation, as shown in upper right of the figure; scale 8°. The pairs of axes in the receptive field diagram are reproduced to the left of each record. Background and stimulus intensities and conventions as in Fig. 6. (Same unit as in Fig. 6.) *A.* 1, horizontal slit covering lower flanking region of right eye; 2, same for left eye; 3, pair of slits covering the lower flanking regions of the two eyes. *B.* 1, pair of horizontal slits covering both flanking regions of the right eye; 2, same for left eye; 3, simultaneous stimulation of all four flanking regions. *C.* 1, horizontal slit in central region of right eye; 2, same for left eye; 3, simultaneous stimulation of central regions of both eyes. Time, 1 sec.

to the 'on' response from the right, producing a response much greater than with either region alone. It is very likely that within a single receptive field opposite-type regions may act in this synergistic way in response to a moving stimulus.

DISCUSSION

In this study most cells in the striate cortex had receptive fields with separate excitatory and inhibitory regions. This general type of organization was first described by Kuffler (1953) for retinal ganglion cells, and has also been found in a prelim-

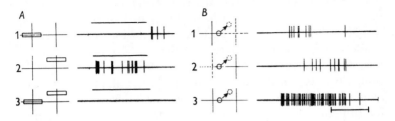

Fig. 10. Same unit as in Fig. 9. Antagonism between inhibitory region in the left eye and an excitatory region in the right eye; stationary spots. 1, horizontal slit in centre of left eye; 2, horizontal slit covering upper flanking region of right eye; 3, simultaneous stimulation of the regions of 1 and 2. *B.* Synergism between inhibitory region in left eye and an excitatory region in the right eye; moving spot of light. 1, right eye covered, spot moved from inhibitory region in left eye, producing an 'off' response; 2, left eye covered, spot moved into excitatory region in right eye, producing an 'on' response; 3, both eyes uncovered, spot moved from inhibitory region in left eye into excitatory region of right eye, producing a greatly enhanced response. Time, 1 sec.

inary study of neurones in the lateral geniculate body (Hubel & Wiesel, unpublished). Thus at three different levels in the visual system a cell can be inhibited by one type of stimulus and excited by another type, while a stimulus combining the two is always less effective. Most retinal ganglion and geniculate cells give clear responses to a large spot of light covering the entire receptive field. At the cortical level the antagonism between excitatory and inhibitory areas appears to be more pronounced, since the majority of units showed little or no response to stimulation with large spots. Similar findings in the cortex of unanaesthetized, freely moving cats (Hubel, 1959) suggest that this is probably not a result of anaesthesia.

Other workers (Jung, 1953, 1958; Jung & Baumgartner, 1955), using only diffuse light stimulation, were able to drive about half the units in the cat striate cortex, while the remainder could not be activated at all. In recent studies (Hubel, 1960) about half the units recorded in striate cortex were shown to be afferent fibres from the lateral geniculate nucleus, and these responded to diffuse illumination. The remainder were thought to be cell bodies or their axons; for the most part they responded poorly if at all to diffuse light. The apparent discrepancy between our findings and those of Jung and his co-workers may perhaps be explained by the exclusion of afferent fibres from the present studies. On the other hand it may be that cells responsive to diffuse light flashes are more common in the cortex than our results would imply, but were not detected by our methods of recording and stimulating. However, cortical cells may not be primarily concerned with levels of diffuse illumination. This would be in accord with the finding that in cats some capacity for brightness discrimination persists after bilateral ablation of the striate cortex (Smith, 1937).

The main difference between retinal ganglion cells and cortical cells was to be found in the detailed arrangement of excitatory and inhibitory parts of their receptive fields. If afferent fibres are excluded, no units so far recorded in the cortex have had fields with the concentric configuration so typical of retinal ganglion cells. Moreover, the types of fields found in the cortex have not been seen at lower levels.

Spots of more or less circular (or annular) form are the most effective stimuli for activating retinal ganglion cells, and the diameter of the optimum spot is dependent on the size of the central area of the receptive field (Barlow, FitzHugh, & Kuffler, 1957). At the cortical level a circular spot was often ineffective; for best driving of each unit it was necessary to find a spot with a particular form and orientation. The cortical units described here have had in common a side-by-side distribution of excitatory and inhibitory areas, usually with marked elongation of one or both types of regions. The form and size of the most effective light stimulus was given by the shape of a particular region. The forms of stimulus used in these studies were usually simple, consisting of slit-shaped spots of light and boundaries between light and darkness. Position and orientation were critical, since imperfectly placed forms failed to cover one type of region completely, thus not taking advantage of summation within that region, and at the same time could invade neighbouring, opposing areas (Fig. 3).

The phenomena of summation and antagonism within receptive fields seem to provide a basis for the specificity of stimuli, in shape, size and orientation. Units activated by slits and boundaries may converge upon units of higher order which require still more complex stimuli for their activation. Most units presented in this paper have had receptive fields with clearly separable excitatory and inhibitory areas. However, a number of units recorded in the striate cortex could not be understood solely in these terms. These units with more complex properties are now under study.

Other types of receptive fields may yet be found in the cortex, since the sampling (45 units) was small, and may well be biased by the micro-electrode techniques. We may, for example, have failed to record from smaller cells, or from units which, lacking a maintained activity, would tend not to be detected. We have therefore emphasized the common features and the variety of receptive fields, but have not attempted to classify them into separate groups.

There is anatomical evidence for convergence of several optic tract fibres on to single geniculate neurons (O'Leary, 1940) and for a more extensive convergence of radiation fibres on to single cortical cells (O'Leary, 1941). Consistent with these anatomical findings, our results show that some single cortical cells can be influenced from relatively large retinal regions. These large areas, the receptive fields, are subdivided into excitatory and inhibitory regions; some dimensions of these may be very small compared with the size of the entire fields. This is illustrated by the fields shown in Figures 1, 2 and 7, in which the central regions were long but very narrow; and by that of Figure 9, in which both flanks were narrow. It is also shown by the field of Figure 4, which had a total size of about 12° but whose in-hibitory region was only about 1° in diameter. Thus a unit may be influenced from a relatively wide retinal region and still convey precise information about a stimulus within that region.

Movement of a stimulus across the retina was found to be a very potent way of activating a cell, often more so than a stationary spot. Transverse movement of a slit usually produced responses only when the slit was oriented in a certain direction. This was sometimes explained by the arrangement within the receptive fields as mapped out with stationary stimuli (Fig. 5).

In many units (Fig. 7) the responses to movement in opposite directions were strikingly different. Occasionally when the optimum direction of movement was established, there was no response to movement in the opposite direction (Fig. 8). Similar effects have been observed with horizontally moving spots in the unanaesthetized animal (Hubel, 1959). It was not always possible to find a simple explanation for this, but at times the asymmetry of strength of flanking areas was consistent with the directional specificity of responses to movement. Thus in the unit of Figure 7 best movement responses were found by moving a slit from the inhibitory to the stronger of the two excitatory regions. Here it is possible to interpret movement responses in terms of synergism between excitatory and inhibitory areas. This is further demonstrated in Figure 10B, where areas antagonistic when tested with stationary spots (Fig. 10A) could be shown to be synergistic with moving stimuli, and a strong response was evoked when a spot moved from an 'off' to an 'on' area.

Inhibition of unitary responses by stimulation of regions adjacent to the excitatory area has been described for the eccentric cell in the Limulus eye (Hartline, 1949) and for ganglion cells both in the frog retina (Barlow, 1953) and in the cat retina (Kuffler, 1953). Analogous phenomena have been noted for tones in the auditory system (dorsal cochlear nucleus, Galambos, 1944) and for touch and pressure in the somatosensory system (Mountcastle, 1957). In each system it has been proposed that these mechanisms are concerned with enhancing contrast and increasing sensory discrimination. Our findings in the striate cortex would suggest two further possible functions. First, the particular arrangements within receptive fields of excitatory and inhibitory regions seem to determine the form, size and orientation of the most effective stimuli, and secondly, these arrangements may play a part in perception of movement.

It is clear from stimulation of separate eyes with spots of light that some cortical units are activated from one eye only, either the ipsilateral or the contralateral, while others can be driven by the two eyes. In view of the small number of cells studied, no conclusion can be drawn as to the relative proportions of these units (ipsilaterally, contralaterally and bilaterally driven), but it appears that all three types are well represented.

Studies of binocularly activated units showed that the receptive fields mapped out separately in the two eyes were alike. The excitatory and inhibitory areas were located in homologous parts of the retinas, were similarly shaped and oriented, and responded optimally to the same direction of movement. When corresponding parts of the two receptive fields were stimulated summation occurred (Fig. 9). Assuming that the receptive fields as projected into the animal's visual field are exactly superimposed when an animal fixes on an object, any binocularly activated unit which can be affected by the object through one eye alone should be much more strongly influenced when both eyes are used. The two retinal images of objects behind or in front of the point fixed will not fall on corresponding parts of the fields, and their effects should therefore not necessarily sum. They may instead antagonize each other or not interact at all.

It is possible that when an object in the visual field exerts, through the two eyes, a strong influence on binocularly activated units, those influences may lead in some way to an increased awareness of the object. If that is so, then objects which are the same distance from the animal as the object fixed should stand out in relief. On the other hand such units may be related to mechanisms of binocular fixation, perhaps projecting to mid-brain nuclei concerned with the regulation of convergence.

SUMMARY

1. Recordings were made from single cells in the striate cortex of lightly anaesthetized cats. The retinas were stimulated separately or simultaneously with light spots of various sizes and shapes.

2. In the light-adapted state cortical cells were active in the absence of additional light stimulation. Increasing the depth of anaesthesia tended to suppress this maintained activity.

3. Restricted retinal areas which on illumination influenced the firing of single cortical units were called receptive fields. These fields were usually subdivided into mutually antagonistic excitatory and inhibitory regions.

4. A light stimulus (approximately 1 sec. duration) covering the whole receptive field, or diffuse illumination of the whole retina, was relatively ineffective in driving most units, owing to mutual antagonism between excitatory and inhibitory regions.

5. Excitatory and inhibitory regions, as mapped by stationary stimuli, were arranged within a receptive field in a side-by-side fashion with a central area of one type flanked by antagonistic areas. The centres of receptive fields could be either excitatory or inhibitory. The flanks were often asymmetrical, in that a given stationary stimulus gave unequal responses in corresponding portions of the flanking areas. In a few fields only two regions could be demonstrated, located side by side. Receptive fields could be oriented in a vertical, horizontal or oblique manner.

6. Effective driving of a unit required a stimulus specific in

form, size, position and orientation, based on the arrangement of excitatory and inhibitory regions within receptive fields.

7. A spot of light gave greater responses for some directions of movement than for others. Responses were often stronger for one direction of movement than for the opposite; in some units these asymmetries could be interpreted in terms of receptive field arrangements.

8. Of the forty-five units studied, thirty-six were driven from only one eye, fifteen from the ipsilateral eye and twenty-one from the contralateral; the remaining nine could be driven from the two eyes independently. In some binocular units the two eyes were equally effective; in others various degrees of dominance of one eye over the other were seen.

9. Binocularly activated units were driven from roughly homologous regions in the two retinas. For each unit the fields mapped for the two eyes were similar in size, form and orientation, and when stimulated with moving spots, showed similar directional preferences.

10. In a binocular unit excitatory and inhibitory regions of the two receptive fields interacted, and summation and mutual antagonism could be shown just as within a single receptive field.

REFERENCES

Barlow, H. B. Summation and inhibition in the frog's retina. *J. Physiol.*, 1953, **119**, 69-88.

Barlow, H. B., FitzHugh, R., & Kuffler, S. W. Change of organization in the receptive fields of the cat's retina during dark adaptation. *J. Physiol.*, 1957, **137**, 338-354.

Davies, P. W. Chamber for microelectrode studies in the cerebral cortex. *Science*, 1956, **124**, 179-180.

Frank, K., & Fuortes, M. G. F. Potentials recorded from the spinal cord with microelectrodes. *J. Physiol.*, 1955, **130**, 625-654.

Galambos, R. Inhibition of activity in single auditory nerve fibers by acoustic stimulation. *J. Neurophysiol.*, 1944, **7**, 287-304.

Hartline, H. K. The response of single optic nerve fibers of the vertebrate eye to illumination of the retina. *Amer. J. Physiol.*, 1938, **121**, 400-415.

Hartline, H. K. Inhibition of activity of visual receptors by illuminating nearby retinal areas in the *Limulus* eye. *Fed. Proc.*, 1949, **8**, 69.

Hubel, D. H. Tungsten microelectrode for recording from single units. *Science*, 1957, **125**, 549-550.

Hubel, D. H. Single unit activity in striate cortex of unrestrained cats. *J. Physiol.*, 1959, **147**, 226-238.

Hubel, D. H. Single unit activity in lateral geniculate body and optic tract of unrestrained cats. *J. Physiol.*, 1960, [**150**, 91-104.]

Jung, R. Neuronal discharge. *EEG. clin. Neurophysiol.*, 1953, Suppl. 4, 57-71.

Jung, R. Excitation, inhibition and coordination of cortical neurones. *Exp. cell Res.*, 1958, Suppl. 5, 262-271.

Jung, R., & Baumgartner, G. Hemmungsmechanismen und bremsende Stabilisierung an einzelnen Neuronen des optischen Cortex. *Pflüg. Arch. ges. Physiol.*, 1955, **261**, 434-456.

Kuffler, S. W. Discharge patterns and functional organization of mammalian retina. *J. Neurophysiol.*, 1953, **16**, 37-68.

Mountcastle, V. B. Modality and topographic properties of single neurons of cat's somatic sensory cortex. *J. Neurophysiol.*, 1957, **21**, 408-434.

O'Leary, J. L. A structural analysis of the lateral geniculate nucleus of the cat. *J. comp. Neurol.*, 1940, **73**, 405-430.

O'Leary, J. L. Structure of the area striata of the cat. *J. comp. Neurol.*, 1941, **75**, 131-164.

Smith, K. U. Visual discrimination in the cat: V. The postoperative effects of removal of the striate cortex upon intensity discrimination. *J. genet. Psychol.*, 1937, **51**, 329-369.

Talbot, S. A., & Marshall, W. H. Physiological studies on neural mechanisms of visual localization and discrimination. *Amer. J. Ophthal.*, 1941, **24**, 1255-1263.

Talbot, S. A., & Kuffler, S. W. A multibeam ophthalmoscope for the study of retinal physiology. *J. opt. Soc. Amer.*, 1952, **42**, 931-936.

[ADDENDA FROM THE ORIGINAL PRINTING OF THIS ARTICLE: *From the Wilmer Institute, The Johns Hopkins Hospital and University, Baltimore, Maryland, U.S.A. Received 22 April 1959.* IN REFERENCE TO THE AUTHORS: *Present address, Harvard Medical School, 25 Shattuck St., Boston 15, Massachusetts.* ACKNOWLEDGEMENT: *We wish to thank Dr S. W. Kuffler for his helpful advice and criticism, and Mr R. B. Bosler and Mr. P. E. Lockwood for their technical assistance. This work was supported in part by U.S. Public Health Service grants B-22 and B-1031, and in part by U.S. Air Force contract AF 49 (638)-499 (Air Force Office of Scientific Research, Air Research and Development Command).*]

ABLATION OF TEMPORAL CORTEX AND DISCRIMINATION OF AUDITORY PATTERNS

▓ *Irving T. Diamond and W. D. Neff*

A CORTICAL PROJECTION AREA of the auditory system in the cat has been defined by combining the results of experiments in which retrograde degeneration, cytoarchitectural, and evoked potential techniques have been used (1, 3, 6, 14, 15, 18, 19). The role played by this projection area in auditory discrimination has been examined in studies which have measured absolute thresholds for tonal stimuli (8), difference thresholds for intensity (13, 16), difference thresholds for frequency (4, 11), and localization of sound in space (2, 12). In none of these experiments has a complete loss in the discriminatory ability tested been found after ablation of auditory cortex. In a one-stage, bilateral ablation, amnesia for the learned habit usually occurs, but the discrimination can be relearned. A permanent but only partial deficit in ability to localize sound in space has been reported by Neff, Fisher, Diamond, and Yela (12).

Results of both clinical and experimental investigations of

REPRINTED FROM THE *Journal of Neurophysiology*, 20:300-315. COPYRIGHT © 1957 BY THE AMERICAN PHYSIOLOGICAL SOCIETY.

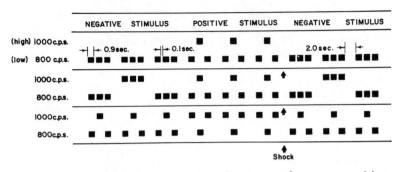

Fig. 1. Schematic representation of patterns of tones comprising discriminatory tasks. Positive group of three tones is presented three times, or for a duration of approximately 15 sec., and is followed by shock. Duration of negative stimulus varies from trial to trial but is always longer than diagram shows. Time constants shown in top patterns apply to both positive and negative stimuli. Thus, 2 sec. is interval between any successive group of three tones, including interval between last negative group and first positive group. Finally, it is to be noted that in patterns represented in middle and bottom lines, same frequency components are present in both positive and negative stimuli.

Fig. 2. Cortical auditory areas in cat.

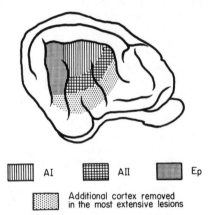

brain function suggest that a loss in sensory discrimination may occur after cortical damage if the discrimination is one which involves patterns of sensory cues (see, for example, 5, 7, 9, 17). The experiment reported below was undertaken, therefore, to examine the effects of ablation of auditory cortex on a learned discrimination of tonal patterns.

Apparatus and Procedure

Six cats were trained and tested in a double-grill box placed in a quiet room. Crossbars of the floor of the box served as electrodes. The box was divided into two parts by a partition with a doorway; animals could be shocked in either compartment. The correct response consisted of avoiding shock by passing through the doorway of the partition at the presentation of the positive stimulus. Stimulus tones were produced by a loudspeaker which was driven by the amplified current from either one of two audio-oscillators. In all training trials, one oscillator was set at 800 c./sec. and the other at 1000 c./sec. A timing circuit controlled the sequence of tones used as stimuli. Tones were presented in groups of three, each tone on for 0.9 sec. with 0.1 sec. between tones of a group. A 2-sec. silent interval separated the groups of tones. Figure 1 shows in diagrammatic form examples of the patterns presented to experimental animals. The sequence of events illustrated in the top line of Figure 1 may be called a frequency discrimination since the positive stimulus introduces a 1000 c./sec. tone not present in the negative stimulus. For the sequences shown in the next two lines, the animal is required to discriminate on the basis of the temporal patterning of the tones. During presentation of the negative stimulus, the animal was permitted to remain at rest in one compartment of the double-grill box. The duration of the presentation period for negative stimuli was varied from 30 to 300 sec. After three presentations of the positive stimulus, shock was given and the animal was forced to move from one to the other compartment of the box. Shock could be avoided by a prompt response. Training on any given pattern was continued until 10 out of 10 avoidance responses were made during a daily test period.

When preoperative training had been completed, auditory cortex was ablated in each animal. Surgery was done under aseptic conditions; the cortical tissue was removed by subpial aspiration. In two animals, D-199 and D-228, the aim was to ablate only AI (see Fig. 2 for map of auditory cortex and identification of subdivisions). In animals D-229 and D-218, the intent was to ablate all of AI, AII, and Ep, but care was taken not to go beyond the boundaries of these areas. In the final two animals, D-138 and D-134, the ablation was extended ventrally to be sure that no remnant of AII or of Ep remained. A recovery period of 18–22 days was allowed before postoperative testing was begun.

After recovery from surgery, animals were returned to the double-grill box and were retrained on the same discrimination they had last learned before operation. Retraining was continued until the criterion of 10 out of 10 consecutive correct responses had been made during the test period of one day or until a stage had been reached at which it appeared that no further learning was going to take place. One animal that failed to relearn pattern discrimination was given training subsequently on frequency discrimination. When postoperative testing had been completed, animals were perfused with saline and 10 per cent formalin. The brains were then removed, dehydrated in alcohol, and embedded in celloidin. Each tenth section was stained by the Weil technique and the adjacent section was stained with thionin. The surface lesion was reconstructed and serial sections through the thalamus 0.5 mm. apart were studied for retrograde degeneration.

In the four animals where an effort was made to restrict the lesion either to AI or to AI, AII, and Ep, an additional check on the lesion was provided by a study of evoked potentials. Before the animals were sacrificed and the brains prepared for histology, the temporal lobes of cats D-199, D-228, D-229 and D-218 were exposed under deep Nembutal anaesthesia and in each case the region around the lesion was explored in the following manner: Small patches (1 × 1 mm.) of filter paper soaked in a solution of strychnine sulfate were applied to the cortex; an electrode was placed over the wet paper; and, after permitting the strychnine to diffuse into the underlying tissue, tonal pulses were delivered to the contralateral ear. The characteristic strychnine spike potentials, spontaneous and evoked, were observed on a cathode-ray oscilloscope. The procedure and instrumentation used in these electrophysiological tests has been fully described by Hind (6).

RESULTS

Anatomical

Drawings of the reconstructed cortical surfaces and of representative cross sections through the cortex and thalamus for each animal are shown in Figures 3–8. The region ablated is shown as solid black. Degeneration of underlying fibers was not systematically plotted in the frontal sections but, in the drawings of cross sections of the cortex, stippling is used to signify degenerated subcortical fibers where otherwise the particular region might be misinterpreted to be normal cortical tissue. Severe gliosis and marked cell loss in the thalamus are indicated by shaded areas (diagonal stripes).

In the thalamus, only sections through the medial geniculate (GM) are shown, with the exception of one case in which there was degeneration in nucleus ventralis posterior (VP). Following Rose and Woolsey, we have used the designation posterior group (Po) to include the suprageniculate and the region which some workers have called n. posterior. In the sections which include the caudal part of Po, the principal division (GMp) of the medial geniculate is a densely populated, curved band of small cells. Proceeding dorsomedially, the cells become larger and more sparse and, without a sharp line of demarkation separating the two, the medial geniculate is replaced by Po. In depicting an approximate boundary between GMp and Po, we have made a conservative estimate of the extent of the medial geniculate. Some atlases of the cat thalamus show Po as a dorsomedial continuation of GMp. Directly ventral to the posterior group, the cells increase further in size and decrease in density.

D-199

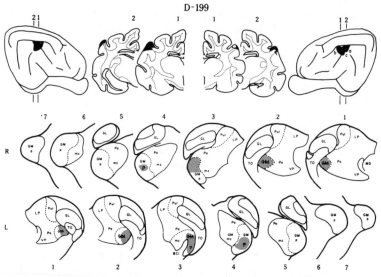

Fig. 3. Cortical reconstruction and thalamic degeneration of cat D-199. In Figs. 3-8, reconstructions of lateral surfaces of cerebral hemispheres for each animal are shown at top of each figure. Cortical lesion is represented by black area. Similarly in representative frontal sections through lesion, blackened area shows extent of ablation. Stippled regions below lesion are degenerated fiber tracts. Letters appearing adjacent to cortical lesion depict points from which evoked potentials were obtained in response to tonal pulses. (See text for further discussion.) Serial sections through thalamus are drawn at bottom of each figure. With exception of left thalamus in D-138, drawing labeled 1 is most anterior section through corpus geniculatum medialis. Number 2 is 0.5 mm. posterior to 1, 3 is 0.5 mm. behind 2, etc., throughout rest of thalamus. In labeling anatomical structures, following abbreviations were used: BCI—brachium colliculus inferioris; CM—nuculeus centrum medianum; GL—corpus geniculatum lateralis; GMp—corpus geniculatum medialis pars principalis; GMmc (or mc)—corpus geniculatum medialis pars magnocellularis; LP—nucleus lateralis posterior; MD—nucleus medialis dorsalis; Mid—midbrain; Po—posterior group of nuclei (see text); Pul—nucleus pulvinaris; TO—tractus opticus; VP—nucleus ventralis posterior; VPL—nucleus ventralis posterolateralis.

This region is usually called the magnocellular division (GMmc) of the medial geniculate.

Lesions restricted to AI. In D-199 (Fig. 3) the ablation of auditory cortex in both the right and left hemispheres is restricted to the middle ectosylvian gyrus. The anterior and posterior ectosylvian gyri are intact bilaterally and most of the

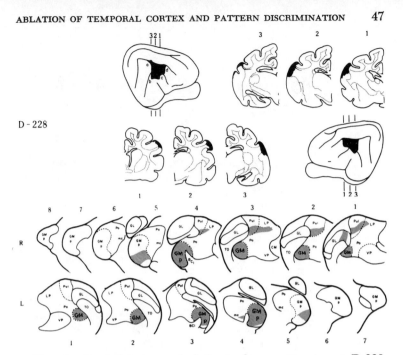

Fig. 4. Cortical lesion and thalamic degeneration in cat D-228. For explanation, see legend of Fig. 2.

cortex between the anterior and posterior ectosylvian sulci is preserved. Degeneration in the thalamus is confined to the principal division of the medial geniculate. In this nucleus, the rostral tip is totally degenerated on one side and largely degenerated on the other side. Degeneration extends into the middle of the medial geniculate on both sides; the caudal portions are intact. When the region of ablation of cat D-199 was explored by the evoked potential technique before the animal was sacrificed, responses were obtained from a band of cortex surrounding the lesion. Three responsive points on the left hemisphere are shown in Figure 3. At point "a" synchronous strychnine responses were evoked by frequencies centered around 2000 c./sec. Point "a," therefore, appears to be a remnant of the low tone region of AI. Point "b" was found to give responses typical of low tone AII. It was most sensitive to 1000 c./sec. and 2000 c./sec.; good responses were elicited by stimuli as low as 250 c./sec. The response curve obtained for point "c" was more flat; the point of greatest sensitivity was 4000 c./sec. Point "c" apparently is part of the middle region of AII.

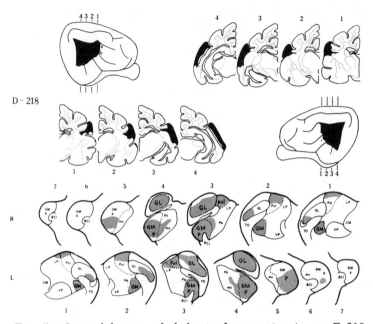

Fig. 5. Cortical lesion and thalamic degeneration in cat D-218. For explanation, see legend of Fig. 3.

The lesion in D-228 (Fig. 4) is more extensive than that of D-199, but in this case, too, electrophysiological study revealed that a remnant of AI was present. Point "a" appeared to be sharply tuned to 500 c./sec. and, therefore, was judged to be part of posterior AI. Excellent responses were elicited at "b" by frequencies from 2000 c./sec. to 35,000 c./sec. At point "c" responses were evoked by intense tones from 5000 c./sec. to 20,000 c./sec. Point "d" responded to intense tones of 500 c./sec. to 1000 c./sec. Points "b" and "c," therefore, appear to lie in middle AII and point "d" in anterior AII. In the thalamus, only the rostral half, approximately, of the principal division of the medial geniculate is degenerated; the caudal half of the principal part and the magnocellular division are intact. On the right side, some degeneration may be noted in the pulvinar and in the lateral geniculate.

In both "AI" animals (D-199, D-228), then, a remnant of AI, as defined by evoked potentials, was located. Furthermore, in both cases, no degeneration of cells is to be seen in the caudal half of the principal part of the medial geniculate.

Lesions restricted to AI, AII, and Ep. In two animals (D-218, D-229), the ablated areas follow closely the boundaries of AI, AII, and Ep. The lesion in the right cerebral hemisphere of D-218 is bounded by the posterior and middle suprasylvian sulci; the depths of the latter are preserved (Fig. 5). Ventrally, the lesion reaches to the tip of the pseudosylvian sulcus. Most of the anterior ectosylvian gyrus appears to be intact. The lesion in the left hemisphere is very similar to that in the right. Auditory cortex appears to be spared in the anterior ectosylvian gyrus. That the lesions are in fact incomplete was verified by electrophysiological examination. Labels "a" and "b" in the right hemisphere refer to patches of cortex from which evoked potentials were elicited. At "a" responses were evoked by frequencies from 125 c./sec. to 16,000 c./sec. Maximum sensitivity occurred at 1000 c./sec. It is likely that part of the low tone area of AII was preserved. At point "b" weak responses were obtained to tones of high intensity from 500 c./sec. to 25,000 c./sec.

In the thalamus of D-218, degeneration in the medial geniculate pars principalis is more extensive than in the two cases with lesions confined to AI (cats D-199, D-228); yet the caudal one-third of the nucleus is preserved and the magnocellular portion is largely intact. Degeneration is found bilaterally in the lateral geniculate and in the pulvinar. As compared to D-218, the lesion in D-229 extends further into the anterior ectosylvian gyrus and deeper in the depths of the middle suprasylvian sulcus (Fig. 6). The electrophysiological exploration of cortex surrounding the area of ablation in cat D-229 was inconclusive. Neither spontaneous nor evoked strychnine spikes were obtained.

The thalamic study of D-229 reveals that invasion of the optic radiations and ablation of cortex in the middle suprasylvian gyrus led to total atrophy of the lateral geniculate and massive degeneration in the pulvinar and n. lateralis posterior. Degeneration in the medial geniculate pars principalis is almost identical to that in cat D-218; the rostral half of the principal division is completely degenerated; caudal to the region of total degeneration the dorsal part of the medial geniculate is preserved; still further in the posterior direction the area of degeneration decreases and finally in the final sections through the posterior tip the geniculate is completely intact. Gliosis and

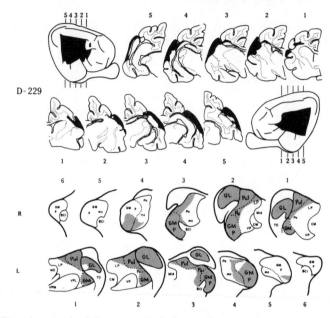

Fig. 6. Cortical lesion and thalamic degeneration in cat D-229. For explanation, see legend of Fig. 3.

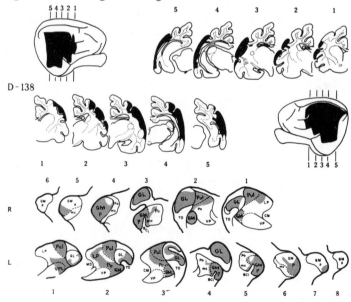

Fig. 7. Cortical lesion and thalamic degeneration in cat D-138. For explanation, see legend of Fig. 3.

cell loss extend medially and dorsomedially beyond the boundaries of the principal division. Still, much of the magnocellular division appears preserved.

Lesions extending beyond AI, AII, and Ep. In the final two cases (cats D-138, D-134), the ablation of cortex was extended further than in the other animals of the series to insure that no cortex responsive to auditory signals remained. The reconstructed cortical surface for D-138 (Fig. 7) appears to satisfy this criterion. In the right hemisphere, the lesion includes much of the anterior ectosylvian gyrus and follows the pseudosylvian sulcus almost to its union with the anterior rhinal fissure. Some question as to the completeness of the ablation might be raised by the presence of cells in the depths of the anterior ectosylvian sulcus (cf. frontal section 2, Fig. 7). The posterior half of the lesion is deep and involves subcortical pathways. On the left side, the reconstruction of the lateral surface shows that rostrally the lesion reaches beyond the anterior suprasylvian sulcus. Throughout the length of the lesion the middle suprasylvian gyrus has been partially removed. Caudally, the lesion invades the posterior suprasylvian gyrus and, ventrally, it extends below AII. The preserved depths of the anterior ectosylvian and pseudosylvian sulci are probably beyond the limits of AII.

Retrograde degeneration is found in n. ventralis posterolateralis on the left side of the thalamus of D-138. This is interpreted as the effect of damage to cortex and fiber tracts rostral to the anterior suprasylvian sulcus. On this same side severe gliosis and cell loss can be observed in a region dorsal and lateral to the posterior part of VP. This pattern of degeneration resembles that found after lesions which include somatic area II in addition to AI, AII, and Ep (4). Extensive bilateral deterioration is found in the lateral geniculate and in the pulvinar. Degeneration in the principal division of the medial geniculate is more extensive than in the four previous cases, but again the posterior tip is preserved. The region of degeneration extends into that part of the magnocellular division of the geniculate adjacent to the principal division; more medially, normal appearing large cells are present.

In both area and depth, D-134 has the largest lesion of any animal in the present series. AI, AII, and Ep were removed bilaterally and, in addition, neocortex ventral to AII was ablated. The study of the thalamus shows total degeneration of the lateral

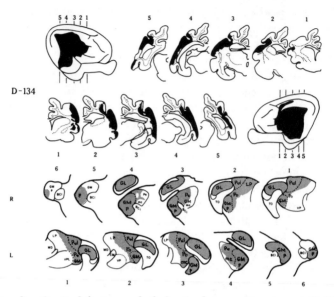

Fig. 8. Cortical lesion and thalamic degeneration in cat D-134. For explanation, see legend of Fig. 3.

geniculate bodies and massive area of degeneration that includes the pulvinar, n. lateralis posterior, and the posterior group. In the principal division of the medial geniculate, severe degeneration penetrates into the posterior tip and, on the left side, only a fragment of the dorsal posterior tip remains. A considerable part of the magnocellular division of the medial geniculate is also degenerated bilaterally.

Behavioral

The six animals fall into three groups on the basis of postoperative tests. Two animals with lesions of AI, D-199 and D-228, suffered little or no loss in the pattern discrimination habit and attained the learning criterion in a fraction of the preoperative training period (Fig. 9). Two animals, D-229 and D-218, were unable to discriminate changes in tonal patterns in the early training sessions following the ablation but were able to relearn (Fig. 9). The remaining two cases, D-134 and D-138, did not reach preoperative levels of performance in the postoperative training period (Figs. 9, 10). One of these animals, D-134, was first trained preoperatively with three low tones as

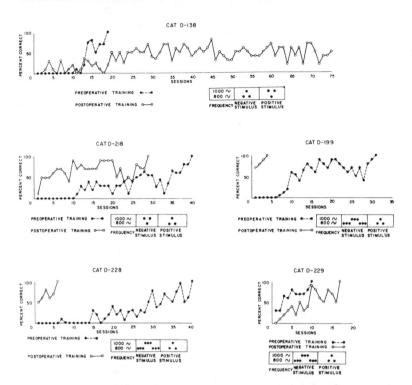

Fig. 9. Pre- and postoperation learning curves for five experimental animals. Pattern used for each animal is symbolized below record of training. For a more complete explanation of discriminatory patterns, see Fig. 1 and text.

the negative and low, high, low as the positive stimulus (Fig. 1, top line). Even though the tones were presented in groups of three, this task is a simple frequency discrimination. Initial training on frequency discrimination has been found to facilitate the learning of pattern discrimination. After the frequency discrimination was learned, pattern discrimination training was given. Following surgery, the animal was unable to recover the pattern habit and was then presented with the frequency discrimination. After 29 sessions, the frequency problem was learned and once again an unsuccessful attempt was made to train the animal to make a pattern discrimination. The inability to respond to pattern differences clearly cannot be attributed to an inability to discriminate differences in frequency.

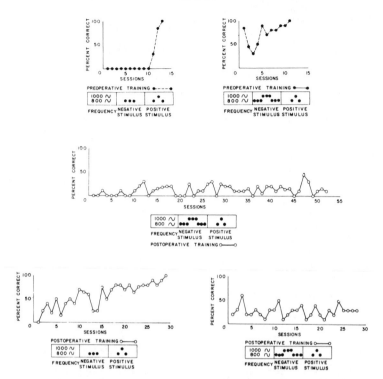

Fig. 10. Behavioral record for cat D-134. The five curves show successive training periods. Upper left graph is record of initial learning of a change in frequency. The upper right curve shows subsequent training on a pattern discrimination. Training on this same pattern discrimination was given after operation (middle curve). After failure to relearn the pattern discrimination, the animal succeeded in relearning to discriminate a change in frequency (lower left record). This experience had little or no effect on ability to learn the pattern discrimination (lower right curve).

Functioning of small remnants of sensory cortex. The evidence from both the electrophysiological and behavioral tests indicates that small remnants of AI or AII can function as normal cortical tissue. Evoked potentials were obtained from small areas immediately adjacent to regions of ablation and animals with only a very small patch of auditory projection area intact behaved entirely differently from animals with all of the projection areas removed.

DISCUSSION

Thalamo-cortical connections. The ablation of a large part of auditory area I without damage to surrounding areas results in retrograde degeneration that is confined to the principal division of the ipsilateral medial geniculate. This evidence is in agreement with the results of other investigators (15, 18). The finding that as much as the entire caudal half of the medial geniculate principal division is preserved with such lesions is not inconsistent with these earlier reports. When the amount of cortex ablated is extended beyond AI to include most of AII and Ep, degeneration in the principal division of the medial geniculate extends somewhat further caudally. When the ablation is increased still further to include neocortex ventral to AII, still less of the caudal portion of the medial geniculate remains intact. In the largest lesion of the present series (cat D-134, Fig. 8), only a small dorsal area remained preserved in the caudal tip. Removal of cortex between the rhinal fissure and the ventral boundary of AII and Ep appears responsible for this further degeneration of the medial geniculate. The suggestion that complete degeneration of the medial geniculate may follow a lesion that includes sufficient cortex between the rhinal fissure and AII is compelling. Attention is thus focused upon a region of the cortex which has not previously been considered as part of the auditory system.

The magnocellular portion of the medial geniculate was completely preserved in the case of the two smallest cortical lesions (D-199, D-228) and was largely preserved in lesions intermediate in extent (e.g., D-218). Only where the cortical lesion contained almost all tissue between the suprasylvian sulcus and the rhinal fissure does a major portion of the large cell division degenerate. These findings are consistent with earlier reports as to the cortical projection of this part of the thalamus. Waller (18) found that a large lesion of the cat's temporal cortex resembling that of our D-134 leads to degeneration in both large and small cell portions of the medial geniculate. Rose and Woolsey (15) failed to find degeneration in the magnocellular part of the medial geniculate after much less extensive ablations.

Relation of behavioral deficit to lesion. The problem of behavioral deficit resulting from cortical ablation has been analyzed historically in terms of two alternative hypotheses. On the

one hand, there may be a quantitative relation between size of
lesion and degree of deficit; on the other hand, the behavioral
capacity studied may depend on the presence, either in entirety or in part, of specific anatomical units. On the basis of
postoperative behavior, the animals of the present study may
be divided into three groups: those who retained the pattern
discrimination habit, those who lost the habit but were able to
relearn, and those who failed to relearn. However impressive
this classification, it must be pointed out that individual differences are apparent from an inspection of the learning curves.
For the present discussion, we will assume, however, that the
three classes are distinct, with the qualification that when more
data are at hand more than three classes may emerge or individual differences may blur all classes.

Are there clear anatomical distinctions to correspond to the
three behavioral classes? This question requires the analysis of
the brain damage according to anatomical criteria. If the
criterion of retrograde degeneration in the medial geniculate is
applied, the answer is no.[1] This is simply because no discon-
tinuity in the amount of degeneration of the medial geniculate
was found. When the maps of medial-geniculate degeneration
are placed in rank order (D-199, D-228, D-218, D-229, D-138,
D-134) there is no sharp separation between adjacent members
of the series. On the other hand, if the results of electrophysiology are compared with the behavioral findings, a case can be
made for three anatomical classes corresponding to the three
behavioral classes. With some part of AI remaining intact, two
animals retained the discriminatory habit. With AI, Ep, and
most but not all of AII removed, two animals relearned the
habit. Finally, the discrimination could not be relearned by the
two animals in which no active auditory cortex remained. To
support these conclusions, additional evidence needs to be obtained from behavioral experiments in which all of AI, AII, and
Ep are removed except for a fragment which is spared by
design.

The difference between the implications of the two anatomical criteria can, of course, be traced to the relationship between

---

[1] It appears that degeneration in nuclei other than the medial geniculate is unrelated to the behavioral deficit. At least massive atrophy of the
lateral geniculate and pulvinar did not prevent cat D-229 from relearning
the discriminatory task.

the cortical subdivisions AI, AII, and Ep and thalamic degeneration. The data show that there is not a simple one-to-one correspondence between cortical subdivision and thalamic source. It has been suggested by Rose and Woolsey (15) that much of the projection to AII consists of collaterals of axons that end in AI. On the assumption that the thalamic cell body degenerates only if both axon and collateral are destroyed, this hypothesis would account for our finding that degeneration in the medial geniculate body forms a continuous series even though the corresponding series of cortical lesions shifts from AI alone to a combination of AI, AII, and Ep. Whatever the effect of cutting collaterals may be, it is easy to see how subdivisions in the cortex might become blurred when retrograde degeneration in the thalamus is used as a criterion for analysis. An entirely new complication is introduced by the finding that still further degeneration occurs in the medial geniculate after lesions which invade cortex outside of AI, AII, and Ep. These considerations lead us to emphasize the electrophysiological findings in interpreting the behavioral results: A large lesion in AI has little or no effect on the habit of pattern discrimination; ablation of all but a remnant of the auditory projection areas (AI, AII, Ep) results in an amnesia for the discrimination habit, but the habit can be relearned; a permanent incapacity to discriminate tonal patterns results from the elimination of all of AI, AII, and Ep.

The capacity of small remnants of the auditory projection areas to give normal evoked responses and to serve in auditory discrimination is in agreement with Lashley's findings for the visual cortex in the rat (10). Despite some temporary disturbance to its circulation and partial interruption of intracortical neuronal connections, the cortex immediately adjacent to a region of ablation appears to retain much of its normal function.

SUMMARY AND CONCLUSIONS

1. Six cats were trained to discriminate between sequences of tones which differed only in their temporal pattern. Bilateral lesions were than made in the temporal cortex and, after recovery from operation, the animals were tested and retraining was initiated. The extent of cortical ablation was checked by histology and, in appropriate cases, by electrophysiology as well.

2. Three classes of postoperative behavior were readily distinguishable. These three behavioral classes corresponded to three kinds of cortical lesions. When the ablation was restricted to AI, the habit of discriminating a change in tonal pattern was retained following the operation. With more extensive lesions involving AII and Ep as well as AI, the discriminatory habit was temporarily lost but could be regained by postoperative training. Still more extensive lesions in which no part of AI, AII, or Ep remained preserved resulted in a postoperative loss of the habit which was not overcome by a long period of retraining.

3. The present study bears on the question of thalamocortical relationships in the auditory projection system of the cat. The anterior half of the principal division of the medial geniculate projects to auditory area I. The entire principal division projects to an extensive cortical region that includes AI, AII, and Ep as well as cortex lying between the ventral border of AII and Ep and the rhinal fissure. Extensive retrograde degeneration was found in the magnocellular division of the medial geniculate only after a large part of this total cortical sector was removed.

4. Normal evoked responses may be obtained from small remnants of projection cortex immediately adjacent to regions of ablated tissue. These small areas of intact auditory cortex also have functional significance in auditory discriminations.

REFERENCES

1. Ades, H. W. Connections of the medial geniculate body in the cat. *Arch. Neurol. Psychiat., Chicago,* 1941, **45,** 138-144.
2. Arnott, G. P. Localization of sound in space. *Amer. Psychologist,* 1949, **5,** 474.
3. Bremer, F., & Dow, R. S. The acoustic area of the cerebral cortex in the cat: A combined oscillographic and cytoarchitectonic study. *J. Neurophysiol.,* 1939, **2,** 308-318.
4. Butler, R. A., Diamond, I. T., & Neff, W. D. Role of auditory cortex in discrimination of changes in frequency. *J. Neurophysiol.,* 1957, **20,** 108-120.
5. Head, H., & Holmes, G. Sensory disturbances from cerebral lesions. *Brain,* 1911-1912, **34,** 102-254.
6. Hind, J. E. An electrophysiological determination of tonotopic organization in auditory cortex of cat. *J. Neurophysiol.,* 1953, **16,** 475-489.
7. Holmes, G. Disorders of sensation produced by cortical lesions. *Brain,* 1927, **50,** 413-427.

8. Kryter, K. D., & Ades, H. W. Studies on the function of the higher acoustic nervous centers in the cat. *Amer. J. Psychol.,* 1943, **56,** 501-536.
9. Lashley, K. S. The mechanism of vision. IV. The cerebral areas necessary for pattern vision in the rat. *J. comp. Psychol.,* 1931, **53,** 419-478.
10. Lashley, K. S. The mechanism of vision. XVI. The functioning of small remnants of the visual cortex. *J. comp. Neurol.,* 1939, **70,** 45-67.
11. Meyer, D. R., & Woolsey, C. N. Effects of localized cortical destruction upon auditory discriminative conditioning in the cat. *J. Neurophysiol.,* 1952, **15,** 149-162.
12. Neff, W. D., Fisher, J. F., Diamond, I. T., & Yela, M. Role of auditory cortex in a discrimination requiring localization of sound in space. *J. Neurophysiol.,* 1956, **19,** 500-512.
13. Raab, D. W., & Ades, H. W. Cortical and midbrain mediation of a conditioned discrimination of acoustic intensities. *Amer. J. Psychol.,* 1946, **59,** 59-83.
14. Rose, J. E. The cellular structure of the auditory region of the cat. *J. comp. Neurol.,* 1949, **91,** 409-440.
15. Rose, J. E., & Woolsey, C. N. The relations of thalamic connections, cellular structure, and evocable electrical activity in the auditory region of the cat. *J. comp. Neurol.,* 1949, **91,** 441-46.
16. Rosenzweig. M. Discrimination of auditory intensities in the cat. *Amer. J. Psychol.,* 1946, **59,** 127-136.
17. Ruch, T. C., Fulton, J. F., & German, W. J. Sensory discrimination in monkey, chimpanzee, and man after lesions of the parietal lobe. *Arch. Neurol. Psychiat., Chicago,* 1938, **39,** 919-938.
18. Waller, W. H. Thalamic degeneration induced by temporal lesions in the cat. *J. Anat., Lond.,* 1940, **74,** 528-536.
19. Woolsey, C. N., & Walzl, E. M. Topical projection of nerve fibers from local regions of the cochlea to the cerebral cortex of the cat. *Johns Hopk. Hosp. Bull.,* 1942, **71,** 315-344.

[ADDENDA FROM THE ORIGINAL PRINTING OF THIS ARTICLE: IN REFERENCE TO THE AUTHORS: *Department of Psychology, University of Chicago, Chicago, Illinois. Received for publication October 30, 1956. This work has been supported by the Office of Naval Research.* ACKNOWLEDGEMENTS: *We are indebted to Dr. Joseph E. Hind and Dr. Nelson Kiang for their aid in the electrophysiological aspects of this study. We wish to thank Mr. Russel Smith who designed and constructed testing apparatus and Mrs. Francis Karapas who prepared material for histological study.*]

PRELIMINARY ANALYSIS OF FUNCTIONS OF THE TEMPORAL LOBES IN MONKEYS ❧ *Heinrich Klüver and Paul C. Bucy*

IN PREVIOUS COMMUNICATIONS[1] we pointed out that the chief symptoms following bilateral temporal lobectomy in the rhesus monkey consist in "psychic blindness" (*Seelenblindheit*) or visual agnosia, strong "oral" tendencies and profound emotional changes. Our results were primarily based on an analysis of the behavioral symptoms of a female rhesus monkey which had been studied for a period of four months following the operations. The type of disturbance analyzed in that case seemed to be similar to the "associative mind blindness" of Lissauer.[2] It is

---

[1] Klüver, H., and Bucy, P. C.: (*a*) "Psychic Blindness" and Other Symptoms Following Bilateral Temporal Lobectomy in Rhesus Monkeys, Am. J. Physiol. **119**:352-353, 1937; (*b*) An Analysis of Certain Effects of Bilateral Temporal Lobectomy in the Rhesus Monkey, with Special Reference to "Psychic Blindness," J. Psychol. **5**:33-54, 1938.

[2] Lissauer, H.: Ein Fall von Seelenblindheit nebst einem Beitrage zur Theorie derselben, Arch. f. Psychiat. **21**:222-270, 1890.

REPRINTED FROM *Archives of Neurology and Psychiatry*, **42**:979-1000. COPYRIGHT © 1939 BY THE AMERICAN MEDICAL ASSOCIATION.

true that the diagnosis "agnosia" can be only of practical importance and merely serves to raise a number of questions. A review of the clinical literature indicates that the more carefully a case is studied the more difficult it may be to decide whether there is really an "agnostic" or merely a "visual" defect, that is, whether the variety of "agnostic" symptoms can be reduced to disturbances of "elementary" or "higher" visual functions. Von Monakow[3] and Mourgue[4] even raised the question whether the disturbances in the process of recognition commonly referred to as "agnosia" are the result of an emotional indifference of the subjects, or, in other words, whether "agnostic" symptoms represent merely disturbances in the affective sphere. In view of this situation, we can consider the "psychic blindness" and related symptoms, as described in our first report, merely the starting point for further analysis. It seemed desirable to produce, if possible, the same symptoms in a larger number of cases and to extend the behavioral analysis in certain directions in order to gain a better understanding of the nature of the disturbance following removal of both temporal lobes.

Testing Procedures

In addition to general observations on locomotion, drinking, eating, sleeping and other forms of activity displayed by the animals while kept in cages, we made use of a variety of special tests. Most of these procedures represent methods or modifications of methods previously devised by one of us for analyzing the behavior of subhuman primates.[5] With the exception of our first monkey,[1b] which was observed previous to the operations only generally, all animals were tested before and after operation. In case the operation was performed in two or more stages, the animal was also subjected to interoperative tests. In the following sections, we shall briefly indicate the procedures and test situations employed. A detailed description of the tests will be published later.

[3] von Monakow, C.: Die Lokalisation im Grosshirn und der Abbau der Funktionen durch kortikale Herde, Wiesbaden, J. F. Bergmann, 1914.

[4] Mourgue, R.: Neurobiologie de l'hallucination: Essai sur une variété particulière de désintégration de la fonction, Bruxelles, Maurice Lamertin, 1932.

[5] Klüver, H.: (a) Behavior Mechanisms in Monkeys, Chicago, University of Chicago Press, 1933; (b) An Auto-Multi-Stimulation Reaction Board for Use with Sub-Human Primates, J. Psychol. 1:123-127, 1935; (c) Certain Effects of Lesions of the Occipital Lobes in Monkeys, ibid. 4:383-401, 1937.

1. *Investigation of sensory and motor factors.* In addition to utilizing conditioned differential reactions as indicators (see "Differential Reactions"), we recorded the reactions of the animal to various stimuli and test situations. Although in most instances quantitative data were not obtained, the tests were designed to enable us to determine at least the presence of gross sensory and motor defects. The procedures used have been briefly described in our first report.[1b] The investigation of visual reactions was confined to the following items: visual reflexes; the ability to appreciate differences in brightness, size, shape, distance or position of objects; and visual field defects. For example, in obtaining data on visual acuity we utilized pulling-in reactions; the caged-in animal was required to pull in black or white threads a fraction of a millimeter in diameter and lying on a black or white ground or on surfaces exhibiting complex visual patterns. In determining visual field defects, various methods of "food perimetry" and the "hemianopic testing board"[5c] were used. The application of the pulling-in technic[5a] made it possible to obtain data on the speed of motor reactions, handedness and various motor habits.

2. *Determination of lateral tendencies.* Two or more similar objects were placed before the experimental cage. In reacting to objects in a row, any monkey may display strong right or left tendencies; that is, it may tend to pick up or pull in such objects as pieces of food, strings or boxes from the right to the left or vice versa. The test situations employed have been extensively used in a previous study of hemianopic monkeys.[6]

3. *Multiple object tests.* Different objects were placed in a row on a table on a piece of cardboard or were suspended from a horizontal string running parallel with the front of the cage and then brought within reach of the animal. In some tests the animal could view the objects before they were placed within reach; in others they were kept out of view until presented. The rows of objects contained either one or more pieces of food or none at all. The objects presented included such items as objects made of glass, wood, paper or metal; feces; live animals; toys; spots of moisture, and drawings made with ink or chalk. In most tests each object was different, but in some tests two or more of the inedible objects were alike.

4. *Investigation of reactions when monkey was free in room.* The animal was turned loose in a large room which contained pieces of apparatus and furniture, and on the floor of which had been placed various objects, including several pieces of food. During a thirty minute period the reactions were observed by the experimenter and an assistant, who sat in different corners of the room.

5. *"Concentration" test.* The apparatus, previously described,[7] consists essentially of a rotating platform on which the center of a board, 180 cm. long and 3.5 cm. wide, is fastened. The positions of the apparatus and the experimental cage were so adjusted that the monkey

---

[6] Klüver,[5c] pp. 386 and 387.
[7] Klüver and Bucy.[1b] Klüver.[5a]

was able to reach one end of the rotating board for a short time every thirty seconds. A piece of food was placed on one end of the board and a nail or metal nut on the other. The animal could, therefore, obtain one edible and one inedible object per minute.

6. *Pulling-in tests.* The tests either represented "string experiments"[5a] or required the pulling-in of a box under different conditions. One, several or all of the strings lying within easy reach of the monkey were baited with food or some inedible object. Different "string configurations" were obtained by varying the number, position, length, direction and distance of the strings from each other.

7. *Differential reactions established by training.* The technics used, which have been previously described, included: (a) the "form board," for establishing reactions to visual differences;[8] (b) the "automultistimulation reaction board," with two plates for establishing reactions to differences in sound;[5b] and (c) the pulling-in technic, with movable stimulus boxes for establishing reactions to differences in weight.[5a] It should be remarked that "form boards" with one as well as with two holes were used. In tests with the one hole "form board" the animal simply had to push aside the stimulus object, for instance, a circle, to gain access to the food. Differential reactions were established only in four of the eight animals with bilateral temporal lobectomy and in monkey 16 (see "Subjects"). This was done partly in view of Munk's results with dogs. It was thought desirable to have available a series of animals which had not been subjected to systematic training procedures. Monkeys 1, 5 and 6 were trained to respond positively to a circle and negatively to a square of the same size. In critical trials following the training, groups of equivalent and nonequivalent stimuli were determined. Monkey 8 was trained to react negatively to a sound, the sound being produced by a Cenco impulse counter, and positively to "silence." Monkey 6 was trained to react positively to the lighter of two weights in the 1,050 and 350 Gm. pair. Finally, monkey 16 was trained to respond positively to a circle instead of a square and to respond positively to a 1,150 instead of a 350 Gm. weight.

8. *Investigation of reactions in the presence of animate and inanimate objects.* The response of the animal to the presentation of single objects likely to elicit characteristic forms of behavior, especially emotional reactions, was studied. We employed such objects as a snake, a cat, a dog, a rat, a mirror, a metal stick (such as is used in transferring a monkey from one cage to the other) and a catcher (used in catching monkeys).

9. *Investigation of implement-using behavior.* Analysis of the ability to utilize objects as "tools," as previous studies have indicated,[9] seems worth while only in the case of Cebus monkeys. The present

---

[8] Klüver.[5c] Klüver and Bucy.[1b]

[9] Klüver, H.: Re-Examination of Implement-Using Behavior in a Cebus Monkey After an Interval of Three Years, Acta psychol. 2:347-397, 1937; footnote 5a.

series includes one Cebus monkey (case 5); all the other animals were macaques. Implement-using behavior was studied only in the case of the Cebus monkey.

Surgical Procedures

We shall briefly indicate the procedures employed in temporal lobectomy. In all cases anesthesia was induced by intraperitoneal injection of pentobarbital sodium. A temporal osteoplastic flap was reflected downward from over the temporal lobe. The pia-arachnoid membrane was coagulated and then cut with the Bovie high frequency current just below and parallel to the sylvian vessels and transversely across the temporal lobe at the level of the anastomotic vein of Labbé, if it occupied its usual position, or at a point just posterior to the lower end of the central sulcus. A blunt spatula was then inserted along these lines of incision and the lobe, including its medial surface, removed. Bleeding was controlled with the Bovie cautery. Whenever possible, the tissue was removed in a single block, weighed and preserved for histologic examination. The wound was carefully dried and the bone flap replaced. Muscle and scalp were closed with several layers of silk sutures.

Some of the animals have been killed, while others are still being studied. The brains of the animals killed have been or are being serially sectioned, and the sections have been stained both for myelinated fibers (by Weil's method) and for cellular elements (with cresyl violet).

A preliminary microscopic examination, for instance, of the brain of monkey 4 has shown that the extirpation included Brodmann's areas 22, 21 and 20, with the exception of the upper part of area 22 lying anterior to area 19. The uncus and almost the entire hippocampus were removed. Throughout the extent of the lesion only a thin dorsomedial strip of the hippocampus remained. Posteriorly, as the hippocampus turns dorsally toward the hippocampal commissure, about one fifth of this structure remained. The basal ganglia were not damaged except for the amygdala, which had been largely removed, and the tail of the caudate nucleus, which had been removed or seriously damaged.

Subjects

In the following list we have indicated the species, the sex and weight of the animal, the type and date of the operation and the date of death, if it has occurred. In seven of the eight cases of bilateral temporal lobectomy the operation was performed in two stages. In one case both lobes were removed simultaneously (case 8). Cases 9 to 15 represent animals in which the temporal lobes were severed from either the frontal or the occipital lobes or in which one or portions of one or of both temporal lobes were removed. In case 16 one temporal lobe was extirpated subsequent to removal of both prefrontal areas.

CASE 1.—A female rhesus monkey (Macaca mulatta), weighing 6.3 Kg., underwent extirpation of the left temporal lobe on Dec. 7, 1936 and extirpation of the right temporal lobe on Jan. 25, 1937. The animal was killed on Dec. 7, 1938.

CASE 2.—A male rhesus monkey, weighing 3.8 Kg., underwent extirpation of the left temporal lobe, on Feb. 1, 1937 and extirpation of the right temporal lobe on Feb. 23, 1937. The animal was killed on July 8, 1937.

CASE 3.—A male rhesus monkey, weighing 3.42 Kg., underwent extirpation of the right temporal lobe on Feb. 4, 1937 and extirpation of the left temporal lobe on Sept. 17, 1937. The animal was killed on Oct. 27, 1937.

CASE 4.—A female rhesus monkey, weighing 3.36 Kg., underwent extirpation of the right temporal lobe on Feb. 11, 1937 and extirpation of the left temporal lobe on February 23, 1937. The animal was killed on Mar. 18, 1937.

CASE 5.—A male Cebus monkey (Cebus capucina), weighing 2.82 Kg., underwent extirpation of the left temporal lobe on Sept. 17, 1937 and extirpation of the right temporal lobe on Oct. 15, 1937. The animal is still living.

CASE 6.—In a male rhesus monkey, weighing 2.72 Kg., the olfactory tracts were cut on July 22, 1938. The right temporal lobe was extirpated on Nov. 25, 1938 and the left temporal lobe on Jan. 27, 1939. The animal is still living.

CASE 7.—In a male rhesus monkey, weighing 4.65 Kg., the left temporal lobe was extirpated on Dec. 20, 1938 and the right temporal lobe on Feb. 6, 1939. The animal is still living.

CASE 8.—A male rhesus monkey, weighing 4.9 Kg., underwent simultaneous bilateral extirpation of the temporal lobes on Jan. 23, 1939. The animal is still living.

CASE 9.—A male rhesus monkey, weighing 4.04 Kg., underwent extirpation of the first convolution of the left temporal lobe on April 14, 1938 and extirpation of the first convolution of the right temporal lobe on July 8, 1938. The animal is still living.

CASE 10.—A female rhesus monkey, weighing 3.17 Kg., underwent extirpation of the second and third convolutions of the right temporal lobe on May 26, 1938 and extirpation of the second and third convolutions of the left temporal lobe on July 16, 1938. The animal is still living.

CASE 11.—In a female Java monkey, weighing 1.4 Kg., the connections between the temporal and the frontal lobe were severed, i.e., the anterosuperior margin of the lesion produced by temporal lobectomy was duplicated, on the left side on April 18, 1938. Connections between the temporal and the frontal lobe on the right side were severed on July 19, 1938. The animal is still living.

CASE 12.—In a male rhesus monkey, weighing 3.07 Kg., the connections between the temporal and the frontal lobe were severed on the left side on July 12, 1938 and on the right side on Sept. 27, 1938. The animal is still living.

CASE 13.—In a male rhesus monkey, weighing 3.2 Kg., the connections between the temporal and the occipital lobe were severed, i.e., the posterior margin of the lesion produced by temporal lobectomy was duplicated, on the right side on July 13, 1938. The connections between the temporal and the occipital lobe on the left side were severed on Sept. 29, 1938. The animal is still living.

CASE 14.—A female rhesus monkey, weighing 4.36 Kg., underwent extirpation of the left temporal lobe on Feb. 4, 1937 and was killed on May 17, 1937.

CASE 15.—A male rhesus monkey, weighing 4.2 Kg., underwent extirpation of the second and third convolutions of the left temporal lobe on April 15, 1938. The animal was killed on April 23, 1938.

CASE 16.—A female rhesus monkey, weighing 4.22 Kg., underwent extirpation of the left prefrontal area on Feb. 11, 1937, of the right prefrontal area on May 12, 1938 and of the left temporal lobe on Jan. 30, 1939. The animal is still living.

EFFECTS OF BILATERAL TEMPORAL LOBECTOMY

We shall describe the polysymptomatic picture as observed in the "bilateral temporal" monkey. It should be said first that the present investigation has essentially confirmed the results[1b] obtained in case 1. Such symptoms as were exhibited in case 1 can be observed immediately after extirpation of the second temporal lobe or after simultaneous removal of the two lobes, and although certain changes occur in the course of time, it is worthy of note that the picture found in case 1 about two years after the operations is in most of its characteristic features essentially the same as can be observed in the bilateral temporal monkey as early as twenty-four hours after the operations. We shall first describe forms of behavior which seem to indicate that the ability to recognize and detect the meaning of objects on the basis of visual criteria alone is either lost or seriously disturbed, although the animal exhibits no, or at least no gross, defect in the ability to discriminate visually. We have summarized this group of symptoms under the term "psychic blindness."

"Psychic Blindness."—The bilateral temporal monkey shows a strong tendency to approach animate and inanimate objects without hesitation. This tendency appears even in the presence of objects which previously called forth avoidance reactions, extreme excitement and other forms of emotional response. The animal tends to contact every object in sight and to examine it by mouth rather than by hand.

In multiple object tests, the caged-in monkey, even when hungry, will pick up objects indiscriminately either one after the other or, by using both hands, two at a time. After an oral examination, the object, if inedible, such as a nail, a glass, a live mouse, feces or a piece of sealing wax, is discarded, but if edible is immediately consumed. In general, all available objects are examined, even though the first object examined may be the only piece of food present among the objects presented and even though the row of objects lying before the cage may contain no food at all. In a given test situation, an inedible object which has been discarded after a first examination may be reexamined several times. If the row of objects contains, let us say, one piece of food and four inedible objects, the reexamination of such an object as an electric bulb or a socket may take place before or after the food has been picked up. If the same objects are presented again in the next test or on succeeding days the animal examines them as if they were being presented for the first time. In such a way, a given object may be examined again and again in the course of several months as if it had never been responded to before. The animal tends to examine all available objects, even if two or more of the objects lying in a row are alike. If the inedible objects are not removed after each test, the animal may frequently reexamine them not only between tests but also while a new series of objects is lying before the cage.

Although it has been our endeavor to present as great a variety of objects as possible in the various multiple object situations, we have not succeeded in finding any object which the bilateral temporal monkey did not want to examine. Objects are examined, no matter whether they are very large or very small, dead or alive, edible or inedible, moving or stationary, silent or noisy, solid or figures printed on paper. The monkey seems to be just as eager to examine the tongue of a hissing snake, the mouth of a cat, feces, a wire cage or a wagon as a piece of food.

The tendency to respond indiscriminately to various objects not only appears in the multiple object tests but may be just as strong when the animal is left to itself in its home cage or when it is turned loose in a room. When in its home cage the animal may examine at random pieces of food, the food pan itself, stones, cigaret stubs and wires lying among the pieces of food, the head of a screw in the wall of the cage and a chain hanging down from the door. If free in a large room the animal may contact and examine more than 100 objects in thirty minutes and may pass the pieces of food lying on the floor many times before picking them up. The examination includes such heterogeneous objects as a steel nut in a motor, an iron pipe, the tail of a monkey, a windowpane, the fingers, shoes and stop watch of the experimenter and a piece of soap. When free in a room, the monkey again tends to reexamine most objects at intervals, so that a given object, let us say an iron pipe, may be examined a dozen times in the course of half an hour. It is worthy of note that the monkey never changes the position of any of the objects in the room and that even very small objects are not carried around. Occasionally an object may be picked up for examination, but then is dropped at the same place. The animal in moving about behaves as if all available objects belonged to one general class, as if they were merely "something to be approached and examined."

In the "concentration" test, in which a piece of food or a metal object passes the experimental cage every thirty seconds, the monkey picks up both the food and the metal object until it ceases reacting to both. The food is eaten, whereas the nail or the steel nut is discarded after an examination by mouth. In some experimental periods, both the food and the inedible object are picked up in 100 per cent of the trials. Even after as many as 260 successive trials the monkey may remove the nail each time it passes, so that finally more than a hundred nails may lie on the floor of its cage. As a rule, however, the monkey is not content with removing and examining the metal object in all, or practically all, trials; it will frequently pick up a nail or a steel nut from the floor of the cage in the intervals between removing an object every thirty seconds. It should be pointed out that the normal monkey in this test situation will let the nail pass by in all trials or pick it up only the first few times.

In pulling-in tests, the animal tends to pull in the strings indiscriminately, no matter whether edible or inedible objects or no objects are attached to them. In fact, the monkey may first examine the cardboard on which the strings are lying, then one string after the other and, finally, after the pulling-in, the object fastened to the string. Again, the strings and objects already pulled in may be examined between trials. When pulling in boxes, the monkey may examine the string repeatedly during the pulling-in and the box itself before reaching into it.

Oral Tendencies.—There exists a strong tendency to examine all objects by mouth. The fact that in the multiple objects tests and in other test situations we have not discovered any kind of object the monkey did not want to examine means, therefore, that we have found no object the animal was not prone to examine orally. This oral examination consists in putting the object into the mouth, biting gently, chewing, licking, touching with the lips and "smelling" by holding the object before the nostrils. At times the object is first put into the mouth and then "smelled"; sometimes the "smelling" occurs first. Either reaction is rarely absent in examining an object. Oral tendencies are present not only in the sense that the animal examines the object orally but also in that it tends to contact the object directly by mouth instead of using its hands. Even in the multiple object tests, in which the objects are lying before the cage, the animal may often attempt to press its head through the bars to establish direct contact with its mouth. Since this is not possible, the monkey is forced to pick up the objects for oral examination. "Objects" which cannot be picked up, such as spots of moisture, drawings made on the table or designs on wallpaper, are frequently touched, rubbed or scratched after futile attempts have been made to pick them up. Such reactions are frequently followed by holding the hand or one finger before the nostrils. The "smelling" of fingers is also observed if an object is beyond reach so that no contact can be established by hand or mouth. Occasionally this "smelling" even precedes the touching or picking up of an object within reach. The monkey may repeatedly stick out its tongue to contact a metal object moving back and forth before the cage, although such an object can be easily reached by hand. The tendency to examine objects orally is not interfered with, of course, when the animal is turned loose in a room. The monkey will run from one object to another and contact and examine the various objects, or parts of them, by mouth. At times the reaction seems to be confined merely to "smelling" glass, metal or other objects, since the mouth does not come in direct contact with the object. When transferred to another cage, the monkey frequently first makes an oral examination of the door, chain, galvanized iron of the floor, heads of nails or other parts of the cage. In the "concentration" test, the hundredth nail picked up is examined orally in the same way as was the first nail removed from the board. In pulling-in tests the monkey examines not only the various objects pulled in but also the stick or the hand of the experimenter used for removing these objects from the experimental cage after completion of the test.

The tendency to examine objects orally is present even though the objects may have acquired "meaning" through previous training. For instance, in the "form board" test the animal is required to choose a circle instead of a square. For the normal monkey which has learned this problem the circle merely points to, or signifies, the presence of food. It is not reacted to for its own sake. It is an object to be pushed aside to gain access to the piece of food. For the bilateral temporal monkey the circle does not signify another object, that is, food, but both circle and square are treated as any other object, that is, as something to be examined. At times both stimulus figures are picked up, examined by mouth and discarded before even an attempt is made to take the piece of food lying in one of the holes. When the "automultistimulation reaction board" is placed before the cage, the animal may try to contact the apparatus by mouth and, since this is impossible, may at least remove the brass squares, take them into the cage and examine them orally.

It is of great interest that the normal rhesus monkey which gets hold of an inedible object is generally dominated by the tendency to tear it rapidly to pieces by using the hands and mouth. In contrast to this, the bilateral temporal monkey when confronted with a variety of objects evidences a certain lack of aggressiveness toward the objects in the sense that it confines its activities to biting them gently, to licking or to touching them with the mouth; in brief, to examining them orally in different ways. The same type of reaction or, differently expressed, the same lack of aggressiveness toward objects appears when the animal is turned loose in a room. No attempt is made to destroy, break or carry objects around.

The reactions, and especially the oral tendencies, observed in case 6 deserve special comment, as the olfactory tracts of this monkey were cut previous to removing both temporal lobes. After the olfactory tracts were severed, the characteristic gesture of "smelling" an object by holding it before the nostrils was still observed for a week. Thereafter, up to the present, for about ten months, the "smelling," even of pieces of food, has never been observed. After section of the olfactory tracts but prior to removal of the temporal lobes the monkey did not show any tendency to pick up inedible objects; even edible objects, in case the animal was not familiar with them, were frequently not taken. This type of behavior did not change when, after about four months, the right temporal lobe was removed. When the left temporal lobe was extirpated about six months after the olfactory tracts were severed, all of the symptoms characteristic of the bilateral temporal monkey appeared except that no "smelling" was ever observed. Although one of the components in the picture of oral tendencies was absent, it is significant that oral tendencies were present as in any other animal with bilateral temporal lobectomy. The results may be best illustrated by reference to the "concentration" test. After the cutting of the olfactory tracts, the animal picked up the piece of food in 100 per cent and the metal object in 2 per cent of the trials. There was never any "smelling" of the objects. After removal of the right temporal lobe exactly the same results were obtained. When the left temporal lobe was also removed the "smelling" reactions continued to be absent, but the animal now picked up the nail or the steel nut in 92 per cent of the trials and in each case examined the object by mouth before discarding it. In brief, it may be said that the reactions observed in the "concentration" test, the multiple object tests, the pulling-in tests and the other test situations clearly indicated that monkey 6 was not different from any other animal with bilateral temporal lobectomy in its tendency to pick up objects indiscriminately and then examine them by mouth.

"*Hypermetamorphosis.*" Any description of the typical behavior of the bilateral temporal monkey is incomplete without reference to another characteristic reaction tendency. When the reactions of the monkey to animate and inanimate objects are observed, it frequently appears to the observer as if the animal were acting under the influence of some "compulsory" or "irresistible" impulse. It behaves· as if it were "forced" to react to objects, events and changes in the environmental stimulus constellation. Thus, it may be said that in the bilateral temporal monkey there exists an excessive tendency to take notice of and to attend and react to every visual stimulus. The symptom described here has been given various names by neurologists and psychiatrists, for instance, by Wernicke, Sommer, Leupoldt, Steiner and others. For the sake of brevity, we shall adopt the terminology of Wernicke,[10] who spoke of a "hypermetamorphosis" and a "hypermetamorphic impulse to action."

[10] Wernicke, C.: Grundriss der Psychiatrie, Leipzig, Georg Thieme, 1906.

The monkey immediately attends to and takes in quickly the various details of a visual situation. The close visual inspection is not confined to objects within reach. The objects singled out for inspection may include such items as an eyelet in a board, a speck of dirt on a mirror, a scratch on the table, a nut in a motor, a stone in a ring, the foot of a toy monkey, a whiff of smoke, cuff buttons, a wrist watch and the mouth of the experimenter. When confronted with a series of objects, the monkey frequently looks from one object to the other before seizing one and often picks up two at a time. In the "concentration" test the animal may almost constantly attend to the end of a moving board and in such a way succeed in removing an object every thirty seconds for more than two hours. It seems clear, therefore, that a "paresis of attention" or similar defects cannot be assumed to account for the picture of "psychic blindness."

The outstanding characteristic of the various reactions is not that the monkey attends visually to such a variety of stimuli and evinces such great curiosity in all kinds of objects and events. The most impressive feature is that the presentation of any visual object will, whenever possible, immediately lead to a motor response. For the bilateral temporal monkey the most heterogeneous objects, varying from a dot in a necktie to the tongue of a hissing snake, have become equivalent in the sense that they evoke the same typical forms of motor behavior. Expressed differently, certain properties of the objects, their being "dangerous," "inedible" or "indifferent," have suddenly become ineffective in determining visually guided reactions. The monkey seems to be dominated by only one tendency, namely, the tendency to contact every object as quickly as possible. The speed with which contact is established is especially great when only a single object is presented. Noticing an object and performing the requisite motor response for contact seem to be a continuous process. When turned loose in a room, the monkey often behaves as if it were ceaselessly "pulled" from one object to another. When the experimenter or a stranger enters the laboratory, the animal may be seen standing in its cage as near to the door as possible and with an arm extended in the direction of the person entering. If the monkey is prevented from establishing contact with an object by the experimenter keeping the object out of reach, it may start examining the objects available in its cage.

The "hypermetamorphic impulse to action" is set off by almost any kind of object. It seems, therefore, that the fact of an object being an object, that is, a "segregated whole," a "discrete something" different from its surroundings, is in itself sufficient for eliciting this impulse. The multiple object tests and other tests demonstrate the strong tendency of the animal to respond to every available object, no matter what its character, and to reexamine it whenever it is noticed again. Whether or not an object is noticed, however, seems to depend on various factors. For instance, every attempt to remove one of the discarded objects from the cage may be immediately followed by grabbing and examining this or some other object or the hand of the experimenter. The monkey, which picks up, let us say, a nail for the hundredth time to examine it, is examining the same object, i.e., a nail, but the very fact that something is presented within reach, either by the experimenter or by an apparatus, makes possible what was impossible a few seconds ago, namely, a transformation of the "hypermetamorphic impulse to action" into action. At any rate, on appearance of the nail the monkey responds by picking it up.

Sensory and Motor Factors.—The question may be raised whether the picture of "psychic blindness," oral tendencies and "hypermetamorphosis" results from a combination of various sensory and motor defects. It appears that defects in "elementary" sensory functions either do not exist or are of a kind not apt to account for the typical behavior of the monkey.

In cases of visual agnosia the attempt must be made to determine whether visual defects of various kinds can in some way account for the reactions observed. One of us[5e] has shown that visual field defects alone, even if they should exist, cannot be considered sufficient to produce the picture of "psychic blindness." It was found that the various differential responses to visual stimuli established by training were not lost, or were only slightly disturbed, after unilateral occipital lobectomy or bilateral destruction of the macular cortex. In these cases Brodmann's areas 18 and 19 were also injured. Since in these cases even very extensive damage to the visual system did not lead to inability to recognize objects visually, it is difficult to understand why such a defect should appear as a consequence of much smaller field defects, as found in some of our bilateral temporal animals. In some cases of temporal lobectomy no field defects can be demonstrated. Yet the previously described symptoms following bilateral temporal lobectomy are the same in animals with and in those without visual field defects. In case 7 the tests indicate the existence of right homonymous hemianopia. The ability to appreciate differences in brightness, size, shape, distance, position and movement is as little impaired in this monkey as it is in monkeys with the left occipital lobe removed.

Our previous analysis of case 1 made the existence of defects in the upper quadrants highly probable.[1b] Since then, the existence of these defects has been supported by anatomic investigation of the brain. When microscopically examined, the right hemisphere showed interruption of the ventral half of the visual radiation close to its origin in the lateral geniculate body. There was presumably a defect involving the upper homonymous quadrants of the left halves of the visual fields, extending probably as far as the horizontal meridians and including the macula. The functional defect to be postulated on the basis of an examination of the left hemisphere was far less extensive and was probably confined to the upper part of the temporal crescent of the right eye. Despite the defects in the upper left quadrants, the monkey would jump without hesitation from the floor to high stands or tables. Anatomic investigation of the brain in case 4 indicates that one must postulate a defect confined to the upper parts of the temporal crescents. Anatomic data on other cases are not as yet available.

In studying visually induced reactions, the question is of interest whether the sequence of reactions in multiple object tests and other test situations is determined by strong lateral tendencies. Such right or left tendencies appear in normal animals, but especially in hemianopic monkeys when series of similar objects are presented. Lateral tendencies also occur at times in cases of bilateral temporal lobectomy, but our observations in multiple object tests and other tests, in which dissimilar objects are introduced, do not support the view that strong right or left tendencies, combined with an excessively strong impulse to action, enforce on the animal a certain sequence of reactions.

The temporal lobes have been of interest chiefly because of their importance for auditory function. In studying the anatomic relationship of the medial geniculate body to the cerebral cortex, Walker[11] has found that in the rhesus monkey the medial geniculate body projects only to a small area on the superior surface of the first temporal convolution. It is of historical interest that work on the functional significance of the temporal lobes has really been concerned with this small area. In our operations no attempt was made to remove this area, since our interest in temporal lobe functions was aroused by the discovery of one of us (Klüver) that the injection of mescaline or chemically related substances into monkeys produces peculiar chewing and licking movements as well as convulsions, in other words, symptoms resembling those found in the "uncinate group of fits" described by Hughlings Jackson and Stewart.[12] It was thought desirable, therefore, to remove the temporal lobes, including the uncus. In passing, it should be noted that the symptoms produced by mescaline are the same in the bilateral temporal monkey as in the normal monkey.

The bilateral temporal monkeys in our series did not exhibit any disturbance in auditory function if judged by the motor reactions to various sounds. Although quantitative data are lacking, it seems justifiable to assume that at least gross defects were absent. The anatomic data so far available support this view. In case 1 only the caudal tips of the medial geniculate bodies were degenerated. In case 4 the posterior one fourth or one third of the medial geniculate bodies was degenerated, the degeneration being more extensive on the right side. For several weeks, and even months, these animals do not vocalize; no sound is uttered in response to other monkeys. The monkey is likely to remain silent even if it is attacked or if the whole colony is shouting at feeding time. The vocal behavior which appears there-

[11] Walker, A. E.: The Primate Thalamus, Chicago, University of Chicago Press, 1938.

[12] Jackson, J. H., and Stewart, P.: Epileptic Attacks with a Warning of a Crude Sensation of Smell and with the Intellectual Aura (Dreamy State) in a Patient Who Had Symptoms Pointing to Gross Organic Disease of the Right Temporo-Sphenoidal Lobe, Brain 22:534-549, 1899.

after seems to differ from that of the normal monkey. The fact that the animals respond to and yet do not seem to recognize the meaning of sounds suggests the possibility of "agnosia" in the auditory field.

The possibility of a tactile agnosia must also be considered, although we failed to detect changes in cutaneous sensitivity in most cases. None of the monkeys was satisfied with touching, grasping or manipulating the objects. Seizing an object was merely preparatory to transporting it to the mouth. With the methods at our disposal, it was difficult to obtain reliable data on the gustatory and the olfactory sense, but it is noteworthy that inedible objects were never swallowed. Inedible objects were always discarded after an oral examination, although even feces was often chewed several times before being removed. Nevertheless, the type and speed of removing objects, such as feces, a piece of food soaked in quinine or a wooden or metal object, were often strikingly different. In view of the fact that the lesions involved all or the greater part of the hippocampus and uncus, it is of special interest that the "smelling" of objects and the characteristic gesture of holding an object before the nostrils represent some of the most typical reactions of the bilateral temporal monkey. It is significant that such reactions were absent in case 6, in which the olfactory tracts had been cut.

The motor reactions involved in grasping, holding, picking up and pulling in objects were essentially the same as in normal monkeys. In some cases abnormalities of gait were observed. Although the tendency to approach and contact every object seemed equally strong in all animals, there were considerable differences in the amount of spontaneous activity. All of the more active monkeys tended to perform "antics," not only when they could not get certain objects beyond reach but also when they were left to themselves in their home cages. In our previous description of case 1 it was pointed out that we frequently observed a "sequence of gesticulations, involving arms, head and most of the body."[1b] These gesticulations and similar movement patterns in other cases are difficult to describe. The many peculiar movements executed by the animal while sitting, lying, jumping or hanging from the top or sides of the cage frequently arouse the mirth of a casual observer. The monkey may repeatedly put both feet, or one foot and one hand, simultaneously behind its neck. It may jump around on the floor of the cage while holding on to one foot with one hand and then without letting the foot go may jump to the seat of the cage. In jumping from the seat to the floor, it may seize the wire mesh at the top of the cage first with its hands, then with its feet, and then may drop to the floor, landing on its hands first. It may swing and perform peculiar twists of its body while hanging with its feet from the top of the cage. It may grab one forearm with one hand and move both arms up and down. It may hang with its hands from the top of the cage and, after pulling its body through the space between its arms, may swing back and forth with its feet almost touching the floor of the cage. It may repeat such movement patterns many times and combine them in different ways.

In fact, the general picture is that of a Witzelsucht of the extremities.

Emotional Changes. In the bilateral temporal monkey we find either profound changes in emotional behavior or complete absence of all emotional reactions in the sense that the motor and vocal reactions generally associated with anger and fear are not exhibited. This change in effectivity is especially remarkable in view of the fact that care has been taken to use only "wild," aggressive monkeys in this work.

The fact that the monkey approaches every object without hesitation, no matter whether it be a catcher, a large bull snake or a strange person, represents in itself a striking deviation from normal behavior. Even bodily contact with an object does not produce avoidance reactions or other forms of behavior indicative of fear. Movements, for instance, of a live animal when being examined, or other forms of sensory stimulation may, because of their suddenness, lead to retreat, but often immediately thereafter a new attempt is made to establish contact with the object.

The typical reaction of a "wild" monkey when suddenly turned loose in a room consists in getting away from the experimenter as rapidly as possible. It will try to find a secure place near the ceiling or hide in an inaccessible corner where it cannot be seen. If seen, it will either crouch and, without uttering a sound, remain in a state of almost complete immobility or suddenly dash away to an apparently safer place. This behavior is frequently accompanied by other signs of strong emotional excitement. In general, all such reactions are absent in the bilateral temporal monkey. Instead of trying to escape, it will contact and examine one object after another or parts of objects, including the experimenter, strangers or other animals. The experimenter may walk over to it, touch and stroke and even pick it up. The monkey often confines itself almost entirely to examining objects which are on or can be reached from the floor. After being attacked and bitten by another animal, it may approach this animal again and again in an attempt to examine it.

While this is the general picture of emotional behavior, individual animals present differences. Expressions of emotions, such as vocal behavior, "chattering" and different facial expressions, are generally lost for several months, but they may reappear. In some cases the loss of anger and fear reactions is complete. In case 6, for instance, the animal is restlessly active most of the time, constantly attending to and responding to numerous stimuli, never resenting any form of handling, always eager to engage in playful activities with the experimenter or to follow him around the room. In fact, it may be said that the picture of normal "wildness" has been replaced by that of "hypomania." The bodily expressions of emotions associated with aggressive tendencies can be observed in some monkeys after a few months. Although such a monkey, with teeth bared and ears laid back, may jump toward the experimenter as if to attack him, it will merely lick or otherwise examine the fingers of the experimenter. The animal may exhibit expressions of intense emotional excitement in case the floor is swept near its cage or a wagon rolled by, but the moment the monkey is allowed to contact and to examine the broom or the wagon, the anger expressions will immediately subside. It seems that emotional behavior, when it occurs, occurs chiefly in connection with events preceding or following the oral examination of an object, especially when the attempt to contact an object is thwarted.

Changes in Sexual Behavior. In some monkeys the increase in sexual activity is so marked and the manifestations of sexual behavior are so diverse that we are forced to include sexual changes among the symptoms produced by bilateral temporal lobectomy. Such changes are not immediately apparent. We have noticed them first three to six weeks after the operation. It should be noted that two of the monkeys in our series were killed before this period. Our observations are, therefore, chiefly concerned with male macaques.

The monkeys appear hypersexed, not only when with other animals but also when alone. The reactions to be recorded either are overt sexual responses or represent forms of behavior involving some sexual element. When the monkey is confined alone in a cage, the following states and activities can be observed: frequent erection of the penis, often without previous manipulation, the glans penis being clearly visible, or semierection, even while the animal is sitting quietly; long-continued licking and sucking of the penis, the animal at times apparently falling asleep with the penis in the mouth; manipulating or pulling at the penis or scrotum, even while the animal is standing; "yawning" (as seen in copulatory reactions) and, at the same time, manipulation of the genitalia while lying on the back or side; oral and manual exploration of the genitalia while the animal is in all kinds of positions, for instance, biting of the penis while swinging back and forth with the feet suspended from the top of the cage and with the hands pressed against the hindquarters; long-continued biting of the fingers, toes, feet, legs and other parts of the body; grabbing the bars of the cage and pressing the hindquarters rhythmically against them, and "presenting reactions" on approach of an observer. Grabbing the finger of the observer may be immediately followed by general bodily activity and penile erection.

Whenever other monkeys are put into the same cage, various forms of heterosexual and homosexual behavior can be observed. The monkey may, for instance, copulate almost continuously for half an hour. It may leave the female only to mount again immediately. If two bilateral temporal male monkeys are put together, sexual behavior may take forms which make it necessary to separate the animals. One of the monkeys while lying on the seat of the cage may reach with one hand toward the floor to grab the erect penis of the other monkey and practically lift the animal from the floor. The animal which is being lifted may do nothing but utter a grunt. Or one monkey may grab the tail of the other and in pulling it across the edge of the seat incidentally break the tail. While one monkey mounts the other and performs copulatory movements, the other one may be seen standing with erect penis. Or both monkeys may lie on the floor and mutually explore each other's genitalia. One monkey may ride on the back of the other and at the same time suck one of its ears. Although they frequently bite each other's legs, arms or tail, fights never develop, and injuries are merely the by-product of heightened sexual activity.

Since such striking manifestations of sexual behavior are completely absent in the normal animals of our colony and do not appear in unilateral temporal monkeys kept on the same diet and under the same conditions, or in monkeys with differently situated lesions, we feel justified in assuming that these sexual changes are dependent on removal of the second temporal lobe or simultaneous removal of both lobes.[13]

GENERAL CONSIDERATION OF BEHAVIORAL CHANGES

Munk failed to produce "psychic blindness" in rhesus monkeys, and although he thought that he had succeeded in producing it in dogs, it was subsequently shown by a number of investigators that visual disturbances and field defects could account for the behavior of the animals. We have found a picture of "psychic blindness" following bilateral temporal lobectomy in the monkey. The importance of this result lies, first of all, in the fact that such a picture can be produced by a cortical operation in animals. At the start, questions such as the duration of the symptoms or the exact nature of the lesions are of secondary importance.

In studying the various reactions and reaction tendencies, we have arrived at a group of symptoms which we may consider "typical" for the bilateral temporal monkey. We are aware that the picture may be modified by a variety of factors. The animals in the present series were studied for varying periods, ranging from three weeks to about two years from the date of the operation. They differed in age, weight, sex and other factors. Nevertheless, in all cases the typical symptoms, which we have briefly summarized under "psychic blindness," oral tendencies, "hypermetamorphosis" and emotional changes, appeared almost

[13] It is perhaps significant that in case 1 typical "presenting reactions" were frequently observed after a period of one and a half years in spite of the fact that the uterus and both ovaries had been previously removed. This animal, as well as three other monkeys that had had similar operations, were supplied to us by Dr. G. W. Bartelmez. Two of these animals were even "wilder" and more "vicious" than the average untamed rhesus monkey. Only one of these four animals was used in the present study (case 1).

immediately and remained remarkably constant for the periods of observation indicated. It is true that changes occurred, but that these changes were not more marked deserves special emphasis. For instance, the experimenter could at all times touch, stroke or slap six of the eight monkeys. Such treatment of the other two animals was not possible after several months, but their emotional behavior remained profoundly altered. Monkey 1, which was studied for about two years, tended during the last few months, in multiple object tests, to pick up food first and then to examine the remaining objects, but was inclined to pick up objects indiscriminately again when they were kept out of view until presented or when injections of mescaline were given. It should be remembered that many of the objects used in these tests had been presented again and again in the course of previous experiments. In brief, even the long-continued study in this case revealed little change in the general picture presented by "psychic blindness," oral tendencies, "hyper-metamorphosis" and emotional changes.[13a]

In considering the polysymptomatic picture following bilateral temporal lobectomy, the question may be raised whether the various symptoms point to one basic defect or disturbance. Conceivably, any of the symptoms described may be indicative of a disturbance in some fundamental mechanism, so that all other symptoms could be understood by reference to one factor. At present, however, any attempt to reduce the variety of behavioral manifestations to one simple formula seems rather hopeless. To determine the mechanisms operative in the behavior of these monkeys further analysis is needed. Preliminary information was obtained in studying various conditioned differential reactions.

In the "form board" test, the monkey was required to react positively to a circle instead of a square. The normal monkey may learn this without even making one error if the tests are preceded by a few trials with a one hole "form board." We shall briefly state the results in cases 1, 5 and 6. In case 1 training was started after removal of both temporal lobes. The animal

---

[13a] In checking on possible changes in dietary habits, we recently found that the rhesus monkeys with bilateral temporal lobectomy which are still living (monkeys 6, 7 and 8) eat animal foods, such as bacon, liver sausage, boiled ham, boiled tongue, smoked whitefish, ground beef and broiled lamb chops. We have never seen normal rhesus monkeys accept such articles of diet.

acquired the differential response only with difficulty and after hundreds of trials. For a long time stimulus figures and food were responded to indiscriminately, but finally an errorless performance was reached. Monkeys 5 and 6, which had been trained before the operations, showed a marked disturbance of the differential response after removal of both lobes, but it was possible to reestablish the response through training. The same marked disturbance occurred in the reactions of monkey 8, which had previously been trained to respond negatively to a sound. However, when vibratory stimulation was included by use of a buzzer or a bell fastened below the floor of the cage instead of the original source of sound (a Cenco impulse counter placed at a considerable distance from the cage), the animal immediately obtained food in 100 per cent of the trials by opening the proper receptacle of the "automultistimulation reaction board." Only one of the responses established preoperatively was found intact after bilateral temporal lobectomy, namely, the response in case 6 to the lighter weight in the 1,050 and 350 Gm. pair.

More important than these findings, perhaps, is the fact that we were able to demonstrate that the animals had not lost the ability to "generalize" when responding to visual stimuli. In the "form board" tests the properties of the stimuli were changed by introducing variations in size, brightness, color and even shape (by presenting, for instance, an ellipse and a triangle instead of a circle and a square) or by substituting "figures" drawn on cardboard for the circle and the square. Despite these changes, all three monkeys continued to react positively to the circle or responded immediately to the curvilinear figure.

It may be said that the ability to respond to different objects in terms of such relations as "larger than," "brighter than" or "nearer than," or such properties as "angular" or "curvilinear" implies "generalizations" of a very primitive order. It can be readily understood that adaptive behavior, as long as it occurs at all, presupposes the effectiveness of such properties or the existence of such primitive forms of "generalization," and it is apparently for this reason that investigators have frequently insisted that the *Beziehungsfunktion* cannot really be destroyed by cerebral lesions.

In view of this situation, the results obtained in the Cebus monkey (case 5) are of special interest. The "form board" tests give no evidence that the ability to "generalize" in responding to visual stimuli was impaired. At the same time, the ability to utilize objects as "tools" in obtaining food was completely lost. It is apparently one thing to recognize that a stick is "longer than" another one or "nearer than" a piece of food; it is another thing to recognize the "tool" character of a stick. As previous work indicates,[9] being "longer than" and being a "tool" are properties which become effective at different levels of adaptive behavior. At any rate, monkey 5 was unable to solve even the simplest problem in which a piece of food lying beyond reach on the floor could be obtained by using a stick lying near the food and within reach of the animal. The response consisted in repeatedly making an oral examination of the stick and again and again reaching for the food with one hand. When different objects were available at the same time, such as a stick, a sack, a wire or a leather belt, the monkey, instead of seizing one of them to obtain food in a few seconds, as it would have done in preoperative tests, repeatedly reached for the food and walked around for half an hour or longer examining one object after another. None of the objects was ever carried around. It is of great theoretic interest to learn whether these results will be confirmed by future work on suitable animals.

EFFECTS OF OTHER LESIONS

The behavioral changes following the removal of one temporal lobe were studied in eight monkeys (cases 1 to 7 and 14) for periods ranging from about two weeks to seven months. The extirpation of one lobe produced none of the symptoms characteristic of the bilateral temporal monkey. In some cases, however, there was a change in the direction of greater "tameness." This seems significant in view of the fact that we have failed to observe a similar change in monkeys with occipital, parietal or frontal lesions. There was no disturbance in differential responses established before the operation.

Furthermore, the forms of behavior typical of monkeys with both temporal lobes removed did not appear after (1) bilateral removal of the first temporal convolution (case 9); (2) unilateral or bilateral removal of the second and third temporal convolutions (cases 10 and 15); (3) severing the connections between the temporal and the frontal lobes (cases 11 and 12), or (4) severing the connections between the temporal and the occipital lobes (case 13). Only in case 13 was there uncertainty as to whether at least some of the symptoms existed in an attenuated form.

Of special interest are the results in case 16. The chief effect of removing the left temporal lobe subsequent to removal of both prefrontal areas was disappearance of the restlessness and the hyperactivity characteristic of the prefrontal monkey and a marked change in the direction of greater "tameness."[14]

COMMENT

In view of the fact that the anatomic study of the brains has not yet been completed, a detailed discussion of the relations between behavioral and neural mechanisms is out of the question. At this point it seems worth while, however, to relate some of the results of our behavorial analysis to data furnished by human pathology.

We may consider the outstanding characteristic of the behavorial changes following bilateral temporal lobectomy to be that they affect the relation between animal and environment so deeply. A monkey which approaches every enemy to examine it orally will conceivably not survive longer than a few hours if turned loose in a region with a plentiful supply of enemies. We doubt that a monkey would be seriously hampered under natural conditions, in the wild, by a loss of its prefrontal region, its parietal lobes or its occipital lobes, as long as small portions of the striate cortex remained intact.

The fact that removal of both temporal lobes in the monkey may result in such profound behavior changes, particularly in the emotional sphere, becomes of special interest in view of the insistence of previous writers, such as Anglade, Takase and Marburg, that the temporal lobes in man are in some way concerned with emotions or "affective tonus."[15] The possible significance of the temporal lobes for emotional behavior has also

---

[14] Spontaneous activity was registered by utilizing vacuum tube amplification. The floor of the cage was covered with pieces of galvanized iron separated by gaps of about 1.5 cm. A minute current passing through the body of the animal operated a relay control whenever the animal walked or ran across these gaps. In such a way the number of circling movements

been brought out in recent discussions of the nonolfactory functions of the "olfactory" cortex. It should be recalled that our
extirpations include structures generally represented as subserving some phase of olfactory function. Herrick[16] expressed
the view that the olfactory cortex may serve as a nonspecific
activator for all cortical activities and that it may act on "the
internal apparatus of general bodily attitude, disposition and
affective tone." In studying the rhinencephalon of the dolphin,
Addison[17] found that the hippocampus, fornix, mamillary bodies
and habenular and amygdaloid nuclei are present, although the
olfactory bulbs and tracts are lacking. Langworthy[18] made similar observations in the porpoise. It is of interest that the parolfactory cortex, which Edinger termed a center for the *Oralsinn,*
was present in both forms. In the opinion of Langworthy, "the
fact that the hippocampus, fornix, and mamillary bodies persist
. . . suggests that they must have functions other than olfactory."

The nonolfactory functions of these structures have recently
been emphasized in a different connection by Papez,[19] who attempted to find an "anatomic basis of the emotions" by correlating anatomic, clinical and experimental data of various kinds.
He stated:

> It is proposed that the hypothalamus, the anterior thalamic nuclei,
> the gyrus cinguli, the hippocampus and their interconnections con-
> stitute a harmonious mechanism which may elaborate the functions of
> central emotion, as well as participate in emotional expression.

Papez suggested that "the central emotive process of cortical
origin" may be built up in the hippocampus and transferred to
the mamillary body and thence through the anterior nuclei of
the thalamus to the cortex of the cingular gyrus, from which the
process may spread to other regions in the cerebral cortex.

---

or other movements from one part of the cage to the other could be automatically recorded by an electric counter.

[15] von Economo, C., and Koskinas, G. N.: Die Cytoarchitektonik der
Hirnrinde des erwachsenen Menschen, Berlin, Julius Springer, 1925.

[16] Herrick, C. J.: The Functions of the Olfactory Parts of the Cerebral
Cortex, Proc. Nat. Acad. Sc. **19:**7-14, 1933.

[17] Addison, W. H. F.: On the Rhinencephalon of Delphinus Delphis, L.,
J. Comp. Neurol. **25:**497-522, 1915.

[18] Langworthy, O. R.: A Description of the Central Nervous System of
the Porpoise (Tursiops Truncatus), J. Comp. Neurol. **54:**437-499, 1932.

[19] Papez, J. W.: A Proposed Mechanism of Emotion, Arch. Neurol. &
Psychiat. **38:**725-743, (Oct.) 1937.

He found "no clinical or other evidence" to support the view that these structures mediate olfactory function.

In our experiments, the cortical circuit proposed by Papez has been definitely interrupted by removal of the hippocampus. The fact that none of the typical symptoms appeared in animals in which the hippocampus was left intact may also be interpreted as lending further support to Papez' theory. As pointed out before, the behavioral reactions characteristic of the bilateral temporal monkey were absent when only the first convolution or the second and third convolutions of the temporal lobes were removed, or when the connections between the frontal and the temporal lobes or between the occipital and the temporal lobes were severed. Whether the hippocampal formation and its connections play such a decisive role in emotional behavior, as suggested by Papez, can only be determined by subsequent experimentation. To throw further light on the symptomatology of the bilateral temporal monkey, it will be necessary to study not only the effects of differently situated subtotal lesions but also the changes following a resection of the fornix or an isolated removal of the hippocampus. Herrick[16] has called attention to the fact that most ablation operations performed in connection with studies of behavior have involved only the neopallium, leaving the olfactory cortex entirely intact or but slightly injured. He pointed out the necessity for removing the various parts of the olfactory cortex in an isolated manner, although this may involve "difficult, but probably not impossible surgical operations."

Kleist[20] has advanced ideas similar to those of Papez in proposing an anatomic substratum for enteroceptive functions, i.e., drives, attitudes, personality traits, moods and emotions. Spatz[21] expressed doubt that the highly developed *Orbitalhirn* of Kleist and the primitive allocortical olfactory region are intimately related and emphasized the importance of the "basal cortex" of the temporal and the frontal lobe for personality changes. He advanced the opinion that no other disease is more important for advancing knowledge of cortical localization than Pick's disease.

[20] Kleist, K.: Bericht über die Gehirnpathologie in ihrer Bedeutung für Neurologie und Psychiatrie, Ztschr. f. d. ges. Neurol. u. Psychiat. **158:** 159-193, 1937.

[21] Spatz, H.: Ueber die Bedeutung der basalen Rinde, Ztschr. f. d. ges. Neurol. u. Psychiat. **158:**208-232, 1937.

In this disease there are not only fundamental changes in personality and character but also such symptoms as echolalia, echopraxia and palilalia.[22] Even in the last stages of the disease the patient may still visually attend to everything that is going on and seize every object within reach to put it into his mouth.[23]

In considering the "hypermetamorphosis" and "hypermetamorphic impulse to action" in the bilateral temporal monkey, we commented on the "compulsory" nature of the reactions. The question may be raised whether the lack of inhibition displayed in seizing every object and the tendency to respond to the same object again and again find their parallel in the symptomatology in cases of lesions in the human temporal lobe. It is perhaps significant that the analysis of speech disorders led Pick[24] to the view that the temporal lobes form the anatomic basis of inhibition, the absence of which leads to logorrhea, various echo symptoms (echolalia, echographia, echopraxia) and paraphasia. According to him, the speech utterances accompanying the epileptic aura or the "dreamy states" of Hughlings Jackson also involve the same mechanism of disinhibition.

In studying the similarities of catatonic and encephalitic disturbances in motility, Steiner[25] found postencephalitic children who touched and examined every object in sight by hand without uttering a word. He expressed the view that a "hypermetamorphosis" which takes the form of touching and tactually examining every object is closely related to echopraxia and echolalia. It is of interest that Leyser,[26] Lotmar[27] and others stated that "hypermetamorphosis," profound changes in affectivity and changes in sexual behavior are the outstanding symptoms in cases of epidemic encephalitis.

The fact that a picture of "psychic blindness," as described by Munk, should result from lesions of the temporal lobe is not

[22] Benedek, L., and Lehoczky, T.: The Clinical Recognition of Pick's Disease: Report of Three Cases, Brain 62:104-122, 1939.

[23] von Braunmühl, A., and Leonhard, K.: Ueber ein Schwesternpaar mit Pickscher Krankheit, Ztschr. f. d. ges. Neurol. u. Psychiat. 150:209-241, 1934.

[24] Pick, A.: Aphasie, in Bethe, A.; von Bergmann, G.; Embden, G., and Ellinger, A.: Handbuch der normalen und pathologischen Physiologie, Berlin, Julius Springer, 1931, vol. 15, pt. 2, pp. 1416-1524.

[25] Steiner, G.: Encephalitische und katatonische Motilitätsstörungen, Ztschr. f. d. ges. Neurol. u. Psychiat. 138:553-561, 1922.

[26] Leyser, E.: Untersuchungen über die Charakterveränderungen nach Encephalitis epidemica, Arch. f. Psychiat. 72:552-609, 1925.

[27] Lotmar, F.: Die Stammganglien und die extrapyramidal-motorischen

readily explained at present. The close relation of aphasic and agnostic symptoms has been frequently emphasized. It is known from Walker's study of the thalamocortical projection of the rhesus monkey that the temporal lobe has few or no thalamic connections except from the medial geniculate body.[11] The functional significance of this observation is not clear, but it seems that the elaboration of impulses relayed from the periphery by way of the thalamus cannot be one of the chief functions of the temporal lobes. The importance of the corticifugal fiber connections of the temporal region, as studied by Mettler,[28] must also be considered. Niessl von Mayendorf[29] has advanced the theory that visual agnosia is due to lesions of the left macular bundle of the visual radiation or of the cortical representation of the macula in the left hemisphere. We consider it safe to assume that the picture of "psychic blindness," as found in the bilateral temporal monkey, is not due to such lesions. The anatomic investigation, for instance, of the brain of monkey 4 has clearly demonstrated that both macular bundles are intact. The behavioral tests applied to animals still living definitely suggest that visual field defects do not exist in the majority of cases.

SUMMARY

The behavioral effects of the removal of both temporal lobes, including the uncus and the greater part of the hippocampus, were studied in macaques. The monkeys exhibited the following symptoms: (1) forms of behavior which seem to be indicative of "psychic blindness"; (2) strong oral tendencies in examining available objects (licking, biting gently, chewing, touching with the lips, "smelling"); (3) a strong tendency to attend and react to every visual stimulus ("hypermetamorphosis"); (4) marked changes in emotional behavior or absence of emotional reactions in the sense that the motor and vocal reactions generally associated with anger and fear are not exhibited, and (5) an increase in sexual activity. These symptoms also appeared if the olfac-

Syndrome, in Foerster, O., and Wilmanns, K.: Monographien aus dem Gesamtgebiete der Neurologie und Psychiatrie, Berlin, Julius Springer, 1926, no. 48, pp. 1-169.

[28] Mettler, F. A.: Corticifugal Fiber Connections of the Cortex of Macaca Mulatta: The Temporal Region, J. Comp. Neurol. 63:25-47, 1935.

[29] Niessl von Mayendorf, E.: Beiträge zur Lehre von der Seelenblindheit: VIII, Ztschr. f. d. ges. Neurol. u. Psychiat. 159:326-344, 1937.

tory tracts were cut previous to removing both temporal lobes. Even the oral tendencies, except for the "smelling," were present.

The symptoms typical of monkeys with both temporal lobes removed did not appear after (1) bilateral removal of the first temporal convolution; (2) bilateral removal of the second and third temporal convolutions; (3) severing the connections between the temporal and the frontal lobes, i.e., duplicating the anterosuperior margin of the lesion produced by temporal lobectomy; (4) severing the connections between the temporal and the occipital lobes, i.e., duplicating the posterior margin of the lesion produced by temporal lobectomy. The symptoms also did not appear after unilateral temporal lobectomy, except that there was in some cases a change in the direction of greater "tameness." This "tameness" was also observed when after previous extirpation of both prefrontal areas one temporal lobe was removed.

Differential reactions to visual stimuli established preoperatively were seriously disturbed after bilateral temporal lobectomy, but it was possible to reestablish the response through training. The ability to "generalize" in responding to visual stimuli did not seem to be impaired.

[ADDENDA FROM THE ORIGINAL PRINTING OF THIS ARTICLE: IN REFERENCE TO THE AUTHORS: *Chicago. Read at the Sixty-Fifth Annual Meeting of the American Neurological Association, Atlantic City, N. J., June 7, 1939. From the Otho S. A. Sprague Memorial Institute and the Division of Neurology and Neurosurgery, University of Chicago. This research has been aided by a grant from the Committee for Research in Dementia Praecox, founded by the Supreme Council, Thirty-Third Degree, Scottish Rite, Northern Masonic Jurisdiction, U.S.A.*]

A PROPOSED MECHANISM OF
EMOTION ❖ *James W. Papez*

THE WORK of Cannon,[1] Bard,[2] Penfield,[3] Ranson[4] and others has greatly advanced knowledge of the functions of the hypothalamus. In the light of these researches the connections of the hypothalamus to the medial wall of the cerebral cortex gain a new significance. The following discussion presents some anatomic, clinical and experimental data dealing with the hypothalamus, the gyrus cinguli, the hippocampus and their interconnections. Taken as a whole, this ensemble of structures is

[1] Cannon, W. B.: The James-Lange Theory of Emotion: A Critical Examination and an Alternative Theory, Am. J. Psychol. **39:**10-124, 1927; Again the James-Lange and the Thalamic Theories of Emotion, Psychol. Rev. **38:**281-295, 1931.

[2] Bard, P.: (*a*) The Central Representation of the Sympathetic Nervous System as Indicated by Certain Physiologic Observations, Arch. Neurol. Psychiat. **22:**230-246 (Aug.) 1929; (*b*) Emotion: I. The Neuro-Humoral Basis of Emotional Reactions, in Murchison, C. A.: A Handbook of General Experimental Psychology, Worchester, Mass., Clark University Press, 1934, chap. 6, pp. 264-331.

[3] Penfield, W.: Wesley M. Carpenter Lecture: Influence of the Diencephalon and Hypophysis upon General Autonomic Function, Bull. New York Acad. Med. **9:**613-637, 1933; Canad. M. A. J. **30:**589-598, 1934.

[4] Ranson, S. W.: The Hypothalamus: Its Significance for Visceral Innervation and Emotional Expression, Tr. Coll. Physicians Philadelphia **2:**222-242, 1934.

REPRINTED FROM *Archives of Neurology and Psychiatry,* **38:**725-744. COPYRIGHT © 1937 BY THE AMERICAN MEDICAL ASSOCIATION.

proposed as representing theoretically the anatomic basis of the
emotions.

It is generally recognized that in the brain of lower vertebrates
the medial wall of the cerebral hemisphere is connected anatomically and integrated physiologically with the hypothalamus and
that the lateral wall is similarly related to the dorsal thalamus
(Herrick[5]). These fundamental relations are not only retained
but greatly elaborated in the mammalian brain by the further
development of the hippocampal formation and the gyrus cinguli
in the medial wall and of the general cortex in the lateral wall
of each cerebral hemisphere.

The main steps in the phyletic history of these structures are
clearly represented in the various classes of vertebrates. It is not
surprising, therefore, to find that the literature on this fascinating
subject presents on the whole a congruent account. Step by step,
the structures of the medial wall become differentiated into the
hippocampal formation, which establishes the first efferent connection of the cortex, namely, the fornix with the hypothalamus,
and as the adjacent cingular cortex appears, it receives, per
contra, an afferent connection from the hypothalamus. Step by
step, the lateral wall above the pyriform cortex becomes differentiated into the lateral nonolfactory cortex, which through the
medium of the internal capsule maintains its afferent and recurrent connections with the nuclei of the dorsal thalamus. The
histories of the two walls of the hemispheres owe their disparity
and distinctive structure to two totally different kinds of integration—the hippocampus and the cingular cortex participating in
hypothalamic activities and the lateral cortex in the general
sensory activities mediated by the dorsal thalamus. It is also
noteworthy that in both systems two-way connections exist between the cortical and the thalamic level.

The account which follows will be concerned chiefly with the
reciprocal connections which exist between the hypothalamus
and the gyrus cinguli and hippocampus. Its chief purpose is to
point out that these connections may mediate by means of the
cortical circuit the important function commonly called emotion.

The term "emotion" as commonly used implies two conditions:
a way of acting and a way of feeling. The former is designated
as emotional expression; the latter, as emotional experience or

[5] Herrick, C. J.: Morphogenesis of the Brain, J. Morphol. **54**:233-258
(March 5) 1933.

subjective feeling. The experiments of Bard[2a] have demonstrated that emotional expression depends on the integrative action of the hypothalamus rather than on that of the dorsal thalamus or cortex, since it may occur when the cerebral hemispheres and the dorsal thalamus are totally removed. For subjective emotional experience, however, the participation of the cortex is essential. Emotional expression and emotional experience may in the human subject be dissociated phenomena. Hence, emotion as a subjective state must be referred to the higher psychic level. Concerning the theory of emotion based on diencephalic processes, Bard[2b] wrote:

As we have seen, every relevant experimental fact points away from the periphery and directly toward the brain as the site of the processes which determine whether or not a stimulus shall give rise to emotional feeling. What is the nature and the locus of these all-important central processes?

Cannon[1] (1927, 1931) and also Dana[6] (1921) have proposed the theory that emotion results from the action and reaction of the cerebral cortex and the diencephalon. This theory, unlike the James-Lange theory, has considerable experimental support and takes into account anatomical and physiological facts ignored by the older view. First of all, there is the evidence that at the base of the diencephalon are located the neural patterns responsible for emotional behavior, mechanisms capable of independent discharge but normally held in check by the cerebral cortex. At the same time the cerebral cortex is the immediate site of emotional consciousness, and, as we have seen, emotional experience and emotional expression may be dissociated by disease or surgical intervention. But we know that thalamic processes are a source of affective experience, that bodily sensations such as are sometimes associated with emotion may be thalamic in origin. Well-established anatomical facts show that, with the possible exception of the olfactory, all sensory impulses are interrupted at the thalamic level before gaining the cerebral cortex, and Head's (1920) studies suggest how there may be regrouping of corticopetal impulses in the thalamus. Cannon's theory has its basis in these facts and it proposes that, at the same time that the diencephalon discharges downward the motor impulses which produce the emotional behavior, it discharges upward to the cortex impulses which throw into action the processes which underlie emotional consciousness.

In order to make clear at the outset the general anatomic picture which I wish to propose as the probable corticothalamic mechanism of emotion, a diagram has been constructed, showing

[6] Dana, C. L.: The Anatomic Seat of the Emotions: A Discussion of the James-Lange Theory, Arch. Neurol. Psychiat. 6:634-639 (Dec.) 1921.

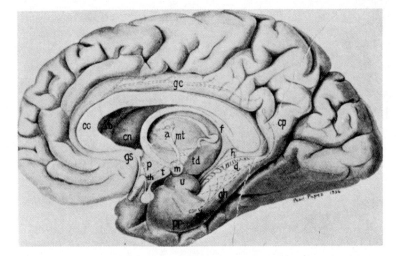

Medial view of the right cerebral hemisphere, showing the hippocampus and its connection with the mamillary body through the fornix and also the connections of the mamillary body to the anterior thalamic nuclei and thence to the cortex of the gyrus cinguli. In this specimen an unusually large exposed (nude) hippocampus is seen.

Abbreviations

a, anterior nucleus
ab, angular bundle
cc, corpus callosum
cn, caudate nucleus
cp, cingulum posterius
d, gyrus dentatus
f, fornix
gc, gyrus cinguli
gh, gyrus hippocampi
gs, gyrus subcallosus

h, hippocampus nudus
m, mamillary body
mt, mamillothalamic tract
p, pars optica hypothalami
pr, pyriform area
sb, subcallosal bundle
t, tuber cinereum
td, tractus mamillotegmentalis
th, tractus hypophyseus
u, uncus

its main features (figure). I shall start with the hypothalamus, the three parts of which are illustrated. The pars optica is connected through the infundibulum with the pars neuralis of the hypophysis. The tuber cinereum is connected downward with the lower sympathetic centers. In the human brain a large tract can be seen passing down, ventral to the red nucleus. The pars mamillaris is connected in an efferent way to the cortex of the gyrus cinguli. The pars mamillaris also receives afferent connections from several other sources, the most prominent being the fornix from the hippocampal formation.

As the figure shows, it is the mamillary body which bears the main hypothalamic relations to the cerebral cortex. This is a two-way connection in the nature of a circuit through the cerebral cortex, at the upper level, and through the mamillary body, at the hypothalamic level. In this circuit impulses may be incited at two points: the cerebral cortex and the hypothalamus. Incitations of cortical origin would pass first to the hippocampal formation and then down by way of the fornix to the mamillary body. From this they would pass upward through the mamillothalamic tract, or the fasciculus of Vicq d'Azyr, to the anterior nuclei of the thalamus and thence by the medial thalamocortical radiation (in the cingulum) to the cortex of the gyrus cinguli.

The central emotive process of cortical origin may then be conceived as being built up in the hippocampal formation and as being transferred to the mamillary body and thence through the anterior thalamic nuclei to the cortex of the gyrus cinguli. The cortex of the cingular gyrus may be looked on as the receptive region for the experiencing of emotion as the result of impulses coming from the hypothalamic region, in the same way as the area striata is considered the receptive cortex for photic excitations coming from the retina. Radiation of the emotive process from the gyrus cinguli to other regions in the cerebral cortex would add emotional coloring to psychic processes occurring elsewhere. This circuit would explain how emotion may arise in two ways: as a result of psychic activity and as a consequence of hypothalamic activity.

The hypothalamus is accessible to both visceral and somatic sensory impressions from many peripheral sources, and it is well known that emotional coloring, or affect, may be associated with all sorts of sensory experiences of bodily and receptor origin. Most of the afferent receptor systems evoke sensations with characteristic qualities, perceptions, etc., which at the conscious level are accompanied by a more or less distinctive affective tone. The question arises as to how these afferent sensibilities, which pass through the dorsal thalamus and then by way of the internal capsule to the cerebral cortex, are capable of acquiring emotional coloring. Physiologic results imply that the emotive process is mediated by the hypothalamus, and anatomic data suggest that it is the mamillary body which sends the excitations to the cortex of the gyrus cinguli.

It has been aptly said that the hypothalamus is the recipient of the vague and undefined impressions from many bodily sources which in their totality represent afferent material capable of influencing the regulative functions of the hypothalamus. It is not yet generally recognized that there are primitive sensory centers in the ventral thalamus, the chief connections of which appear to pass to the hypothalamus. These primitive receptive centers in the ventral thalamus (subthalamus) are known as the pars ventralis of the lateral geniculate body, the nucleus praegeniculatus, the pars ventralis of the medial geniculate body, the reticular nucleus and the nucleus of the mamillary peduncle. These primitive centers receive certain terminals from various afferent systems: for example, the optic tract ends in part in the pregeniculate nucleus and in the pars ventralis of the lateral geniculate body; the acoustic system ends in part in the pars ventralis of the medial geniculate body; the spinothalamic and trigeminothalamic tracts end in part in the reticular nucleus, and the medial lemniscus appears to contribute fibers to the nucleus of the mamillary peduncle.

These nuclei of the ventral thalamus send to the hypothalamus diffuse fiber connections, some of which are better known as the supra-optic decussations. They end in general in the pars optica and the tuber cinereum, the regions which regulate visceral activities and emotional expression. However, the pars optica and the tuber are connected with the mamillary body, which also receives afferent connections through the medial bundle of the forebrain, the mamillary peduncle and the fornix. Thus, the mamillary body is the ultimate recipient of various afferent excitations, which reach the hypothalamus especially through the afferent centers of the ventral thalamus.

It is thus evident that the afferent pathways from the receptor organs split at the thalamic level into three routes, each conducting a stream of impulses of special importance. One route conducts impulses through the dorsal thalamus and the internal capsule to the corpus striatum. This route represents "the stream of movement." The second conducts impulses from the thalamus through the internal capsule to the lateral cerebral cortex. This route represents "the stream of thought." The third conducts a set of concomitant impulses through the ventral thalamus to the hypothalamus and by way of the mamillary body and the anterior thalamic nuclei to the gyrus cinguli, in the medial wall of the cerebral hemisphere. This route represents "the stream of feeling." In this way, the sensory excitations which reach the lateral cortex through the internal capsule receive their emotional coloring from the concurrent processes of hypothalamic origin which irradiate them from the gyrus cinguli.

The aim of the following discussion is to call attention to a number of anatomic regions and their connections, which taken as a whole may be regarded as an integrated mechanism. This, with the aid of clinical data, may be interpreted as subserving the physiologic emotive processes and the psychologic function of emotion itself.

THE HIPPOCAMPAL FORMATION

In an interesting essay, Lewis[7] has given an account of the history and significance of the term hippocampus, as applied to the cerebral structure first described in the human brain by Arantius, in 1587. Golgi,[8] in an excellent monograph described and illustrated the fine histologic structure of this region, including the pyramidal cells of the hippocampus and the small granule cells of the fascia dentata.

Ramón y Cajal,[9] in his unique studies of the histologic structure of the brain, gave an exhaustive and lucid description of the minute structure of the hippocampal formation and its fiber connections, which he included in the olfactory apparatus. Briefly, the main points are as follows: The central olfactory apparatus consists of (1) the olfactory bulb, which is the primary olfactory receptive center, (2) the pyriform (sphenoid) lobe, which is the center of the olfactory perception and (3) the hippocampal formation, which is an association center dealing with the retention and recall of olfactory impressions and their integration with the ideomotor processes of the brain in general. The olfactory nerve terminates in the olfactory bulb. The lateral olfactory tract carries the excitations to the pyriform cortex, terminating there in an external fiber stratum. The pyriform cortex, in particular its

[7] Lewis, F. T.: The Significance of the Term Hippocampus, J. comp. Neurol. 35:213-230, 1923-1924.

[8] Golgi, C.: Istologia normale, in Opera omnia, Milan, U. Hoepli, 1903, vol. 2, chap. 16, pp. 397-536; Sulla fina anatomia degli organi centrali del sistema nervoso, Riv. sper. di freniat. 9:1-17, 1883.

[9] Ramón y Cajal, S.: Die Riechrinde beim Menschen und Säugetier, in Studien ueber die Hirnrinde des Menschen, Leipzig, A. Barth, 1900, no. 4. Histologie du système nerveux de l'homme et des vertébrés, Paris, A. Maloine, 1909.

posterior part, the angular nucleus (centrum spheno-occipitale or *noyau angulaire*), gives origin to a tract of fibers, the angular bundle *(Winkelstrang oder spheno-ammonische Bahn* or *faisceau angulaire ou temporo-ammonique)*, which gains an internal position and follows the closed medial angle of the temporal horn of the lateral ventricle, adjacent to the hippocampus—hence its name, the angular bundle. The fibers of this bundle perforate the subiculum of the hippocampal gyrus *(perforierende Fasern* or *fibres perforantes)* and on its external surface form the substantia reticularis alba (Arnoldi), which enters the hippocampal fissure. Here they end in two ways. Part of them synapse with the dendrites of the granule cells of the gyrus dentatus (fascia dentata), and part enter the lacunar layer of the hippocampus. A portion of the angular bundle does not perforate on the same side but passes dorsally to cross in the hippocampal commissure and terminate in the hippocampal formation of the opposite side.

The view is generally held (Ariëns Kappers[10] and others) that the gyrus hippocampi and the fascia dentata are the receptive cortex for this region, while the pyramidal cells of the hippocampus major form the emissive, or motor, layer giving rise to the fornix, or the corticohypothalamic tract.

Ramón y Cajal also showed the intimate relation which exists between the posterior portion of the cingulum and the regions from which the angular bundle takes origin. This fiber connection was illustrated schematically by Dejerine (vol. 2, fig. 327),[11] showing the intimate relation which exists between the gyrus cinguli and the hippocampal formation. This bundle forms another connection of special interest in regard to the theory of hippocampal functions presented here.

In a mangabey monkey examined by me, from which Professor Dusser de Barenne had removed both temporal lobes, the subcallosal bundles were completely severed. Sections of this brain showed that the cingulum posterior is the largest bundle which enters the medullary core of the gyrus hippocampi. In addition, there was retrograde degeneration of a conspicuous system of association fibers passing from the gyrus cinguli to the temporal lobe. From the gyrus cinguli these fibers pass laterally and ventrally across the internal capsule. In this animal the presence of

---

[10] Ariëns Kappers, C. U.: The Development of the Cortex and the Function of Its Different Layers, Acta psychiat. et neurol. 3:115-132, 1928.

[11] Dejerine, J.: Anatomie des centres nerveux, Paris, J. Rueff, 1901.

these degenerated fibers was an obtrusive feature. No previous record of them occurs in the literature.

The subcallosal fasciculus of Muratoff[12] is well known. It lies next the ependyma of the lateral ventricle in the angle formed between the corpus callosum and the caudate nuclus. In the dog and other mammals this bundle can be readily peeled away from the corpus callosum and the lateral wall of the ventricle, and thus its curved course can be traced into the temporal horn, into the region of the angular bundle adjacent to the hippocampal formation. Onufrowicz[13] first described this fiber stratum as the occipitofrontal fasciculus in the brain of a microcephalic idiot which possessed no corpus callosum to confuse the picture. Bechterew[14] stated that, according to Muratoff, the bundle degenerates after lesions of the frontal, parietal and occipital gyri. He stated that Shukowski's experiments on the frontal cortex and the gyrus cinguli (illustrated in Bechterew's[14] book) produced degeneration of this bundle, which was particularly profuse following lesions of the cortex of the gyrus cinguli.

Dejerine,[11] in numerous figures, has illustrated the subcallosal bundle as the *substance grise sous-épendymaire* lying between the caudate nucleus and the corpus callosum. In relation to his *substance grise sous-épendymaire*, he showed the occipitofrontal fasciculus of Forel and Onufrowicz as a special, well myelinated bundle, which extends into the wall of the temporal horn of the ventricle and forms there the tapetum of the sphenoid lobe. In his case,[15] Moriceau (page 148), it degenerated after a frontal lesion.

Mettler[16] (page 532) reviewed the literature and contributed his own observations that lesions of the prefrontal area produce degeneration of the descending and ventral parts of the subcallosal fasciculus. He made this observation:

The posterior component continues backward in dorsal association with the caudate nucleus and makes the return loop with it (into the

[12] Muratoff, W.: Sekundäre Degeneration nach Durchschneidung des Balkens, Neurol. Centralbl. 12:316 and 714, 1893.

[13] Onufrowicz, W.: Das balkenlose Mikrocephalengehirn Hofman, Arch. f. Psychiat. 18:305-328, 1887.

[14] Bechterew, W.: Les voies de conduction du cerveau et de la moelle, Lyon, A. Storck & Cie, 1900, p. 604.

[15] Dejerine,[11] vol. 2, p. 148.

[16] Mettler, F. A.: Cortifugal Fiber Connections of the Cortex of Macaca mullatta: The Frontal Lobe, J. comp. Neurol. 61:509-542, 1935.

temporal pole) after sending some fibers to travel more posteriorly beneath the ependyma.

Bechterew and others expressed the belief that the polarity of the bundle is occipitofrontal and that it bears an intimate relation to the caudate nucleus. However, the experimental evidence strongly supports the opposite view that the origin of the subcallosal bundle is frontal, cingular and parietal and that it terminates in a medullary center in the gyrus hippocampi, close to the angular bundle. If this view is correct, the subcallosal bundle and its associated structures constitute another associational link between the general cortex and the hippocampal formation.

The general view of most morphologists, e.g., Ramón y Cajal, Dejerine, Turner and G. E. Smith, has been that the hippocampus, and even the entire limbic lobe, mediate in some obscure way the olfactory sector of functions. The angular bundle is, in fact, of olfactory origin, but it is not the only source of hippocampal incitations. The cingulum posterius brings the cingular gyrus into relation with the hippocampus. Though less important, the subcallosal bundle, including the occipitofrontal fasciculus (tapetum), probably brings the prefrontal region and the gyrus cinguli into functional relation with the hippocampal formation. These make possible the interpretation that central processes from various parts of the cortex may incite hippocampal activity.

For centuries the functional significance of the hippocampus has remained unknown. The hippocampus is by no means a vestigial structure; it may vary greatly in development in different persons. Retzius,[17] commenting on this, stated that the varied development of the hippocampus is independent of age, sex or special prominence of any known psychic function. Ferrier[18] was the first to test the matter experimentally. He destroyed the hippocampus in monkeys and described the depressive effect it produced on cutaneous sensibilities. He expressed the belief that it is the center for these sensibilities. What seems more important now, he described a tendency to somnolence in stating that the monkey was continually tending to drop off to sleep.

[17] Retzius, G.: Das Menschenhirn, Stockholm, P. A. Norstedt & Söner, 1896, vol. 1, p. 67.

[18] Ferrier, D.: The Functions of the Brain, London, Smith, Elder & Co., 1876.

Subsequent observations have placed the zone of cutaneous sensibility in the parietal lobe, leaving the functions of the hippocampus in obscurity.

Since the Negri bodies, the essential lesions of rabies, or hydrophobia, have their site of predilection in the hippocampus and the cerebellum and since the disease is characterized by intense emotional, convulsive and paralytic symptoms, there seems to be offered an important clue to the probable location of the emotive mechanism. The prodromal symptoms—insomnia, irritability and restlessness—usher in the stage of excitement and profound emotional perturbation. There is extreme hyperesthesia to all forms of stimuli, such as light and sound, and every stimulus situation provokes great apprehensiveness and paroxysms of fear. The patient presents the appearance of intense fright and of mingled terror and rage. Hydrophobia, or fear of water, develops as a result of painful pharyngeal spasms when the patient attempts to swallow fluids. Foaming at the mouth is the common symptom of autonomic disturbance. The predominance of hypothalamic lesions in the supraoptic nucleus has been described by Nicolau and Kopciowska.[19] Wood[20] stated:

> The Negri bodies are, as a rule, most abundant in the large ganglion cells of the hippocampus major, but occur in ganglion cells of the cerebral cortex and elsewhere.

Bassoe and Grinker[21] (fig. 13) stated that Negri bodies are demonstrable with ease in the ganglion cells of the cornu ammonis and the adjacent temporal lobe. However, they added:

> It is important to note that from the appearance of the ganglion cell containing the Negri bodies no more degenerative changes were associated with their presence than in the other ganglion cells.

From such evidence it is possible to construct the hypothesis that the hippocampus participates in some important way in the central production of the emotive process.

[19] Nicolau, S., and Kopciowska, L.: Rage du lapin, à virus fixe, et corps de Negri; dénombrement comparatif des inclusions dans la corne d'Ammon et dans la zone élective (noyau optique basal), Compt. rend. Soc. de biol. 112:445-448 (Feb. 10) 1933; abstr., J. A. M. A. 100:1190 (April 15) 1933.
[20] Wood, F. C.: Delafield and Prudden's Text-Book of Pathology, ed. 16, Baltimore, William Wood & Company, 1936, p. 334.
[21] Bassoe, P., and Grinker, R. R.: Human Rabies and Rabies Vaccine Encephalomyelitis: Clinicopathologic Study, Arch. Neurol. Psychiat. 23: 1138-1160 (June) 1930.

THE GYRUS CINGULI

The cortex which borders the corpus callosum on the medial side of each hemisphere is the gyrus cinguli, or the gyrus fornicatus. From the adjacent cortex it is sharply set off by the cingular sulcus. Posteriorly it broadens out into the precuneus, and around the splenium of the corpus callosum it merges with the hippocampal gyrus. Broca assigned the gyrus cinguli to the limbic lobe, and Turner included it in the rhinencephalon. However, as Edinger[22] (page 216) remarked, it is a question whether the gyrus cinguli belongs to the olfactory apparatus. Such a grouping, Berry[23] (page 341) said, is arbitrary and misleading, as it is not in accordance with either morphologic or functional fact.

The cyto-architecture of this gyrus has been described by Campbell[24] and Ramón y Cajal[9] and recently by von Economo and Koskinas[25] (Plate 51). The relations of the fiber bundle, known as the cingulum, to the gyrus have been long recognized. This has been generally interpreted as an association bundle which, according to some authors, is connected with the septal and subcallosal region and, according to others, is more strongly connected to the precuneus and the hippocampal region, through the cingulum posterius.

It was Ramón y Cajal who intimated that the cingulum carries afferent fibers from some unknown source. The recent discovery of an afferent thalamocortical connection from the anterior thalamic nuclei to the gyrus cinguli is to be credited to Clark and Boggon[26] and Waller.[27] These thalamic connections have been shown by the Marchi and the retrograde cell degeneration tech-

[22] Edinger, L.: The Anatomy of the Central Nervous System of Man and of Vertebrates in General, edited by W. S. Hall, Philadelphia, F. A. Davis Co., 1899.

[23] Berry, R. J. A.: Brain and Mind, or the Nervous System of Man, New York, The Macmillan Company, 1928.

[24] Campbell, A. W.: Histological Studies on the Localization of Cerebral Functions, Cambridge, University Press, 1905.

[25] von Economo, C., and Koskinas, G. N.: Die Cytoarchitektonik der Hirnrinde des erwachsenen Menschen, Berlin, Julius Springer, 1925.

[26] Clark, W. E. L., and Boggon, R. H.: On the Connections of the Anterior Nucleus of the Thalamus, J. Anat. 67:215-226, 1933.

[27] Waller, W. H.: Topographical Relations of Cortical Lesions to the Thalamic Nuclei in the Albino Rat, J. comp. Neurol. 60:237-269, 1934.

nics in the rat and cat. There are indications that in the brain of
the monkey similar connections are present (Walker,[28] page 30).
The course of these fibers has not been illustrated or described in
detail. In general they pass laterally and forward from the anterior and anterodorsal nuclei to enter the anterior limb of the internal capsule. They turn dorsally and medially over the anterior
horn of the ventricle to enter the cingulum, in the medial wall of
the hemisphere. I have observed their degeneration in the rat
after injury to the frontal lobe and after incision of the medial
wall of the cortex. According to Clark and Boggon and Waller,
the connections of the small anterodorsal nucleus are with a
small area of cortex of the retrosplenial region, while the anterior
nucleus is connected with the extent of the gyrus cinguli. These
nuclei also have a strong connection through the inferior thalamic peduncle *(ansa peduncularis)* with the anterior part of the
pallidum and by a strong triangular band which passes forward
probably with the head of the caudate nucleus. In considering
the anterior thalamic nuclei as centers in a functional system,
connections with the corpus striatum, as well as with the cingular cortex, must be recognized.

So far as functions of the gyrus cinguli are concerned, experimental evidence is scant, owing to the inaccessibility of this
region. I[29] have noted (pages 50 and 72) that in the two sexes
the precuneus shows a greater difference in size than any other
portion of the cortex, being more highly developed in the male,
and it was suggested that representation of the sex organs may
be localized there. This difference between the sexes has been
confirmed by Mettler[30] (page 319) in the brain of the monkey.
Sensations related to sex matters possess a high degree of emotional coloring.

More important evidence is derived from tumor of the corpus
callosum which involves the surrounding cortex. Bristowe[31] described the symptoms of slowly increasing paralysis, impairment

[28] Walker, E. A.: An Experimental Study of the Thalamo-Cortical Projection of the Macaque Monkey, J. comp. Neurol. 64:1-40, 1936.
[29] Papez, J. W.: The Brain of Helen H. Gardener (Alice Chenoweth
Day), Am. J. Phys. Anthropol. 11:29-79, 1927.
[30] Mettler, F. A.: Brain of Pithecus Rhesus (M. Rhesus), Am. J. Phys.
Anthropol. 17:309-331, 1933.
[31] Bristowe, J. S.: Cases of Tumor of the Corpus Callosum, Brain 7:315-
333, 1885.

of intelligence, progressive drowsiness, profound stupor, coma and death in cases of callosal tumor. Gowers[32] (page 712) expressed the opinion that the symptoms of tumor of the corpus callosum are due to pressure on or extension into the cerebral hemispheres. Ironside and Guttmacher[33] illustrated a number of such tumors, which clearly involved the gyrus cinguli of both sides. They stated:

The mental changes which are so commonly present are often the first symptoms. Apathy, drowsiness and defect of memory are met with more commonly than in growths elsewhere, and occur with such regularity in the corpus callosum syndrome as to be characteristic.

Many similar cases can be found in the literature. In a recent paper, Voris and Adson[34] described the various symptoms and mental changes in thirty-eight cases. They listed the prominent mental changes as: loss of memory, indifference to environment, change in personality or character, drowsiness, stuporous or comatose state and disorientation in time and place. Less important are Witzelsucht, euphoria, puerility, delirium and states of depression. Armitage and Meagher[35] listed as first among the mental symptoms loss of spontaneity in emotion, thought and activity. Ligation or occlusion of the left anterior cerebral arteries produces marked reduction of conscious processes. Dandy[36] removed the various lobes of the hemispheres and ligated the left anterior cerebral artery and noted the effect on consciousness. He localized the seat of consciousness along the mesial aspect of the left hemisphere and near the corpus callosum. He, in agreement with others, recognized that steadily increasing pressure on the brain stem will produce drowsiness and eventually unconsciousness and postulated conduction tracts between the lower parts of the brain stem and the cortex which are responsible for conscious processes.

[32] Gowers, W. R.: A Manual of Diseases of the Nervous System, Philadelphia, P. Blakiston's Son & Co., 1888.
[33] Ironside, R., and Guttmacher, M.: The Corpus Callosum and Its Tumors. Brain 52:442-483, 1929.
[34] Voris, H. C., and Adson, A. W.: Tumors of the Corpus Callosum: Pathologic and Clinical Study, Arch. Neurol. Psychiat. 34:965-972 (Nov.) 1935.
[35] Armitage, G., and Meagher, R.: Gliomas of the Corpus Callosum, Ztschr. f. d. ges. Neurol. u. Psychiat. 146:454-488, 1933; abstr., Arch. Neurol. & Psychiat. 33:1112 (May) 1935.
[36] Dandy, W. E.: Seat of Consciousness, in Lewis, Dean: Practice of Surgery, Hagerstown, Md., W. F. Prior Company, Inc., 1931, vol. 12, p. 57.

Occlusion of the anterior cerebral artery or its branches does not often destroy the gyrus cinguli, and even then rarely bilaterally. Critchley[37] described a case (case 2) in which there was softening of the left paracentral lobule and the gyrus cinguli. The initial symptoms were fright, followed by a hysterical fit, semicoma and unconsciousness. As this condition improved, the patient was emotional, irritable and depressed, till the time of her death.

Cogent argument can be drawn from such evidence in support of the view that the gyrus cinguli is the seat of dynamic vigilance by which environmental experiences are endowed with an emotional consciousness. It seems likely that if ever the purely callosal symptoms are separated from the other cortical symptoms, the loss of emotive dynamics will be attributed to the compression or damage of the gyri cinguli, the strong associations of which with the hippocampal formations have already been outlined. There seems to be ample justification for the ancient view of La Peyronie, professor of surgery at Montpellier, who on the basis of such clinical experience expressed the belief that the region of the corpus callosum is the "seat of the soul" (quoted from Critchley[37]).

THE MAMILLARY BODY

In reptiles the hippocampus is connected with the hypothalamus in a diffuse way through the rudimentary fornix. The mamillary body is still undifferentiated, but this general cellular region is connected with the anterior thalamic nuclei, the connection of which in turn is chiefly with the corpus striatum. One can infer that hippocampal activity, however aroused, influences the hypothalamus in a diffuse way and through the striatal connections regulates attitudes of emotional expression. I[38] have suggested (page 469) that in reptiles the anterior nuclei may have an incipient connection with the frontal, parahippocampal cortex, which would correspond in part to the gyrus cinguli of mammals.

In mammals the mamillary bodies as well as the gyri cinguli,

[37] Critchley, M.: The Anterior Cerebral Artery, and Its Syndromes, Brain 53:120-165, 1930.
[38] Papez, J. W.: Thalamus of Turtles and Thalamic Evolution, J. comp. Neurol. 61:433-475, 1935.

with which they connect, are always well developed. Many descriptions of these nuclear masses exist. For the present purpose it may be assumed that the description given by Aronson and me[39] (page 10) for the monkey is widely applicable to other forms. A good histologic description is that of Ramón y Cajal.[9] Cytologic details and connections were given. In brief, the mamillary body consists of a number of nuclei. The medial mamillary nucleus is the largest. The fornix ends chiefly in its lateral part. The larger medial part emits the mamillothalamic tract, or the fasciculus of Vicq d'Azyr. The lateral mamillary nucleus is a triangular mass of large cells in direct connection with the mamillary peduncle, which, according to the author, is an afferent bundle. This nucleus emits fibers which join the mamillothalamic tract. On the lateral side there also occurs the intercalate nucleus. Dorsally, in the supramamillary decussation is the supramamillary nucleus. A thin layer of cells separates the medial mamillary nuclei of the two sides and extends into the fibrous capsule of the bodies.

There are at least three direct afferent paths to the mamillary body. In general the capsule receives fibers from the tuber cinereum and the medial bundle of the forebrain, which Ramón y Cajal designated as the *faisceau de la capsule du corps mamillaire interne.*

The major part of the fornix ends by terminal collaterals in the medial nucleus of the mamillary body. A part of the fornix in some mammals (*e.g.*, the guinea-pig) decussates dorsal to the mamillary body, and a part of this crossed bundle is continued to the interpeduncular region. This caudal bundle is conspicuous in some reptiles (*e.g.*, Anolis carolinensis).

The mamillary peduncle may be interpreted as an ascending bundle coming from the region of the medial lemniscus and the medial border of the substantia nigra. In this region I[40] have identified (page 98) a special nucleus which I have designated as the nucleus of the mamillary peduncle. It appears likely from the observations of Edinger and Wallenberg[41] that the medial

[39] Papez, J. W., and Aronson, L. R.: Thalamic Nuclei of Pithecus (Macacus) Rhesus: I. Ventral Thalamus, Arch. Neurol. Psychiat. 32:1-26 (July) 1934.

[40] Papez, J. W.: Thalamic Nuclei of the Nine-Banded Armadillo, J. comp. Neurol. 56:49-103, 1932.

[41] Edinger, L., and Wallenberg, A.: Untersuchungen über den Fornix und das Corpus mammillare, Arch. f. Psychiat. 35:1, 1902.

lemniscus is related to this structure. One can infer that proprioceptive impulses are thus brought into the mamillary body. However, the confusing views on the origin and polarity of the mamillary peduncle reviewed by Ramón y Cajal,[9] Huber and Crosby[42] and others must for the present remain an obstacle to any final interpretation of this fiber tract.

From these connections it is evident that the mamillary body receives impulses from the hippocampus, the tuber cinereum and other sources.

The mamillothalamic tract, or fasciculus of Vicq d'Azyr,[43] is the well-known efferent tract from the mamillary nuclei to the anterior and anterodorsal nuclei of the thalamus. Its smaller part arises from the lateral mamillary nucleus. Near its origin the fasciculus bifurcates, giving off a smaller descending mamillotegmental tract, which, according to most authors, terminates in relation to the tegmental nuclei of Gudden. Stimulation along its course gives striking pressor effects, that is, rise of blood pressure. As the main mamillothalamic tract ascends, it gives off these collaterals in the region of the nucleus campi Foreli of the Vogts.[44]

It is thus seen that the mamillary body can mass and relay the impulses it receives to the anterior thalamic nuclei and, to a lesser extent, to the deep tegmental nuclei. Kernohan, Learmonth and Doyle[45] (case 4) reported a case of tumor in the third ventricle which destroyed the tuber cinereum and the corpora mamillaria. The patient was drowsy most of the time; she had diabetes insipidus, and during occasional attacks of weakness she perspired profusely.

The recent work of Ranson,[4] with the aid of Ingram, showed not only that damage in and around the mamillary bodies causes drowsiness and somnolence in monkeys but that during this period the animals are emotionally inactive. They lost their wildness and even after recovery from somnolence were tame and

[42] Huber, G. C., and Crosby, E. C.: Somatic and Visceral Connections of the Diencephalon, Arch. Neurol. & Psychiat. 22:187-229 (Aug.) 1929.

[43] Vicq d'Azyr, F.: Traité d'anatomie et de physiologie, Paris, F.-A. Didot l'Aîné, 1776.

[44] Vogt, O., and Vogt, C.: Zur Kenntnis der pathologischen Veränderungen des Striatum und des Pallidum, Sitzungsb. d. k. Akad. d. Wissensch. Math.-naturw. Cl. (Abt. B) 14:1-56, 1919.

[45] Kernohan, J. W., Learmonth, J. R., and Doyle, J. B.: Neuroblastomas and Gangliocytomas of the Central Nervous System, Brain 55:287-310 (Sept.) 1932.

tractable. When it is remembered that the sensory pathways to the cortex were not interrupted, the importance of the mamillo-thalamic cortical pathway in insomnia and emotional excitement can be appreciated.

THE ANTERIOR NUCLEI OF THE THALAMUS

How the anterior and the anterodorsal nuclei receive the fasciculus of Vicq d'Azyr and how they connect with the gyrus cinguli, on the one hand, and the head of the corpus striatum, on the other, have already been stated.

Clinical data on the anterior thalamic nuclei are meager, but emotional disturbances, such as spontaneous laughing and crying, from thalamic lesions are well authenticated. Perhaps the most vivid case of compression in this region was described by Penfield[46] as one of diencephalic autonomic epilepsy produced by a tumor situated at the interventricular foramen, between the anterior thalamic nuclei and back of the column of the fornix.

The patient lay most of the time in obvious pain. At intervals she had an attack in which the same phenomena appeared regularly. The attack was explosive and was confined to the structures controlled by the vegetative nervous system. Prodromal symptoms were restlessness and a request for ice in the mouth, followed by sudden vasodilatation of the area of the skin supplied by the cervical sympathetic nerves. There were sudden rise of blood pressure, lacrimation, salivation, dilatation of the pupils, protrusion of the eyes, increase in pulse rate, retardation of the respiratory rate, excitability of the pilomotor reflex and loss of consciousness. The attack lasted ten minutes or more. As the symptoms faded, transient hiccup, shivering and respiration of the Cheyne-Stokes type occurred, followed by drowsiness and a tendency to sleep.

Cases of tumors destroying these thalamic nuclei have been recorded. Mott and Barratt[47] (case 1) described a case in which the tumor involved the anterior thalamic nuclei. Among other symptoms the patient exhibited drowsiness, sometimes falling asleep while taking food. Weisenburg[48] discussed the

[46] Penfield, W.: Diencephalic Autonomic Epilepsy: The Vegetative Nervous System, A. Research Nerv. & Ment. Dis., Proc. 10:645-663, 1930.

[47] Mott, F. W., and Barratt, J. O. W.: Three Cases of Tumors of the Third Ventricle, Arch. Neurol. Path. Lab. London County Asyl. Claybury 1:417-439, 1900.

[48] Weisenburg, T. H.: Third Ventricle Tumors, Brain 33:236-260, 1910.

question whether lesions of the third ventricle cause mental symptoms, such as apathetic, dull mentality, drowsiness and somnolence. Fulton and Bailey[49] (case 3) reported a case of hypersomnia due to a cystic tumor of the anterior part of the third ventricle. Hart remarked that "emotional negativism and fatuous serenity are states of mind described by numerous authors." There is little doubt that tumor of this region produces loss of emotive dynamics when it involves the mamillary body, the fasciculus of Vicq d'Azyr or the anterior thalamic nuclei. On the other hand, lesions of the tuber and the pars optica produce diabetes insipidus, Fröhlich's syndrome and other disturbances of the autonomic nervous system, with less marked emotional changes.

THE SUPRA-OPTIC DECUSSATIONS AND THE PARS VENTRALIS THALAMI

The commissures of Meynert, Ganser and Gudden are well entrenched in neurologic literature, though their functional significance is veiled in obscurity. Concerning the origin and ending of these supra-optic decussations the evidence is still conflicting and weighted with the opinions of older authors, e.g., Bechterew,[14] Dejerine,[11] Edinger[22] and others.

By older authors the origin of Meynert's commissure, as well as its termination, was given as pallidal. So closely are the pallidum and its ansa lenticularis applied to the optic tract that they are superimposed on Meynert's commissure, and it looks as if the commissure arose from the pallidum. Hence the classic view.

Somewhat contrary to this view it has been shown that in some of the lower mammals[40] (page 94) and in reptiles[38] (page 452) what appears to be the equivalent of Meynert's commissure arises from the pars ventralis of the lateral geniculate body and the pregeniculate nucleus. Passing along the optic tract, it appears to end in the pars ventromedialis of the supra-optic nucleus. In part it decussates, to end in the hypothalamus of the other side. Accordingly, it represents an afferent connection

[49] Fulton, J. F., and Bailey, P.: Tumors in the Region of the third Ventricle: Their Diagnosis and Relation to Pathologic Sleep, J. nerv. ment. Dis. **69**:1-25, 1929.

between the primitive optic centers of the ventral thalamus and the hypothalamus. This point of view has already been indicated by Vonderahe.[50]

In the same papers it has also been intimated that the dorsal supra-optic decussation corresponds to the fibrae ansulatae, Ganser's commissure or the anterior hypothalamic commissure in the anterior part of the tuber cinereum. In reptiles these fibers arise from the nucleus of the dorsal supra-optic decussation (Huber and Crosby[42] and others), situated in the course of the lateral bundle of the forebrain. My own observations on the brains of various mammals (e.g., dog, monkey and man) lead me to believe that the fibers issue in part from a fiber mass situated lateral to the pillar of the fornix, in area P_3 of Winkler,[51] which is interpolated in the course of the oral portion of the pallido-rubro-olivary and other fibers of ansa lenticularis. In Carnivora the pallidohypothalamic fibers come from the entopeduncular nucleus, and in the monkey and in man, from a comparable region, namely, the medial nucleus or segment, of the globus pallidus (Grünthal[52]). I have verified experimentally in the cat that the other coarse fibers of the anterior hypothalamic commissure come from the region of the interstitial nucleus of the midbrain, as described by others.[42]

Concerning Gudden's commissure, it is generally admitted that its origin is in the inferior colliculus, the posterior portion of the tectum (Huber and Crosby[42]), and in most lower vertebrates also in the nucleus isthmi or parabigeminal body. En route, as it joins the optic tract, it also receives fibers from the pars ventralis of the medial geniculate body (Papez[53] and others). Decussating with the optic tract, it probably ends in the anterior portion of the tuber cinereum, and according to the classic view, many of its fibers may reach the medial geniculate body of the opposite side. Thus, it represents an afferent connection between the primitive acoustic and static centers and the hypothalamus.

[50] Vonderahe, A. R.: The Representation of Visceral Function in the Brain, Ohio State M. J. 31:104-109, 1935.

[51] Winkler, C.: Manuel de neurologie. Le corps strié et le diëncéphale, Haarlem, de Erven F. Bohn, 1933, vol. 1, pt. 5, p. 34.

[52] Grünthal, E.: Vergleichend anatomische Untersuchungen über den Zellbau des Globus pallidus und Nucleus basalis der Säuger und des Menschen, J. f. Psychol. u. Neurol. 44:403-428, 1932.

[53] Papez, J. W.: Evolution of the Medial Geniculate Body, J. comp. Neurol. 64:41-61, 1936.

As has already been said, it is possible that the mamillary peduncle represents a similar primitive connection of the medial lemniscus, the proprioceptive pathway and of the substantia nigra, to the mamillary body.

Concerning the olfactory centers and the amygdala, the case is simple. The medial bundle of the forebrain connects the septal region and the olfactory tubercle with the whole extent of the lateral hypothalamic nuclei. The stria terminalis connects the amygdala, the function of which is unknown, with the pars optica hypothalami (Johnston,[54] Krieg[55] and others).

The question remains how the reticular nucleus and the remaining receptive portions of the pars ventralis thalami are connected with other regions of the brain. Some good evidence was derived from the myelinization studies of Bechterew,[14] from the Marchi experiments of Wallenberg[56] and from the observations of others that ascending spinothalamic and bulbothalamic tracts end in part in these nuclei. The reticular nucleus is generally credited with sending fibers broadcast to the cerebral cortex. Connections with the pallidum and the hypothalamus are possible. What function it mediates is unknown, though its primitive nature is certain. In this regard the thalamic pain syndrome of Dejerine and Roussy[57] deserves reconsideration, as do the visceral and gustatory functions of the amygdala.

In recent papers of Krieg,[55] Clark,[58] Papez and Aronson[39] and Walker,[28] the connections in the medial walls of the third ventricle have been emphasized. There is no question of the existence of such periventricular fibers, as they can be clearly seen in the brains of reptiles and of most mammals. Especially important are the connections between the medial nucleus and centrum medianum and the hypothalamus. The view of Nathan[59]

[54] Johnston, J. B.: Cell Masses in the Forebrain of the Turtle, Cistudo Carolina, J. comp. Neurol. 25:393-468, 1915.

[55] Krieg, W. J. S.: The Hypothalamus of the Albino Rat, J. comp. Neurol. 55:19-89, 1932.

[56] Wallenberg, A.: Sekundäre sensible Bahnen im Gehirnstamme des Kaninchens, ihre gegenseitige Lage und ihre Bedeutung für den Aufbau des Thalamus, Anat. Anz. 24:142 and 357, 1904.

[57] Dejerine, J., and Roussy, G.: Le syndrôme thalamique, Rev. neurol. 14:521-532, 1906.

[58] Clark, W. E. L.: Structure and Connections of the Thalamus, Brain 55:406-470, 1932.

[59] Nathan, M.: Le troisième ventricule constitue-t-il un cerveau affectif? Presse méd. 39:857-858 (June 10) 1931.

on the localization of emotions and personality in the region of the third ventricle appears to have considerable anatomic support. He reviewed the historical development of this idea from Haškovec (1910, 1925 and 1929) to Camus (1921, 1924), Roussy and Lhermitte (1924), Rosenfeld (1925) and Küppers (1929).

The left basal region was suspected by Alford.[60] His observations showed that emotion and consciousness are not located primarily in the lateral cortex of the cerebral hemispheres and that they are more disturbed by basal lesions of the left hemisphere.

SUMMARY

Is emotion a magic product, or is it a physiologic process which depends on an anatomic mechanism? An attempt has been made to point out various anatomic structures and correlated physiologic symptoms which, taken as a whole, deal with the various phases of emotional dynamics, consciousness and related functions. It is proposed that the hypothalamus, the anterior thalamic nuclei, the gyrus cinguli, the hippocampus and their interconnections constitute a harmonious mechanism which may elaborate the functions of central emotion, as well as participate in emotional expression. This is an attempt to allocate specific organic units to a larger organization dealing with a complex regulatory process. The evidence presented is mostly concordant and suggestive of such a mechanism as a unit within the larger architectural mosaic of the brain.

Negative and contradictory evidence has not been presented. The structures described here are usually represented as dealing with some phase of the olfactory function. There is no clinical or other evidence to support this view. The new interpretation which I propose can be supported by much more data at present available in the literature, but it is evident that any such doctrine will have to stand the test of experimental and clinical experience if it is to be useful in science. Emotion is such an important function that its mechanism, whatever it is, should be placed on a structural basis.

The organization presented here meets adequately the physio-

[60] Alford, L. B.: Localization of Consciousness and Emotion, Am. J. Psychiat. 12:789-799, 1933.

logic requirements proposed by Cannon and Bard in respect to the theory of emotion based on diencephalic-cortical processes. It is also in agreement with the observations of Dandy[36] that the seat of consciousness is located somewhere near the midline, between the limits set by the corpus callosum and the basal structures of the brain.

[ADDENDUM FROM THE ORIGINAL PRINTING OF THIS ARTICLE: IN REFERENCE TO THE AUTHOR: *Ithaca, N. Y.*]

SOME FOREBRAIN MECHANISMS INVOLVED IN EXPRESSION OF RAGE WITH SPECIAL REFERENCE TO SUPPRESSION OF ANGRY BEHAVIOR ❖ *Philip Bard and Vernon B. Mountcastle*

INTRODUCTION

IT HAS BEEN ESTABLISHED by the work of a number of investigators (see 3) that after removal of all cerebral cortex a cat or dog is capable of displaying a mode of response which in intensity and pattern closely resembles the activity which constitutes the expression of fury in normal members of the same species. The rage reactions of these decorticate animals differ from those of their normal fellows only in being poorly oriented in respect to the provoking stimulus.

The impression gained from studies of chronically decorticate

REPRINTED FROM *Research Publications of the Association in Nervous and Mental Disease*, 27:362-404. COPYRIGHT © 1948 BY THE ASSOCIATION FOR RESEARCH IN NERVOUS AND MENTAL DISEASE, INC.

carnivores is that such animals tend to display anger rather more readily than when the brain is intact. Thus the decorticate dog of Goltz (11) and the two decorticate cats described by Dusser de Barenne (9) gave violent exhibitions of anger when merely lifted from the floor or from their cages, and Rothmann's dog (28) was sent into a full fit of rage by the mere presence of a fly on its nose. The dog studied by Bromiley (7) invariably exhibited, throughout its survival of 33 months, an intense rage reaction in response to the most trivial disturbances. A consideration of the writings of these and other investigators of the behavior of decorticate carnivores certainly suggests that decortication leads to the development of a *hyperexcitability* in the sense that mild stimuli, which preoperatively had proven indifferent or even productive of signs of pleasure, suffice to provoke a marked exhibition of anger. This has led to the idea that the cerebral cortex normally holds in check the subcortical mechanism or mechanisms which are responsible for the bodily expression of rage. According to this view, the low threshold of the rage-responses of dogs and cats without cortex represents a *release phenomenon.*

In a study of four cats which were deprived of all neocortex and additional portions of the forebrain Bard and Rioch (5) compared the reactions to given stimuli before and after operation. This same comparison was made in the case of three similarly prepared dogs that were used in a study (22) of forebrain influences upon temperature regulation. Commenting on the results obtained on these seven animals Bard (3) stated:

"On the whole, the evidence suggests that the cortex, or possibly some part of the upper brain stem, does normally exert an inhibitory influence on the hypothalamic mechanism. Doubtless the cortex has an excitatory as well as an inhibitory effect on most of the activities of the brain stem. Such a double action would make it extremely difficult to secure unequivocal results by studying the effects of large cortical ablations. Further analysis, especially the determination of the pathways over which the cortex may exert its influences, is badly needed."

A review of the descriptions, given by seven or eight authors, of the rage reactions of some 20 chronically decorticate cats and dogs indicates that these responses may vary, especially in threshold, from animal to animal. It is reasonable to suppose that these differences between preparations are due to differences in the extent of the ablations, especially in respect to rhinencephalic and subcortical portions of the forebrain since the neocortex was wholly or almost wholly extirpated in each instance. Bard and Rioch (5), having had at their disposal several such animals, the brains of which had been carefully studied histologically, devoted some attention to this obvious question, but it cannot be said that any wholly satifactory correlation was established. Even more puzzling are the variations which have occasionally been noted in one and the same animal during long periods of survival, and which cannot be attributed to alterations in health or in any other readily determined physiological condition. Such changes apparently occurred in Rothmann's dog and they unquestionably appeared in Bard and Rioch's *cat 103*. On the other hand, they were slight or absent in many similar preparations. In this connection one notes with interest that Kennard (14) has reported that the "sham rage" exhibited by decorticate cats and by cats from which portions of frontally located cortex had been removed "became with time less frequent, less extreme and more difficult to elicit." Such has not been the general experience of one of us (P. B.) in observing eight cats and two dogs that were kept for periods of from 4 to 33 months after removal of all neocortex and various additional portions of the forebrain. A regression of the rage reaction occurred in only one of these animals, *cat 228* of the study by Bard and Rioch (5).

Diencephalic and Mesencephalic Mechanisms

The question of the locus of the subcortical region responsible for the well-patterned and vigorous display of anger of which the decorticate carnivore is capable is not an immediate concern of the present communication. It must, however, enter into any consideration of the *modus operandi* of forebrain mechanisms discussed below and for this reason we propose to outline what we regard as the present status of this cognate problem.

The older evidence that the hypothalamus is concerned in the production of angry behavior has been reviewed at length by one of us (2, 3) and by Ranson (23, 24). This evidence consists of two groups of experimental facts. First came the demonstration that in acute experiments removal of all cerebral tissue rostral, lateral and dorsal to the caudal hypothalamus is followed by "sham rage," whereas this patterned activity fails to develop after truncation of the brain stem at an upper mesencephalic level or at the zone of transition between diencephalon and midbrain (1). Further, it has long been recognized by all who have studied acutely decerebrate cats that these animals do not exhibit an integrated rage response even when subjected to strong nociceptive stimulation. Thus acute experiments suffice to reveal an extraordinary difference between hypothalamic preparations and animals with all brain removed above any mesencephalic, pontile or bulbar level. This fact strongly suggests that the hypothalamus is prepotent among the neural mechanisms which confer upon the decorticate animal the capacity to exhibit at low threshold a full expression of anger. A second line of evidence indicating that the complex reaction pattern characteristic of rage is dependent on integrating and executive mechanisms located in the hypothalamus was secured by Ranson and his collaborators (23, 24). On stimulating the hypothalamus in the unanesthetized or lightly anesthetized cat with brain intact, behavior fully expressive of rage was obtained —"the cats behaved as they would had they been threatened by a barking dog." This reaction appeared to be specifically hypothalamic; it was not evoked from thalamus, internal capsule or septum. Although in similar experiments Magoun, Atlas, Ingersoll and Ranson (17) obtained coordinated facial and vocal activity expressive of anger on stimulation of a localized area in the midbrain and pons, both when the brain was intact and after acute decerebration, they thought it probable "that a correlation of the faciovocal component with other features of emotional expression in the behavior of the normal animal involves the activity of the more rostrally situated diencephalon or cerebral cortex." As far as we can determine, a fully integrated expression of anger such as that described by Ranson has never been produced by stimulation of any region of the brain except the hypothalamus.

If a neural mechanism situated in the hypothalamus is essential for the ready and complete expression of anger in a cat or dog, it is to be expected that lesions restricted to this part of the brain would produce a considerable degree of paralysis of emotional expression. In experiments on cats and monkeys Ranson (24) obtained somnolence and a definite but not permanent emotional stolidity by placing in the brain stem lesions which partially destroyed the hypothalamic areas, the stimulation of which produces rage responses. On the other hand, Kelly, Beaton and Magoun (13) have shown that after a restricted lesion has destroyed the entire hypothalamus at the mammillary level and interrupted all known descending connections of the hypothalamus, nociceptive stimulation can evoke piloerection, growling, crying, spitting, striking and biting. One of the two cats thus prepared growled, spat and sometimes emitted screaming cries when it was lifted, fed or cleaned. On exposure to barking dogs both cats retracted their ears, hissed, struck with forepaws and showed erection of hair and the ocular signs of a greatly augmented sympathetic discharge. In 1938 and 1939 Magoun and Bard (unpublished work) observed vigorous, well-integrated rage reactions in three cats which had survived for some time quite large hypothalamic lesions. The lesions of two of these animals (*cats E84 and E85*) have been described and illustrated in a paper devoted to a consideration of the central nervous mechanisms involved in sexual behavior (4). There can be no doubt that after a large circumscribed lesion has destroyed the greater part of the hypothalamus, including the entire hypothalamic origin of fibers belonging to the periventricular system as well as to the mammillothalamic and mammillotegmental tracts, and has interrupted the descending fibers of the medial forebrain bundle, a cat is still capable of exhibiting an aggressively effective rage response when appropriately stimulated. This positive result stands in marked contrast to the somnolence, paucity of spontaneous activity and complete lack of temperature control shown by such preparations. An experience which has included studies of more than a dozen cats which have survived for many weeks removal of all neocortex and some or all of the other forebrain structures permits the statement that rage reactions are more readily evoked in them than in the animals with hypothalamic influences excluded by large but restricted lesions. The difference is more one of threshold than of intensity or character of response.

In some of the cats of Kelly, Beaton and Magoun and in those of Magoun and Bard the large lesions interrupted the descending pathways from striatum as well as those from the hypothalamus, but the basis pedunculi was wholly or largely intact on both sides. This fact raises the question whether their capacity to show anger depended on the integrity of the cerebral cortex or other forebrain structures with efferent fibers in the cerebral peduncles. The probability that this was the case appears to be greatly reduced by the fact that the spinothalamic tracts and the lemniscal system were largely interrupted in diencephalon or upper midbrain. But perhaps one should not lose sight of the possibility that in the absence of afferent bombardment from cord and medulla the cerebral cortex is capable of exerting through efferent connections a facilitating effect upon executive mechanisms in midbrain or hindbrain and thereby may make possible a goodly display of anger. It is, as will be pointed out below, reasonable to suppose that the hypothalamus itself plays this kind of role in the determination of the threshold and integration of rage behavior. On the other hand, the rage responses of animals with hypothalmic influences excluded by restricted lesions may be solely the result of activation of neural organizations in mesencephalon, pons and bulb.

Studies of decerebrate animals in the subchronic or chronic state have thrown some light on this problem. Bazett and Penfield (6) were the first to keep cats for more than a number of hours after low mesencephalic truncation of the brain stem. Some of their animals lived for periods of from one to three weeks and showed themselves capable of some "pseudaffective" activity. This consisted of such *isolated items* of behavior as biting, clawing and tail-lashing; it never attained an integrated and convincing exhibition of anger such as is seen in the hypothalamic cat of acute or chronic experiments. But the observations made by Bazett and Penfield were definitely limited by conditions under which their cats were kept, conditions which were designed to keep the body temperature close to a normal level and which did not permit the execution of activities of which we now know their animals were capable. Ten years later Keller (12) reported results obtained on several cats which were kept alive for periods up to 20 days after transection of the brain stem at a mesencephalic level. All cerebral tissue rostral to the lesion was left in place. He stated that a *"typical rage response* can be obtained in a preparation with only the cord, medulla, pons and small ventrolateral portions (essentially a pontile animal) of the midbrain intact." When the section was made through the rostral part of the mesencephalon the response was, as a rule, more difficult to evoke. On being disturbed his cats showed the various signs of augmented sympathetic activity which are part of the normal feline display of rage. These autonomic responses were at times accompanied by spitting, growling, tail-lashing and "aimless pawing or clawing movements." Whether the rage reactions shown by Keller's animals were as vigorous and as well patterned as those displayed by decorticate or hypothalamic cats is a question of much interest. Probably it can be answered in the negative on the basis of the statement, "The end response differs from that obtained in a normal animal only in that the somatic effectors are not coordinated into an 'escape' or 'defensive' pattern." In agreement with Keller's results are those recently obtained by Kelly, Beaton and Magoun (13) in an animal (their *cat 4*) which was observed for one month after transection of the midbrain-diencephalic junction. After the first week nociceptive stimulation and even mere handling evoked growling, spitting and often piloerection. While the animal appears not to have shown a fully integrated rage reaction, the low threshold is worthy of note. A study of serial sections of the brain stem showed that it had been completely divided except for the lateral portion of one medial geniculate body. There is no reason to suppose that this small bridge in any way determined the result.

The securing of further information regarding the capacity of mechanisms located below the hypothalamus to effect rage responses when isolated from all diencephalic and forebrain influences was the chief aim of some experiments carried out in this laboratory several years ago by Macht and Bard (16). Decerebration was accomplished in one stage by first ablating all cerebral structures rostral, lateral and dorsal to olfactory tubercles and ventral diencephalon and then removing by gentle suction a wedge of tissue, 3–5 mm. wide rostro-caudally, just cephalad to the desired plane of brain stem truncation. The neurally isolated island of tissue (composed of ventral diencephalon, olfactory tubercles and hypophysis) thus left with adequate blood supply served to maintain a normal water and carbohydrate balance. This technique gave the operator definite assurance that the brain stem had been completely severed and afforded him, prior to autopsy, a fair impression of what he had actually done. It is felt that this method yields more certain results than can that of Keller (12) which involves transecting the brain stem with a blunt instrument after its partial exposure by elevation of one or both occipital poles. Successful postoperative management demanded vigilance, but was otherwise not especially difficult. Since swallowing reflexes remained excellent, all food and water was given by mouth; weight losses were temporary and small. The chief hazard in the management of these poikilothermic and intermittently active animals was the development of hyperthermia. Eight of the 14 cats decerebrated in this manner were kept in good condition for periods of from 30 to 154 days (average survival, 56 days).

Despite a capacity to right, stand and walk, the cats of this series with brain stem truncated at any level between the exit of the third nerves and the mammillary bodies never exhibited the full pattern of angry behavior shown by decorticate and hypothalamic cats. The responses obtained were brought forth only by definitely nociceptive stimuli. They were: growling; hissing or spitting; tail-lashing; thrashing movements of the forelegs, sometimes with claws protruded; moderate increases in respiratory rate; urination; and signs of increased sympathetic discharge (piloerection, cardiac acceleration, retraction of nictitating membranes). These items of response were not always combined. At no time was retraction of the ears observed. Also wholly lacking was the integrated response typically shown by decorticate and hypothalamic cats, namely, an attack with claws and teeth which is directed forward and downward and supported by an appropriate stance. With very strong nociceptive (faradic) stimulation these animals uttered a shrill cry and moved forward rapidly as if to escape. Somewhat fewer of the items of the rage response were evocable in low mesencephalic and pontile cats—preparations which cannot right the body, stand and walk—but the threshold was about the same as in the high midbrain animals. A recent study of three high mesencephalic dogs (survivals of from 9 to 20 weeks) has disclosed the fact that in these animals quite innocuous stimuli (patting or lifting them) may elicit growling and that somewhat greater disturbances may provoke snarling and biting. The display of anger was never as forceful nor as complete as that seen in decorticate dogs.

As regards the capacity of the decerebrate carnivore to exhibit signs of anger, these studies confirm those of Keller (12) and of Kelly, Beaton and Magoun (13), but they make it quite clear that the rage responses evocable in midbrain cats and dogs and in pontile cats are subtotal responses. In the case of the cats the threshold is very high. When one reviews all the relevant evidence it seems reasonable to suggest that the role of the hypothalamus in the central management of rage behavior is largely the facilitation of lower mechanisms, an influence quite like that which the ventral diencephalon exerts "downstream" on movements induced from cortex or bulbar pyramid (25).

The Problem of the Locus of the Restraining
Influence of Telencephalon

That the brain stem mechanisms responsible for the rage behavior of decorticate and hypothalamic animals are normally subject to one or more restraining influences of forebrain origin appears to be an inescapable fact, but it cannot be said that the precise source or sources of this effect or the pathways over which it is exerted have been conclusively demonstrated. Certain parts of the available experimental evidence pertinent to this problem seem contradictory and some are based on experimental procedures that are hardly capable of giving the desired answer.

Yet there can be no doubt that certain of the results already secured are most suggestive, and they will doubtless acquire considerable significance when the final answer is obtained. We propose to review them briefly, but we shall make no attempt to present the anatomical evidence that indicates the existence of efferent connections of the forebrain with hypothalamus and midbrain. A very useful résumé of this difficult aspect of the subject has been provided by Spiegel, Miller and Oppenheimer. (30).

It is important to bear in mind that the differentiating feature of the rage responses of lower animals is the character of activity in the skeletal musculature. In the cat, for example, retraction of ears, growling, a snarling expression, hissing, tail-lashing, biting and striking with claws unsheathed are the distinguishing aspects of a display of anger. However remarkable they may be, the changes in viceral effectors —largely the result of augmented sympathetic discharge—which accompany this overt activity, are common to a number of very different behavior patterns and to certain homeostatic reactions; they cannot in themselves be taken as evidence that anger is being exhibited. It is therefore scarcely justifiable to assume, as Kennard (14) has done, that the "sham rage" of wholly or partially decorticate preparations is the result of "removal of that portion of the cortex in which autonomic representation lies." This assumption includes the hypothesis that the autonomic alterations which occur in this form of emotional behavior are normally held in check by the cortical autonomic representation. But many of the autonomically determined changes which constitute a part of the rage reaction are induced rather than inhibited by stimulation of this representation.

In a few chronic experiments, which unfortunately have never been fully reported, Fulton and Ingraham (10) found that if a transverse cut 2–3 mm. deep be made at the base of the brain 3–4 mm. rostral to the optic chiasm, the animal (cat) becomes very irritable and exhibits rage on very slight provocation. This result was not obtained after unilateral lesions or when, on one or the other side, the lesion did not reach the midline. Kennard (14) apparently removed the area in which these lesions were made, an area which she designates as "the orbital surface of the frontal lobes," and reported that each of five cats in which this was done exhibited a syndrome resembling in many respects the "sham rage" of decorticate preparations. The behavior changes obtained by Fulton and Ingraham have sometimes been attributed to interruption of descending tracts from the neocortex of the frontal poles. Standing in contradiction to this interpretation of their results is a good deal of evidence indicating that in the cat ablation of all neocortex situated rostral to the ansate sulci is not followed by any clear tendency to show excessive rage behavior (3, 18, 30). In the face of this evidence it is difficult to fit into the pattern of our present knowledge the statement of Kennard (14) that after removal of the "mesial and lateral surfaces of the frontal lobes, in the region of area 4" cats show sham rage "though not to the same degree as those in which the orbital surface had been damaged. . . ." The experiments of Murphy and Gellhorn (20), in which the method of local strychninization was used, indicate that in the cat "frontal" neocortex can discharge impulses which reach the hypothalamus, but they do not provide any information as to how these impulses act. It seems clear enough that all neocortex lying caudal to the frontal pole (*i.e.*, behind the ansate and anterior ectosylvian sulci) can be dismissed from the present consideration (3, 14, 30).

That elimination of parts of the forebrain other than neocortex may be the cause of the augmented tendency of decorticate animals to display anger was strongly suggested by results obtained by Spiegel, Miller and Oppenheimer (29, 30) in acute experiments on cats. Lesions were made under ether anesthesia and the behavior of the animals was studied only during the immediate postoperative period. As indicated above, lesions restricted to neocortical areas, including those of the frontal pole, failed to produce the typical decorticate rage reactions. Very definite signs of readily evoked anger appeared, however, if the olfactory tubercles were injured either by a somewhat restricted lesion or in the course of a wide extirpation of the frontal poles. This result is in agreement with the findings of Fulton and Ingraham (*cf.* 14). Quite marked outbursts of rage behavior occurred after bilateral destruction of the amygdaloid nuclei, but superficial damage of the pyriform lobes or destruction of olfactory bulbs did not produce this effect. Rage reactions that varied in intensity and in degree of integration followed lesions of the hippocampus-fornix system. On the other hand, Klüver and Bucy (15) and Bucy and Klüver (8; see also discussion of paper by Spiegel, Miller and Oppenheimer, 29) obtained a very pronounced diminution or even an apparent abolition of anger and fear reactions in monkeys (the wild and intractable

Macaca mulatta) as a result of bilateral removal of the temporal lobes, the greater part of the hippocampus, the uncus and the amygdala.

Scope of Present Investigation

The foregoing discussion should make it clear that there exist a number of uncertainties concerning the organization of the central mechanisms involved in the management of angry behavior. The work of Klüver and Bucy and of Spiegel, Miller and Oppenheimer directed attention to the role played by rhinencephalic structures in the central management of emotional behavior. Previously Papez (21) had presented the proposition "that the hypothalamus, the anterior thalamic nuclei, the gyrus cinguli, the hippocampus and their interconnections constitute a harmonious mechanism which may elaborate the functions of central emotion, as well as participate in emotional expression." The new experimental work which is reported below had its origin in our desire to test experimentally this interesting and provocative suggestion. We also had in mind at least a partial repetition of the experiments of Spiegel, Miller and Oppenheimer (30). It seemed especially desirable to extend some of their observations by carrying out chronic experiments and determining as precisely as possible by histological studies[1] not only the limits of each ablation or lesion but also any secondary degenerations or atrophies which resulted.

METHODS

Each of the animals used—all have been cats—was observed for days or weeks, occasionally for months, before operation. In this way we gained some knowledge, in most cases intimate knowledge, of the temperaments and individual peculiarities of our subjects when their brains were intact. We especially endeavored to appraise their thresholds to rage-provoking stimuli, but we took care not to alter their dispositions by examining them too frequently or too intensely. We pinched their tails, their feet and their ears. We picked them up by the loose skin of their backs and shook them. We spanked them and determined their responses to restraint. In general we examined the

[1] In the histological aspects of this work we received much help from Dr. Jerzy E. Rose. To him we are indebted for a number of valuable suggestions concerning possible correlations between our anatomical and physiological findings.

effects not only of applying moderately nociceptive stimuli but also
of disturbing that personal dignity the violation of which is so apt
to induce signs of anger in most normal cats. During these preoperative periods of observation we also explored the capacity of each cat
to express pleasure or contentment when petted, and we noted
whether it sought this kind of attention or preferred to remain aloof.
Data secured in this way cannot be expressed in quantitative terms,
but they do afford a fair and absolutely essential basis for determining whether or not a cerebral ablation has changed the threshold,
intensity or character of an emotional response. When, as was usually
the case, bilateral removal of cerebral tissue was effected in two
stages, we had the opportunity to study the animals during the interval between operations. Since in this series we have never encountered changes in emotional response as a result of a unilateral ablation,
these observations have provided an additional basis for evaluating
the original emotional status of the cats.

All operations were carried out under deep pentobarbital sodium
anesthesia (42 mg. per kg. of body weight, intraperitoneally). Rigid
aseptic precautions were taken, but when it was necessary to open
a frontal sinus or when respiratory infections were present in the cat
colony, penicillin (a single dose of 20,000 units) was given on the
day of operation and daily thereafter for periods of from one to three
weeks. The cranial cavity was approached through a large bone defect. Temporal muscle or periosteum or both were incised and reflected in such a way as to permit their being used to close the
opening in the skull. Special care was taken in handling the dura
which in the cat is thin and easily torn. It was incised in such a way
as to obtain adequate exposure and ensure subsequent tight closure
by means of sutures of fine silk. Cerebral tissue was removed by light
suction applied, whenever possible, subpially. This technique permits
a degree of precision in ablation that cannot be achieved in any other
way. Large bilateral ablations were usually done in two stages.

Postoperatively all animals were kept in individual cages. After
certain operations, especially those involving removal of olfactory
bulbs, the cats failed to eat and had to be fed by hand for days or
even several weeks. Postoperative management was almost always
easy unless a respiratory infection intervened. Intracranial infections
have been very few. Whenever one occurred the animal was discarded. When an animal was sacrificed it was anesthetized with
pentobarbital sodium, the chest opened and the head and anterior
parts of the body perfused (through a cannula tied into the ascending aorta) first with a 0.9 per cent solution of NaCl, then with 10
per cent formalin. The brain was removed from the skull and suspended in formalin. A careful gross examination was made of every
brain. The brains of a number of cats, selected on the basis of the
nature of the removal and the postoperative behavior, were imbedded
in paraffin and sectioned serially at 20 μ. Every fourth section was
mounted and stained with thionin.

RESULTS

Production of Placidity

We began this investigation by attempting to prepare cats in which all neocortex had been removed but in which there remained intact, on each side, those forebrain structures which are commonly called rhinencephalic (olfactory bulb and tubercle, amygdala, cortex of pyriform lobe, Ammon's formation) and those cortical areas of the midline which appear to be transitional between rhinencephalic cortex and neocortex (see 26). As is now well known, this midline cortex, which lies ventral to the splenial (cingular) sulcus and extends forward from and downward around the rostrum of the corpus callosum, receives afferent connections from the anterior nuclei of the thalamus. It can be subdivided cytoarchitectonically into (i) the anterior limbic area (area 24), whose thalamic relationship is with the anteromedial nucleus; (ii) the cingular area (area 23), which receives fibers from the anteroventral nucleus; and (iii) the retrosplenial areas (areas 29 and 30), to which the anterodorsal nucleus projects. To these may be added the small infralimbic area (area 25), which receives fibers from the medioventral nucleus, and the postsubicular cortex (area 48).

The operative procedure necessary for the production of an animal with this particular cerebral ablation requires (i) the removal, without damage to pyriform lobe, amygdala or hippocampal formation, of all cortex of the convexity of the hemisphere that lies between the posterior rhinal and the lateral sulci; (ii) ablation of all cortex of the lateral gyrus down to the splenial sulcus without damage to the underlying retrosplenial and cingular cortex; and (iii) the removal of neocortex of the frontal pole without encroaching upon the anterior limbic area. The last is the most difficult part of the procedure because there are few easily determined boundaries between cortex which should be removed and cortex which should be spared. Ventrolaterally there is the anterior rhinal sulcus, but it is not always easily brought into view. On the medial wall the splenial sulcus ends after turning to run in a rostrodorsal direction above the descending limb of the cruciate sulcus, both banks of which are composed of medial extensions of the anterior and posterior sigmoid gyri. Here one must remove all cortex lying above a plane which passes forward and downward from the ascending limb of the splenial sulcus. If the ablation is carried too far ventrally the anterior limbic area will suffer damage. In most cases we guarded against this by sparing the ventral portion of the gyrus proreus, and there are several reasons for believing that the small fragments of the neocortex that were left were not functionally active. Another difficulty is the preservation of the thalamocortical fibers which project to the cingular and retrosplenial areas. In every case, although the entire midline cortex was intact below the splenial sulcus, many of these fibers were interrupted (shown by partial or severe degeneration of anteroventral and anterodorsal nuclei). A source of no little confusion and uncertainty is our considerable ignorance of the efferent connections of all subdivisions of the transitional cortex of the midline. Even if one succeeds surgically in preserving them and in sparing their afferent connections from the thalamus, there is no good anatomical criterion by which one can determine whether they can act on parts of the brain still intact.

We have prepared and studied five cats in which the desired ablation was closely approximated. Each has exhibited throughout a long survival period a state of refractoriness to rage-provoking stimuli, a condition which can best be described as *placidity*.[2] Rough handling, rigid restraint or the application of quite strong nociceptive stimuli invariably failed to evoke any sign of anger. In all other respects these animals behaved like wholly decorticate cats; their general activity, locomotion, postural adjustments, postural deficiencies, feeding reactions and cleaning reactions were essentially the same as those of the cats with more extensive forebrain removals described by Dusser de Barenne (9) and by Bard and Rioch (5). Somewhat detailed descriptions of two of these animals will make clear the rather extraordinary emotional unresponsiveness which was produced by removal of neocortex with sparing of rhinencephalic structures and of the transitional cortex of the midline.

Cat 16. During a preoperative observation period of two weeks this small adult female proved to be a friendly and easily handled animal. She responded to agreeable stimuli with signs of pleasure. Noxious stimuli, such as light pinching of her tail, evoked loud angry vocalization, spitting, snarling, striking, pupillodilatation and piloerection; she usually launched an integrated and effective attack with teeth and claws on the source of the stimulus, *e.g.*, the hand (preferably gloved) of the observer.

On 17 April 1947 the neocortex was removed from the left hemisphere. The extent of the ablation is shown in Figure 1. The operation

[2] We wish to make it clear that our use of this word carries no implication of a subjective experience. It should also be understood that when we describe a cat as "placid" we mean nothing more than that its *behavior* is mild and calm, even when subjected to stimuli which in normal cats would give rise to activities denoting a major affective state.

produced no change in her affective behavior. She remained as friendly as before; petting evoked rubbing, rolling and purring. Noxious stimuli produced the same exhibition of anger as before operation and there was no change in threshold.

After an interval of 42 days the right hemisphere was subjected (on 21 May 1947) to an ablation that closely approximated that performed on the left side (see Fig. 1). There were no postoperative complications. On the third day the cat began to eat of her own accord when food was placed in her cage, and when put on the floor she walked about slowly with a wide base. She remained in good condition throughout her survival of 20 weeks. She always exhibited extensor rigidity when suspended, lacked placing reactions and showed very deficient hopping reactions. The animal pricked up its ears and turned its head toward the source of a sharp sound and, like Bard and Rioch's cat 244, she followed a scraping noise across a large room. When a pan containing food was placed within five feet of her, she sniffed and licked repeatedly, quickly found the food and ate it rapidly in great gulps. There was exaggeration of postprandial nose and chop licking. She spent much time licking her chest and shoulders, but neglected the rest of her coat which rapidly became filthy unless brushed and washed.

The second operation produced a most striking alteration in the animal's response to being violently disturbed or stimulated nociceptively. Throughout her survival of nearly five months it was never possible to obtain any reaction characteristic of the feline expression of anger even when quite intense and prolonged nociceptive stimuli were applied. Such procedures as tying her in the dorsal decubitus on an animal board, picking her up by the loose skin of the back and vigorously shaking her, spanking her or pinching her tail as hard as possible between thumb and forefinger elicited only a few plaintive meows. When her tail was grasped between the jaws of a large surgical clamp and compressed sufficiently to produce a bruise she cried loudly and attempted to escape by moving forward, but there was no growling, spitting, snarling, retraction of ears, striking, tail-lashing, change in respiration, pupillodilatation or sweating from the footpads. Considerable piloerection was present at all times after the second operation, regardless of the level of environmental temperature, but it was not augmented by these noxious stimuli. During the 139 days of survival she was subjected, every two or three days, to a variety of noxious stimuli, each sufficient to provoke in any normal cat or any cat without forebrain a well-patterned and vigorous exhibition of rage. Without exception her response was confined to a few meows and progressive movements of the extremities. On one occasion her tail, shaved and moistened, was stimulated tetanically through electrodes connected with the secondary of a Harvard inductorium the primary circuit of which was activated by 4.5 volts. When the secondary coil was at 13, she mewed; at 11 there was loud crying and an increment in piloerection; at the end of a five-second stimulation with the secondary at 5 she screamed loudly and spat twice. The last

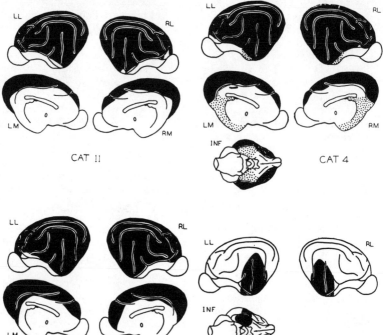

CAT 11

CAT 4

CAT 16

CAT 22

Fig. 1. Representation of the results of studies of serial sections of brains of *cats 11, 4, 16* and *22*. Each chart is based on micrometric measurements of areas of cortex remaining intact. The data were transferred, with allowance for shrinkage, to photographic silhouettes of a standard cat's brain. Solid black: areas which had been completely removed. White: areas which remain intact. Stippled areas (*cat 4*): areas left intact in first and second operations, but removed in third and final operation. LL, LM, RL, RM, INF: left lateral, left medial, etc.

of these stimulations produced a third degree electrical burn of the tail. It was the only one ever applied to this cat that elicited spitting; it did not evoke any other sign of anger.

Cat 16 was sacrificed on 15 October 1947. A study of serial sections of the brain is the basis of its representation in Figure 1 which depicts quite accurately the extent of the forebrain removal. The dorsolateral neocortex had been completely removed except for a small remnant of the gyrus proreus and gyrus compositus on the left.

This is reflected in the fact that sections through the thalamus reveal a definitely greater preservation of the mediodorsal nucleus on the left than on the right. On the medial surface of each hemisphere the orbitofrontal, infralimbic, cingular, retrosplenial and postsubicular cortical fields had been left intact. The anterior limbic region (area 24) was a little damaged on the right, but remained intact on the left. Accordingly the anteromedial nucleus of the thalamus was partly degenerated on the right, but was essentially preserved on the left. Although the rest of the midline cortex was equally well spared on both sides, the anteroventral and anterodorsal nuclei were better preserved on the left than on the right. This difference doubtless reflects a bilaterally unequal interruption of their cortical projections. The drawing of the ventral surface of this brain (Fig. 1) shows that narrow strips of cortex of the pyriform and entorhinal areas, ventral and medial to the posterior rhinal sulci, had been removed. Study of the serial sections showed that there had been no injury to any other rhinencephalic structure. No part of the diencephalon or mesencephalon was involved in the surgical removal.

Cat 11. This animal was the only one of the series in which bilateral removal of neocortex was carried out in a single operation. Reference to Figure 1 shows that the ablation, done on 17 January 1947, was very similar to that performed in *cat 16.* The cat was a handsome yellowish male which during a preoperative observation period of one week, proved to be a restless animal that invariably struggled to escape when handled gently. Rough handling evoked scratching, but no excessive display of emotion. When restrained on an animal board he cried loudly, struggled and spat, but did not bite. Our notes indicate that the responses of this cat to certain rage-provoking stimuli were not adequately determined. They do suggest, however, that he possessed a somewhat higher threshold to such stimuli than did *cat 16.*

The animal made a remarkably good recovery from the extensive removal of cerebral tissue. On the fourth postoperative day he began to take food of his own accord. During the first 30 days he showed very little spontaneous activity. In his cage he remained for long periods in a crouching position with legs flexed beneath his body and engaged in a good deal of loud wailing. Outside his cage he moved about slowly with head low and licked the floor. Spontaneous activity gradually increased; by the end of the sixth week he walked rapidly and even ran when released from his cage. The odor of food always increased his activity. When meat was placed nearby he began at once to chew or gnaw any object—an empty food pan, a stick or a shoe—placed in front of him. When guided to the food (after several weeks he was able to find it unaided) he attacked the meat, burying his nose, jaws and face in it and biting and swallowing it in gulps without chewing. On one occasion he devoured 400 grams (20 per cent of his body weight) of horsemeat and seemed eager to continue his gluttony. His excessive appetite continued and he gained in weight. Doubtless he would have become obese had food been

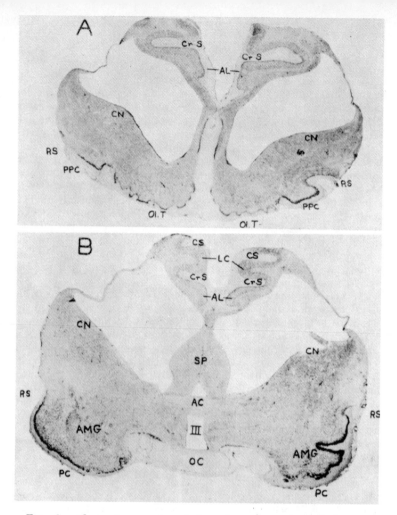

Fig. 2. Photomicrographs of frontal sections through brain of *cat 11.* Thionin. ×4. A. Section just in front of rostrum of corpus callosum. On each side removal followed anterior rhinal sulcus. Rhinencephalic structures and caudate nuclei are bilaterally intact. On medial aspect of each hemisphere the anterior limbic cortex has been preserved. A small sector of neocortex covering dorsal lip of cruciate sulcus is present on both sides. B. Section at level of anterior commissure and optic chiasm. Laterally, on right and left, removal follows posterior rhinal sulcus precisely and rhinencephalic structures are intact. On medial surfaces anterior limbic cortex ventral to caudal end of cruciate sulcus is intact. More dorsally, between tip of cruciate sulcus and rostral extremity of splenial (cingular) sulcus, is rostral portion of cingular cortical field. [For key to abbreviations used in this and other figures in this article see pp. 157, 158.]

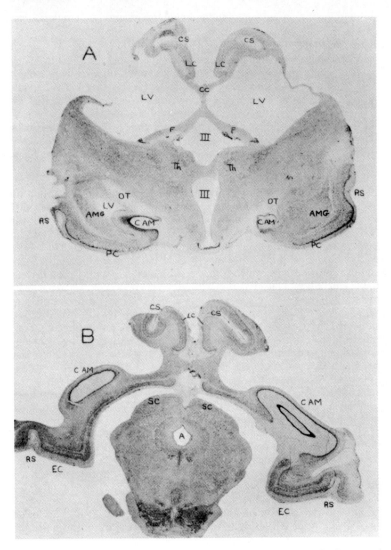

Fig. 3. Photomicrographs of frontal sections through brain of *cat 11.* Thionin. ×4. *A.* Section at the level of rostral extremity of thalamus. Laterally the removal on each side has followed the rhinal sulcus, but all structures medial and ventral to rhinal sulci were left intact. On medial surface of each hemisphere cingular field of transitional cortex of midline is present, and some cortex within the splenial sulcus has been partially preserved. *B.* Section just caudal to splenium of corpus callosum. On each side lateroventral limit of ablation passed just outside the rhinal sulcus. The section illustrates the preservation of the cingular cortical area and cornu ammonis on the two sides.

made available *ad libitum*. In all other respects he was like *cat 16*. He followed a scraping noise about the room, but he showed no response whatever to a dog whistle or to other high-pitched sounds. When held two or three feet from an angry dog that barked loudly and growled he evidenced not the slightest reaction. This animal exhibited particularly well an interesting phenomenon that is seen in all chronically decorticate cats and dogs, namely, what appears to be normal sleep. Especially during the night (when the laboratory was quiet) we frequently found him asleep, curled up in a typical feline sleeping posture with nose tucked under tail and eyes closed.

Throughout his survival of 88 days this animal exhibited "placidity." His only response to being strapped in an extended position on an animal board was a few struggling movements. When suspended by hindfoot or tail he merely cried in a wailing, plaintive manner and licked. Quite strong nociceptive stimulation of any part of the body was equally ineffective in producing signs of anger. Up to the end of the eighth week squeezing his tail between the jaws of a Kelly clamp produced only walking movements and a few cries which were devoid of angry tone. On the 58th day this procedure evoked yells, more suggestive of pain than of anger, and after repeated stimulation he spat twice. During the third month he occasionally hissed when subjected to this intensely nociceptive stimulation, but at no time did it or any other stimulus or disturbance produce biting, striking, tail-lashing, retraction of ears, dilatation of pupils or sweating from the footpads.

On the 88th day (15 April 1947) this cat was found lying on his side in his cage, unable to stand. There was a continuous fine tremor of tongue, head, legs, and tail which became greater in amplitude and lower in frequency during phasic movements. This condition was of quite sudden occurrence, for on the previous day there had been no trace of it and he appeared entirely well. The cat was sacrificed at once, but neither autopsy nor study of serial sections of the brain revealed anything which could account for the disorder. We have occasionally seen it develop in normal cats.

The condition of the brain of *cat 11* is indicated in Figures 1, 2 and 3. Except for small remnants of the gyrus proreus and posterior ectosylvian gyrus on the right and a very narrow strip of the posterior sylvian gyrus on both sides, all neocortex of the dorsolateral aspects of both hemispheres had been removed. On the medial surface of each hemisphere there remained of the neocortex the orbitofrontal fields and small fringes of the anterior and posterior sigmoid gyri. In the thalamus the partial preservation of the mediodorsal nucleus —somewhat more on the right than on the left—signals the sparing of at least portions of neocortical areas corresponding to areas 8–12 of the primate cortex. Any remnants of areas 6, 4, 3, 1 and 2 that remained were unquestionably without efferent connections. As regards the transitional cortex of the midline, it is clear that the anterior limbic, infralimbic, cingular, retrosplenial and postsubicular fields were bilaterally intact. The anteromedial and medioventral nuclei of the thalamus showed scarcely any atrophy on either side. On the other hand; the anteroventral and anterodorsal nuclei were only partly preserved (somewhat better on right than left), and this degeneration certainly resulted from damage to fibers passing to the cortex rather than to any operative injury to the cingular and retrosplenial cortical areas. Examination of serial sections showed that all parts of the rhinencephalon remained wholly intact on both sides. There had been no injury to any subcortical structure.

In a third animal (*cat 4*) a state of placidity was produced by removal—in two stages—of neocortex with sparing of the rhinencephalic structures and the transitional cortex of the midline. It was subjected, however, to a third operation in which a large part of the rhinencephalon was removed bilaterally. The additional ablation converted the animal from a placid creature to one in which a full display of rage could be easily evoked. This change will be described in the following section. Since the third operation involved no removal of neocortex and only barely touched the cortex of the midline (at its caudal extremity) our study of serial sections of the brain has given us some fairly reliable information regarding the extent of the first two removals. They produced a state of placidity equal to that exhibited by *cats 11* and *16*. The following protocol will make this clear.

Cat 4, an adult female, provoked no disturbance when kept for several days before operation in a cage with six other cats. She was easily handled, but did not appear to be especially friendly. When spanked or roughed or when her tail was squeezed moderately she responded with a full display of anger.

In the first operation (17 October 1946) the neocortex of the left hemisphere was removed. During the 47 days that elapsed between this and the second ablation the cat showed no noticeable change in her disposition. Although easily handled she was not friendly and did not spontaneously seek petting. When closely restrained in one's arms she made violent efforts to escape, but did not exhibit any specific sign of anger. Pinching her tail always provoked a fine exhibition of anger (growling, spitting, striking, biting, tail-lashing, pupillodilatation and piloerection).

On 3 December 1946 the right hemisphere was subjected to essentially the same operation as that carried out previously on the left side. All cortex lying between the anterior and posterior rhinal sulci and the rim of the hemisphere at the midline was removed. On the medial surface all cortex above the splenial sulcus was sucked away and this ablation was continued forward to include most of the medial aspect of the frontal pole (see Fig. 1). The rhinencephalic structures were not injured or removed. The animal made an uneventful re-

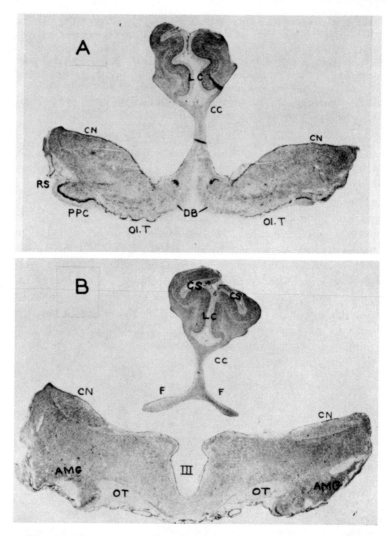

Fig. 4. Photomicrographs of frontal sections through the brain of *cat 4*. Thionin. ×4. A. Section just caudal to rostrum of corpus callosum. On the right side (left in Fig.) line of removal is along the rhinal sulcus. On the left side prepyriform field, ventromedial to rhinal sulcus, has been partially removed. Caudate nuclei are intact. B. Section just caudal to optic chiasm. The entire dorsolateral neocortex has been removed. Except for small remnants in vicinity of the optic tracts pyriform and peri-amygdaloid cortical fields have been removed. Amygdaloid nuclear complex has been largely destroyed on each side.

covery and showed the same general behavior as did *cats 16* and *11.*

The responses of this cat to all sorts of disturbances and to nociceptive stimuli were frequently determined during the interval of 49 days between the second and third intracranial procedures. She exhibited a state of profound placidity. Whereas at all times before the second operation she had responded to light pinching or rough handling with a vigorous and complete rage reaction, she now failed to show any item of angry behavior when subjected to strong nociceptive stimuli. Shaking her immoderately by the loose skin of the back or pinching her tail strongly with a Kelly clamp failed to evoke any trace of any item of the exhibition of rage characteristic of a normal or wholly decorticate cat. She submitted to being tied supine on an animal board as if she enjoyed the maneuver. This was in marked contrast to her preoperative response to this procedure. Before the first and second operations she had never displayed signs of pleasure when petted or stroked. On several occasions during the time of her placidity she purred when petted. Toward the end of this period it was found that when her head was stroked she purred and pressed against one's hand in a way that was suggestive of mild pleasure. On 6, 9 and 14 January she received large intramuscular injections (2,000, 4,000 and 4,000 units, respectively) of estradiol proprionate in oil (Progynon B). This attempt to evoke estrous behavior was wholly unsuccessful. She failed to show either the typical feline "courtship activities" or the "after-reaction," both of which have been seen in female cats without forebrain (3, 4). Mechanical stimulation of the vagina produced loud angry vocalization and spitting. This was the only procedure that ever elicited these expressions of anger during the interval between the second and third operations.

The third operation was carried out on 21 January 1947. The cranial cavity was opened on both sides and a bilaterally symmetrical removal was done. Care was taken not to disturb or injure the midline cortex rostral to the level of the splenium of the corpus callosum. The stippled areas shown in Figure 1 were removed by gentle and careful application of the sucker. On each side the postsubicular, entorhinal, pyriform and periamygdaloid cortical areas were removed as was also all of the hippocampal formation except small fragments situated medially beneath the corpus callosum and at its ventromedial tip adjacent to the amygdala. The only parts of the amygdaloid complex which escaped removal were, on each side, portions of the cortical and medial nuclei (see Figs. 4B and 5A). A study of serial sections shows that the globus pallidus was not injured on either side.

As will be made clear in the next section, the third ablation changed the state of the animal from one of placidity to one of extreme hyperexcitability with respect to rage reactions. But here we are concerned with the extents of the first two removals. As regards the midline cortex there can be little doubt, for only its most caudal extremity was touched in the last operation. Throughout this animal's life the infralimbic, anterior limbic and cingular areas and the greater part of the retrosplenial area remained intact on both sides (Figs. 4

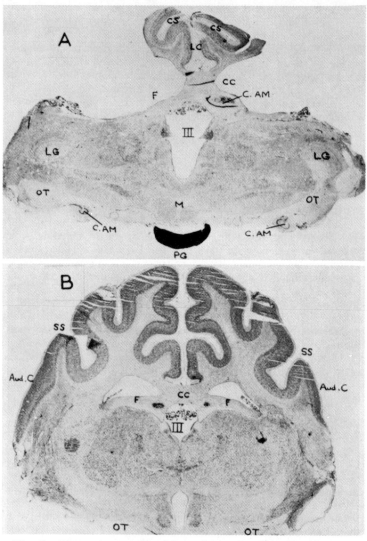

Fig. 5. Photomicrographs of frontal sections. Thionin. ✕4. A. Section through brain of *cat 4* at level of mammillary bodies. All dorsolateral neocortex and entorhinal area situated ventromedial to posterior rhinal sulcus have been ablated on both sides. Of cornu ammonis there remain only a small fragment beneath corpus callosum on left side (right in Fig.) and the extreme ventral tip on both sides. Along medial surface of each hemisphere cingular cortex is intact except for a small injury on left. B. Section through brain of *cat 22* at level of middle commissure of thalamus just caudal to optic chiasm. Pyriform and peri-amygdaloid cortical fields, insular cortex and portions of auditory cortex have been removed bilaterally. The amygdaloid complex is absent on both sides.

and 5A). Examination of the thalamus (Fig. 6C) suggests that in the first and second operations most of the afferent fibers from the anteroventral and anterodorsal nuclei to the cingular and retrosplenial areas were interrupted; these portions of the diencephalon had undergone extensive atrophy. On the other hand, the thalamic projections to the anterior limbic and infralimbic areas were almost wholly undamaged, for the anteromedial and medioventral nuclei showed scarcely any atrophy. A partial preservation of the mediodorsal nuclei (better on the left than on the right) indicates some sparing of those neocortical areas which are homologous to areas 8–12 of the primate brain. As regards the rhinencephalic structures present after the second operation (but removed in the third) there is less certainty. Our operative notes indicate that no damage was done to cortex (of pyriform lobe) lying medial to the posterior rhinal sulci and that amygdala and Ammon's formation were entirely spared on both sides. No structure of the ventral surface of the brain situated medial to the anterior rhinal sulci was damaged in any of the three operations.

Like *cat 4*, two other animals were first made placid by bilateral removal of neocortex and then subjected a third operation which greatly lowered their very high thresholds to rage-provoking stimuli. In them, however, the final procedure was bilateral ablation of the transitional cortex of the midline; the rhinencephalic structures removed in *cat 4* were left intact. Despite some uncertainty as to the exact extent of the operative procedures, we shall describe the change produced in both by removal of neocortex.

Cat 5. This was a large adult male that exhibited preoperatively unusual friendliness and affection. Whenever he had access to a human being he persistently sought petting. On being fondled, stroked or scratched he purred loudly, kneaded with his forepaws, rubbed and rolled. When his tail was pinched he appeared startled and cried out. If the stimulus was continued at high intensity he vocalized loudly and finally snarled, spat and struck with unsheathed claws at the source of the stimulation.

The object of the first operation, carried out 22 October 1946, was removal of all neocortex of the left hemisphere. Care was taken to leave intact the midline cortex and all rhinencephalic structures. The animal made a rapid recovery and showed the various deficiencies characteristic of a hemidecorticate cat. He remained as friendly as before and continued to exhibit a high threshold for rage reactions.

On 18 November 1946 the right hemisphere was subjected to ablation of neocortex and we were confident that it was of the same extent as that performed on the left side. Recovery was uneventful and during the 57 days that elasped before the third operation the cat behaved and reacted in the same manner as did *cats 16, 11* and *4* after bilateral ablation of neocortex. Stroking or rubbing him no

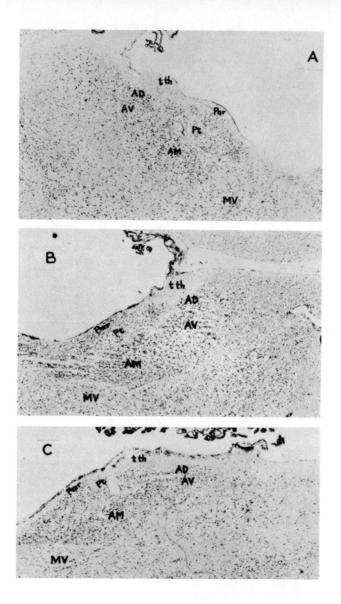

Fig. 6. Photomicrographs of frontal sections through thalami of *cats 11* (A), *16* (B) and *4* (C). In the three brains status of anterior group of nuclei is much the same. The anterodorsal and anteroventral nuclei show considerable atrophy. Anteromedial nucleus has been largely preserved, but in no cat does it appear entirely intact in all sections. Because of changes in pressure relationships due to the large removal of cerebral tissue there is distortion of the thalami in all these brains.

longer produced any signs of pleasure. During this kind of stimulation he remained perfectly still with eyes closed. Placidity was profound. Roughing, hard spanking or strong tail-pinching evoked nothing more than a few weak and plaintive cries. When tied backdown on a board he struggled a little, but gave not the slightest sign of anger. On only one occasion was an item of the normal feline rage reaction evoked: after a very severe nociceptive stimulation of the tail he spat once. Although the threshold of his rage reactions had been quite high before the second operation it was clear that this removal made it almost infinite. In his failure to respond by affective behavior to strongly noxious stimuli he stood in striking contrast to cats which have been deprived of the entire forebrain.

In a third operation (14 January 1947) the transitional cortex of the midline was removed on both sides. On exposure this part of the brain appeared to be entirely intact. As soon as the effects of the anesthetic had disappeared it became evident that the operation had produced a marked change in affective behavior. This change, which will be described in the next section, persisted throughout a further survival of 8.5 months.

The animal was sacrificed on 26 September 1947, but his brain has not been sectioned serially for histological study. Gross examination showed that all neocortex except very narrow fringes just lateral to the posterior rhinal sulci had been removed. The postsubicular, retrosplenial and cingular areas and the greater part of the anterior limbic area were absent on both sides. Of the entire midline cortex there remained on each side only the most ventral portion of the anterior limbic area (and doubtless also the small infralimbic area). It was evident that in the first and second operations the ablation had very closely followed the line of the rhinal sulci. The pyriform lobes were entirely intact and we could find no indication that any rhinencephalic structure had been damaged.

Cat 17. This animal, a small adult female, is still alive and therefore our operative notes and impressions constitute the only evidence we can present regarding the extent of each of the three cerebral removals which were carried out. Nevertheless, it seems reasonable to present this account of our observations, for they are in fair accord with those made on the four animals already described.

The cat was subjected to an unusually long and searching preoperative period of observation. For two months she served as a "normal control" in a class exercise devoted to a study of a number of cats with ablations of one or another part of the central nervous system. During this time she underwent extensive neurological examinations by more than 70 medical students. Although these tests did not involve the application of any nociceptive stimulus, they subjected her to much clumsy handling and no little loss of feline dignity. Such disturbances never evoked signs of bad temper. At the same time, however, it was discovered that fairly strong nociceptive stimuli evoked growling, spitting and a vigorous attack.

Removal of all neocortex of the left hemisphere, except the gyrus proreus and the ventral portion of the medial surface of the frontal pole, was carried out on 26 May 1947. Until the next operation, 19 days later, she remained friendly and affectionate and responded as before to nociceptive stimuli. Then, on 14 June 1947, the same operation was performed on the right side. This produced a greatly raised threshold to rage-inducing stimuli, but the degree of placidity was not as great as that found in the four cats described above. Close restraint on her back, spanking, roughing or shaking did not evoke any sign of anger. Strong pinching of her tail, however, produced some growling and biting and, when prolonged, one or two hisses. Moderate dilatation of the pupils occurred, but there were no other external indications of any alteration in autonomic activity.

In a third operation (17 July 1947) the midline cortex was removed on both sides. In addition, the olfactory stalks were severed and all remaining cortex of the midline of the frontal pole removed. Probably the anterior portions of the olfactory tubercles were included in the ablation, but on each side the amygdala, the pyriform lobe and the hippocampal formation remained intact. Recovery was rapid. From the fifth postoperative day to the time of the present writing (eight months later) this cat has invariably exhibited a vigorous expression of rage in response to any slight disturbance.

These experimental observations make it clear that after a careful bilateral ablation of all neocortex except very small fragments of the medial surfaces of the frontal poles a cat becomes extraordinarily refractory to rage-provoking stimuli. We have evidence that just as great a degree of placidity is produced when the rhinencephalic structures and midline cortex remain on only one side. In the case of two animals (*cats* 38 and 41) removal of the neocortex of one hemisphere was done in a first operation and subsequently all tissue above the mesencephalon except thalamus, hypothalamus, olfactory tubercle and septum was ablated on the other side. Preoperatively both cats showed marked rage reactions in response to restraint or light tail-pinching. We cannot at this time give any detailed description of their brains, for both are still alive. *Cat 41* has been studied for 106 days and throughout this period he has been frequently subjected to stimuli which in normal cats and in wholly decorticate cats invariably produce violent rage responses. Such procedures as squeezing his tail between the jaws of a surgical clamp, swinging him by his tail or a hindfoot or tying him on an animal board have never induced any item of the feline rage reaction; at the most they have evoked progressive movements of the legs and a few meows or a curious, rather loud cackling vocalization. *Cat 38* showed almost the same degree of placidity throughout a period of 67 days, at the end of which a segment of hippocampus and fornix was removed on the side of the first operation. This had no perceptible effect and he has remained placid for an additional 47 days.

The patterned mode of behavior which constitutes the expression of anger in a normal cat is composed in part of autonomically determined bodily changes. Most of these are due to augmented sympathetic activity. We wish to emphasize that when stimulated nociceptively or disturbed violently the placid cats showed as great a paucity of response in visceral effectors as in skeletal muscle. A considerable degree of piloerection existed at all times. It was not related to external temperature or to the very small and quite normal fluctuations in rectal temperature that occurred in these animals. With very strong nociceptive stimulation it was sometimes perceptibly increased. This occurred in *cat 16* when her tail was stimulated with a strong faradic current, but it was not accompanied by pupillodilatation or sweating. None of these changes was ever observed in *cat 11*. When strong continuous bruising pressure applied to the tail evoked a few bites and two hisses in *cat 17* there was a submaximal dilatation of the pupils, but no other external sign of a change in autonomic activity. In *cat 41* this same stimulation caused a small further erection of hair, but there was no increase in the size of his pupils and his toepads remained dry. Although our exploration of alterations in autonomic activity has been limited to observations of changes in superficially situated visceral effectors, we feel justified in stating that placidity includes a sluggishness of autonomic response to rage-provoking stimuli.

Conversion of a State of Placidity to One of Ferocity by an Additional Forebrain Removal

A comparison of the placid animals with cats lacking not only neocortex but also the greater part of the rest of the forebrain, *e.g.*, the cats described by Bard and Rioch (5), naturally led us to suppose that placidity must be due to a restraining influence exerted by the transitional cortex of the midline or the rhinencephalic structures or perhaps by both regions acting together. The correctness of this assumption was demonstrated by the effects of removal of one or the other of these portions of the telenecephalon in three placid cats. These animals (*cats*

4, 5 and *17*) have been described in the protocols of the preceding section. There the reader will find a full account of their
preoperative responses, the degree of placidity displayed and the
operations performed.

Cat 4. It will be recalled that after removal of the neocortex
of both hemispheres this animal was profoundly placid. She
was studied in that condition for a period of 49 days. Then, in
a third operation, certain rhinencephalic structures were removed on both sides, but a study of serial sections has shown
that the cortex of the midline, the globus pallidus, putamen
and caudate and the entire diencephalon and mesencephalon
were not touched. The structures removed on each side were:
the postsubicular, entorhinal, pyriform and peri-amygdaloid
cortical areas, almost the entire hippocampal formation and all
of the amygdaloid complex except portions of the cortical and
medial nuclei. The rather dramatic change produced by this
ablation became very evident in an examination made just 50
hours after completion of the operation. When the cat was
lifted from her cage she growled, spat and bit. Light pinching
of the skin of her tail, flank or back produced growling, spitting,
biting and striking, acceleration and deepening of respiration,
marked dilatation of pupils and piloerection. In her poorly
directed attack she bit herself viciously.

From the second day after the third operation until she was
sacrificed 160 days later *cat 4* invariably responded to the most
trifling disturbance by a savage exhibition of rage. Tactile, pressure and vibratory stimuli were equally effective in eliciting all
the motor phenomena which make up the full expression of
feline anger. Merely placing a hand lightly on her flank or
back produced hissing with lips retracted and tongue curled,
growling, flattening of ears, tail-lashing, acceleration of respiration, dilatation of pupils, erection of hair over tail and back,
and profuse sweating from the toepads. Any stimulus of the
body, extremities or tail greater than a gentle stroke evoked in
addition savage biting and striking with unsheathed claws. If
the stimulus was applied to the tail or near the midline of the
body the attack was directed forward and downward and sometimes she bit her forepaws. When it was applied well to one
side of the midline she turned a little to the stimulated side,
but never sufficiently to reach the source of the stimulation.
The threshold for effective tactile stimulation was higher

around the neck, occiput and top or sides of the head than over the trunk, tail and extremities. A light puff of air directed at her face sufficed to provoke spitting, growling, retraction of ears, widening of pupils, piloerection and the assumption of a belligerently defensive stance, but this reaction was not produced by tapping her on the nose. The cat occasionally hissed in the absence of any apparent external stimulus, but we never observed any spontaneous development of an integrated rage reaction. On the 52nd day it was noted for the first time that *cat 4* salivated profusely during a rage reaction. From that time on this was an invariable accompaniment of a fully developed exhibition of anger.

All attempts to induce any signs of rage by purely auditory stimuli failed. On the other hand, vibratory stimulation was quite effective. Provided she was in her cage, tapping it always elicited several definite signs of anger. The same response could be obtained by knocking on a table when she was sitting or crouching on it. We were never able to induce any sign of pleasure. Stroking her back or lightly rubbing her head or cheeks invariably caused growling and spitting. We were never able to obtain in this cat the definite fear reaction which Bard and Rioch (5) noted when decorticate cats were exposed to loud high-pitched sounds.

The third operation caused certain changes in the nonemotional aspects of the behavior of *cat 4*. During her period of placidity she had been somewhat restless and spent many hours of the day pacing about her cage. Despite its marked effect upon the threshold of the rage reaction, the removal of the rhinencephalic structures reduced the amount of her spontaneous motor activity. When undisturbed in her cage she remained for long periods of time completely immobile in a crouch with back arched, all four feet drawn up under her, and head motionless. In this quiet state the hair of back, flanks and tail was quite smooth; there was little of the piloerection which was conspicuous at all times when she was in the placid state. When immobile the animal did not appear to be asleep, but she was repeatedly found, especially at night, curled up in a posture typical of the sleeping normal cat. When this cat did move about it was in the same awkward manner she had displayed after only neocortex had been removed. In contrast to this was the neatness of her swift striking movements when displaying anger.

Within the first week following the third operation *cat 4* began to eat spontaneously when presented with food and she was always able to find, obviously by olfactory cues, meat placed within three or four feet of her nose. Her search was accompanied by much sniffing and

licking. This response to the presence of odoriferous food was present
after the second operation and was not altered by the third in which
so great a part of the so-called rhinencephalon had been removed.

Cat 5. After removal of the neocortex of both hemispheres this
animal showed as striking a degree of placidity as did *cat 4.* In
the third operation the rhinencephalic structures removed in
that animal were not touched. Instead we removed the transitional cortex of the midline. At autopsy gross inspection of the
brain (serial sections have not been made) showed that except
for the most ventral portion of the anterior limbic field and the
infralimbic area all of this cortex had been removed on both
sides. The olfactory bulbs, tracts and tubercles remained intact.

After the third operation it became almost immediately apparent that removal of midline cortex had abolished the practically total suppression of angry behavior which had existed
throughout the 57 days between the second and third operations. On the first postoperative day he growled, spat and bit
when his tail was pinched. Twenty-four hours later this response
was evoked when he was roughly picked up by the skin of his
back. During the first three weeks the threshold of the rage
reaction underwent a slight further fall, but thereafter it did
not perceptibly change. It was always much higher than in
cat 4, but once crossed by a moderately nociceptive stimulus
the response obtained was a complete and very convincing
exhibition of anger. At all times throughout his survival of 255
days, pinching his tail between thumb and forefinger caused a
very ferocious episode of sham rage. First, he responded by
growling and snarling. Then, as the stimulus was continued,
he spat, bit and struck at the floor, and retracted his ears. Any
object held in front of his mouth was savagely bitten and
chewed. This integrated acivity of skeletal muscle was accompanied by maximal dilatation of the pupils and an increase
in the piloerection always present. On several occasions, when
the tail was stimulated for more than a few seconds, we noted
sweating from the toepads. The skeletal components of the reaction ceased within 3–5 seconds of releasing the tail and during this time the appendage was lashed a few times. The cat
withstood quite rough handling without showing signs of anger.
He could be lifted and shaken or spanked without displaying
any item of the rage response. It is to be remembered that during his period of placidity the most intense nociceptive stimula-

tion of his tail failed to evoke any angry behavior. Also it should be recalled that preoperatively a definitely noxious stimulus was required to obtain any signs of fury.

It is interesting and perhaps quite significant that removal of midline cortex not only restored this animal's capacity to show anger but was followed, after some time, by at least some return of the marked pleasure reaction which had been such a conspicuous feature of his preoperative behavior. The second operation apparently had abolished all responses indicative of pleasure. During the last seven months of his survival, however, he purred when handled gently and if his head or neck was scratched or rubbed he turned or rolled his head to press against the stimulus, closed his eyes and purred. Sometimes he was heard to purr when alone in his cage. For some time after angry behavior had been evoked signs of pleasure could not be obtained. Another effect of the third operation was an increase in spontaneous motor activity. In *cat 4* removal of rhinencephalic structures had the opposite effect. As regards responses to the odor of food and in his manner of eating this animal closely resembled *cat 4*.

Cat 17. The placidity produced in this animal as a result of the first two operations was not as intense as in *cats 4* and *5*. A very strong nociceptive stimulus provoked some signs of anger but a full rage reaction was never obtained (see protocol, p. 135). In the third operation the midline cortex was removed bilaterally as in *cat 5*, but the ablation was carried forward to include the olfactory stalks and tracts and any small fragments of neocortex of the frontal pole that may have been spared in the previous operations. The rostral portion of each olfactory tubercle was probably damaged. Again, we soon saw evidence of release of the rage reaction. On the fifth day, when her tail was pinched, she growled, spat and bit savagely at the floor beneath her chin. Shortly she began to exhibit a full and very energetic rage reaction—the typical sham rage of the decorticate cat—in response to relatively innocuous stimuli. For example, on lifting her gently by the loose skin of her back she snarled, growled, bit, spat repeatedly, struck into the air with forefeet, and lashed her tail. At the same time she showed maximal dilatation of the pupils and moderate piloerection. This activity lasted as long as she was held suspended. Pinching her tail evoked an even more violent episode in which she bit her forefeet and the floor. Quite trifling stimuli sufficed to produce raging behavior. Pulling a single hair on back or flank caused growling, snarling, hissing, and striking with forefeet a little in the direction of the side stimulated. While the rage responses of this cat were just as intense as those of *cat 4*, the threshold was a little higher; blowing in her face or touching her lightly did not evoke signs of anger. This state of emotional hyperexcitability has remained unchanged up to the time of the present writing (eight months after the last operation). She has shown some pressing of the head against a caressing hand, but no purring. She seems to be wholly anosmic, but finds and eats food placed in her small cage.

Comment on conversion of the three cats. In view of the fact that cats deprived of *all* cerebral cortex and the greater part of the rhinencephalon invariably exhibit rage in response to rather mild stimulation, the production of a state of placidity by removal of neocortex *alone* must be due to the exertion of a restraining influence by the remaining forebrain. The results obtained in *cat 4* indicate quite clearly that in the absence of neocortex some part of the rhinencephalon greatly elevates the threshold of the animal to rage-provoking stimuli. But the marked effect produced in *cats 5* and *17* by ablation of the transitional cortex of the midline suggests that under the same conditions this part of the forebrain has almost as powerful a suppressing action. The puzzling feature of these experimental results is that when either of these parts of the forebrain is removed the other fails to maintain the placid state. This is a problem requiring elucidation. We shall return to it after presenting some additional information that is relevant.

Attempts to Produce a State of Ferocity by Restricted Forebrain Ablations

The fact that a cat rendered placid by removal of neocortex develops a specific state of emotional hyperexcitability and hyperactivity when rhinencephalic structures or the transitional cortex of the midline is removed led us to carry out some experiments designed to determine whether in normal cats the extirpation of one or another of these regions would lower the threshold of the rage reaction. This part of our program has not been completed. Some of the results so far obtained seem fairly decisive, but much more work will have to be done before they can be fitted into any general formulation of the role played by the forebrain in the control of angry behavior.

Bilateral removal of transitional cortex of midline. This can be accomplished in two ways, each satisfactory for the purposes of this study. The first involves a surgical procedure that can be carried out without causing any permament damage to other parts of the brain. It is as follows:

Exposure of the medial surfaces of the hemispheres down to the corpus callosum is achieved by (i) removal of a wide medial strip of the calvarium from a point over the occipital poles to the frontal sinuses, (ii) incision and reflection of the dura on one side, (iii) coagulation of the veins entering the sagittal sinus from the cortex of that side, and (iv) gentle lateral retraction of one or the other hemisphere. Having identified the splenial (cingular) sulci on both sides all cortex between them and the corpus callosum is removed by gentle suction. Next, the ablation is extended forwards and downwards to include the anterior limbic and infralimbic areas.

Two cats have been subjected to the surgical procedure just described. The removals have not yet been checked by a study of serial sections, but we are confident that all transitional cortex of the midline was removed from each hemisphere. The first of these animals, *cat 29*, was studied for a postoperative period of 60 days. Preoperatively he had exhibited a friendly and even affectionate attitude toward human beings. The ablation appeared to intensify this characteristic, but it had no detectable influence on the rather high threshold to rage-provoking stimuli that he had shown preoperatively. Just two months after the first operation a bilateral ablation of certain rhinencephalic structures was carried out with a result that will be described later. In the case of *cat 45*, a large friendly male, the same bilateral removal of midline cortex also failed to produce any alteration in his affective behavior except possibly an increase in the intensity of his display of pleasure on being handled gently or petted. He was studied during a postoperative period of 64 days.

The second method we employed to eliminate the transitional cortex of the midline on both sides was first to ablate all cortex of one hemisphere (except all or part of the pyriform lobe) and then, with the medial surface of the other hemisphere widely exposed, to remove from it by gentle and careful suction the retrosplenial, cingular, anterior limbic and infralimbic areas. The large removal on one side is justified by the fact that it has never, in our rather extensive experience, produced any change in the emotional behavior of a cat. It included of course the midline cortex on that side. Such was the operation performed on *cat 25*. Before this he had been a definitely shy and apprehensive animal. Petting had quieted him, but it had never induced signs of pleasure. On mild nociceptive stimulation he displayed anger and directed an attack upon the source of the disturbance. The single operation produced a transitory lowering of the threshold of rage reactions. During the first 10 or 12 days spanking him lightly or picking him up by the loose skin of his back evoked a moderately intense but incomplete exhibition of anger. After the 14th day very hard spanking failed to produce anything more than cowering with retracted ears and erection of hair over back and tail. At the same time he developed a capacity to display a pleasure reaction consisting of purring, rubbing and rolling when petted. In view of our rather frequent attempts to evoke rage reactions in him, it does not seem likely that the appearance of these signs of affability was entirely due to his postoperative handling. During the last two months of his 82-day survival the threshold and intensity of his rage reactions were quite normal. He was sacrificed and his brain prepared for histological study. An examination of the serial sections is the basis of the following statement.

The left hemisphere of *cat 25* is completely devoid of neocortex. All the transitional cortex of the midline had been removed. The ventral surface of the left "frontal pole" had been completely ablated except for small remnants of the olfactory tubercle and prepyriform fields. The entorhinal cortex had been removed, but the pyriform and peri-amygdaloid cortex remains undamaged. The amygdaloid complex, cornu ammonis and striatum are all intact. The left thalamus is almost wholly atrophied.

In the right hemisphere the orbitofrontal, anterior limbic, cingular and retrosplenial cortical fields have been wholly removed from the medial wall. The olfactory bulb, the ventral surface of the gyrus proreus and the medial half of the olfactory tubercle have also been removed. There was no other injury. In the right thalamus there is complete degeneration of the entire anterior group of nuclei and a partial degeneration of the mediodorsal nucleus.

Cat 27 was prepared in the same way as *cat 25*. Before operation he proved to be a very gentle and friendly animal. He actively sought petting. Very rough handling and hard spanking caused no sign of anger. At autopsy a careful gross inspection of his brain revealed the following facts concerning the extent of the cerebral ablation.

On the *left* side all cortex except fragments of the entorhinal and pyriform areas had been completely removed—including the transitional cortex of the midline. Ammon's formation had been injured and at least two-thirds of the amygdala removed. Rostrally the line of removal cut across the caudal third of the olfactory tubercle leaving the diagonal band intact. The medial wall of the frontal pole had been removed back as far as the septum. On the *right* side the transitional midline cortex had been removed except for a small fragment in the cingular area. In front of the callosum the entire medial wall and the lateral portion of the gyrus proreus hed been extirpated. The ventrolateral edge of the ablation cut across the olfactory tubercle, severed the olfactory tract and reached the anterior rhinal sulcus.

During the first week after operation non-nociceptive stimuli applied to the left side caused growling, spitting and accurate striking with the left forefoot. On repeatedly evoking this response the threshold became lower and stimuli applied to the right side of the body became effective. During the second week the threshold at which angry behavior could be evoked definitely rose and at the same time a very pronounced pleasure reaction appeared. After the first month signs of anger could be elicited only by pinching his tail. The friendliness and evident enjoyment of petting that was such a conspicuous feature of this preoperative behavior now became extreme. This condition lasted until he was sacrificed after a survival of 77 days.

Several other cats, all still alive many weeks after being subjected to approximately the same operation as was carried out in *cats 25* and *27*, have also shown a transitory drop in the threshold of their rage-reactions.

Frontal pole removals. We have examined the effects of removing bilaterally various portions of the frontal poles. For example, we have removed all of one hemisphere in front of a curved plane passing around the rostrum of the corpus callosum, from the ansate sulcus to the optic chiasm and then on the other side, about 3 mm. rostral to the chiasm, have sucked away a band of tissue extending across the tuberculum olfactorium from midline to olfactory tract. The latter injury is comparable to the lesion made by Fulton and Ingraham (10) on both sides. We have also removed all tissue on each side back to a line

connecting the ansate with the anterior ectosylvian sulcus and
extending medially from the latter to cross the middle of the
tuberculum olfactorium before reaching the midline again.
When serial sections of the brains of these animals have been
studied we shall report the results of our observations in detail.
Here we merely wish to state that, throughout a long survival
period, each of these cats has failed to exhibit any indication
that the removals lowered the threshold of its rage-reactions.
We shall, however, present herewith the results obtained in one
animal (cat 24) of this group. It was subjected to the most
extensive "frontal" removal we have performed and its brain
has been studied histologically. The following protocol describes
our studies of this animal.

Cat 24 was a friendly and easily handled adult female that invariably responded to agreeable stimuli with signs of pleasure. Roughing or spanking her produced only a struggle to escape. She also
attempted to escape when her tail was pinched strongly between
thumb and forefinger, but if her escape was prevented she turned,
growling and spitting, to attack the source of the stimulus. It became
clear before operation that her threshold for the elicitation of angry
behavior was relatively high and, therefore, she was selected as an
excellent subject for this particular experiment. The operation on
the left side was done on 30 July, that on the right 26 August 1947.
She was sacrificed on 27 October after a survival of 62 days.

The first operation had no effect upon her disposition; she remained
extremely friendly and gentle. Signs of anger could be obtained only
by definitely nociceptive stimulation. Her recovery from the second
operation was uneventful. During the first few weeks she showed the
"propulsive" activity and prancing gait characteristic of cats without
frontal poles, but these abnormalities gradually diminished and had
practically disappeared by the end of the fifth week. Although totally
devoid of olfaction she began to eat spontaneously on the 28th postoperative day and thereafter she exhibited a hearty appetite. She always showed more spontaneous motor activity than before the second operation. Like wholly decorticate animals she failed to lick
parts of her coat other than the hair of chest and forelegs. She exhibited exaggerated postprandial licking of nose and chops. There was
a gradual return of the striking capacity to display pleasure that she
had exhibited at all times before the second operation. At the end of
the sixth week this note was written: "She is friendly and affectionate. On the table she pawed playfully at my hand and pushed a
brush about in a playful manner. Rubbing her head provoked a fine
display of feline pleasure: she closed her eyes and rotated or extended
her head to push against my hand." At no time during her survival
did she ever exhibit any hyperexcitability to rage-provoking stimuli.
On the second postoperative day when held and spanked very hard

she only made running movements, meowed and retracted her ears. She cried loudly and hissed twice when her tail was pinched. At this time petting quieted her, but there was no pleasure reaction. Later, during the first month and from then on, her reaction to hard tail-pinching was, first, angry vocalization, spitting and dilatation of pupils; then, as the stimulus was continued, she bit and chewed any object in front of her mouth. She never turned to attack the source of the stimulus and she did not attempt to escape by going forward. Hard slapping of her hips or back never caused any response other than licking of forefeet or floor. She could be handled roughly without showing the slightest indication of anger.

A preliminary study of serial sections of the brain of *cat 24* has shown that the entire telencephalon anterior to the rostrum of the corpus callosum had been removed. In the *left* hemisphere the margin of the removal runs laterally from a point just behind the ansate sulcus to cross the rhinal sulcus just rostral to the insular cortex. On the ventral surface it passes just in front of the optic chiasm. The entire ventral surface of the "frontal pole" was ablated except the prepyriform fields and small remnants of the olfactory tubercle. On the medial aspect of the hemisphere all cortex rostral to the corpus callosum had been extirpated. The extension of the anterior limbic field into the cingular gyrus and a portion of the cingular field had also been included in the removal. There has been considerable damage to the septal structures and the diagonal band. The removal on the *right* was essentially the same as that on the left, but the insular cortex and the prepyriform fields were more extensively damaged.

The amygdaloid complex and the peri-amygdaloid and pyriform cortical areas remain completely intact on both sides as do also the cornu ammonis and the striatal complex. There is extensive retrograde degeneration in the thalami. The anteromedial nucleus is completely degenerated on each side. The anterodorsal and anteroventral nuclei are almost completely degenerated on the left and, with the exception of their dorsolateral sector, also on the right. On both sides the mediodorsal nucleus is completely atrophied and the midline and intralaminar nuclei severely affected. There are widespread degenerations in the ventrolateral complex of each side, but the lateral group of nuclei is almost entirely intact. The medial geniculate, dorsal lateral geniculate and the pulvinar group of nuclei are all preserved bilaterally.

Bilateral removal of hippocampus. The change produced in *cat 4* by the third operation directed our attention to those so-called rhinencephalic structures that were ablated bilaterally in that animal. In two animals, *cats 20* and *21*, the hippocampal formation from its ventral tip (adjacent to the amygdala) to its medial extremity beneath the corpus callosum was carefully sucked away on both sides at a single operation. The procedure included the extirpation on each side of a segment of the fornix and removal of the subiculum. The approach required taking away a strip of cortex and white matter approximately 1 cm. wide overlying the lateral ventricle. The visual deficiencies that ensued indicated that the greater part of the visual radiations had been interrupted. Nonvisual placing reactions were only temporarily affected. Olfactory responses to the presence of food were quite unaffected. Each cat was studied until sacrificed during the tenth postoperative month.

Preoperatively *cat 20*, a large adult female, demonstrated a very low threshold for pleasure reactions, was most affectionate and took advantage of every opportunity to be petted. She did not display anger unless we applied definitely noxious stimuli. The other animal, *cat 21*, was an undemonstrative adult male in whom we were never able before operation to evoke what are commonly regarded as feline signs of pleasure. While not at all ill-tempered, he was readily induced to display anger. The operation seemed to produce an exaggeration of the pleasure reactions of *cat 20* and to make *cat 21* friendly and demonstrative. We could not detect the slightest change in the reactions of either animal to rough handling or nociceptive stimuli.

Restricted ablations that included bilateral removal of amygdala and pyriform cortex. When it became evident that removal of hippocampus and much of the fornix on each side did not produce any increment in a cat's tendency to exhibit anger, we turned our attention to the amygdala and the cortex of the pyriform lobe. We naturally suspected that the extremely low threshold for the elicitation of rage behavior shown by *cat 4* might be the result of excluding these parts of the so-called rhinencephalon.

A most suggestive result was obtained in *cat 29*. It will be recalled that both preoperatively and after bilateral removal of the transitional cortex of the midline this animal exhibited a high threshold to rage-provoking stimuli and was friendly and gentle. In a second operation there were removed from each side the following structures: most of the cortex of the temporal lobe, the lower third of the hippocampus, the amygdala, and the cortex of the pyriform lobe. The animal is still alive five months after the operation. He has a visual defect confined to the upper half of his fields, but the tactile placing reactions are normal. Within 18 hours of the second operation be began to exhibit anger on slight provocation. This tendency increased so that by the ninth day he had to be handled with great care; unless picked up very gently he bit and scratched. Light tapping of his back evoked a full rage reaction and an attack on the offending hand. After being thus aroused he walked about lashing his tail and when he bumped into any object he struck at it viciously with his forepaws. His bad temper and low threshold for elicitation of rage have not only persisted but have become more prominent despite long periods during which we have refrained from stimulating or handling him. When his tail is slightly squeezed he attacks with teeth and claws—growling, spitting and snarling—retracts his ears and shows pupillodilatation and piloerection. This is not an automatic, stereotyped and undirected exhibition of "sham rage," but an organized, accurately directed and perfectly timed attack on the source of the stimulus.

A smaller ablation of tissue that included the amygdala was carried out on each side in three animals not previously operated upon. The first of these, *cat 22*, was a gentle, friendly male that showed marked pleasure reactions when petted. He could be handled roughly without displaying the slightest sign of anger. On 3 July 1947 a bilateral removal was carried out. On each side the lateral wall of the lateral ventricle was removed to expose the anteroventral half of Ammon's formation. The pyriform lobe and the amygdaloid nuclei were then carefully sucked away.

The precise extent of the ablation in *cat 22* was later determined by a study of serial sections, one of which is shown in Figure 5B. The chart of this brain given in Figure 1 further illustrates the removal. On each side, in addition to some temporal cortex, all parts of the pyriform lobe except the presubicular region and minute portions of the entorhinal and peri-amygdaloid fields were completely removed. On both sides the entire amygdaloid nuclear complex had been ablated and the insular cortex had been damaged. Ammon's formation remained intact except at its junction with the amygdala. There was slight, scarcely detectable, damage to the globus pallidus on each side.

Cat 22 made a quick recovery from the operation and was soon displaying in his cage the usual behavior of a normal cat. From the first, however, he showed a considerable visual defect. On the twelfth postoperative day it was noticed that he failed to show any reaction to petting and that he reacted to moderately noxious stimuli by spitting, growling, piloerection and widening of pupils. From this time on until the eighth postoperative week the cat underwent what was probably a gradual lowering of the threshold of his rage-reactions. He was not frequently examined and therefore the change cannot be attributed to repeated testings of his temper. At the end of the fourth and fifth weeks we noted that he cringed when approached and tried to escape when handled. On 28 August he acted as if frightened when a scraping noise was made in the room. Blowing on his face caused retraction of ears, growling and spitting, maximal piloerection, pupillodilatation, retraction of nictitating membranes and extrusion of claws. Thereafter it became very evident that we had on our hands a very nasty animal. Whenever his cage door was opened and a hand extended slowly toward him, he snarled and spat and then drew himself together to form a ball of upstanding cat fur. He could be removed from his cage only at the risk of injury to his handler. Any stimulus greater than a light touch caused growling, spitting, tail-lashing and then a ferocious and accurately directed attack with teeth and claws; the external signs of sympathetic activity were maximal. At no time after the operation did gentle petting soothe him or evoke any of the signs of pleasure which were so prominent preoperatively. The cat was sacrificed on the 82nd postoperative day.

In *cat 23* the pyriform lobe and amygdala were removed bilaterally, but less temporal cortex was ablated than in *cat 22*. The hippocampus was not injured except at its ventral tip. Such was the impression at operation and it has been confirmed by gross inspection of the brain at autopsy. Serial sections have not yet been studied. Unlike *cat 22* this animal, a female, was an apprehensive "alley" cat evidently not accustomed to petting. She was not in the least bad-tempered and showed a normal aggressive rage-reaction to nociceptive stimulation, but not to lesser disturbances. She was studied for 230 days postoperatively. During the first month she exhibited a good pleasure reaction to petting, but showed no change in her response to noxious stimuli. During the second month there was a gradual diminution in her pleasure reaction and a lowering of the threshold for elicitation of angry behavior. At the end of the third month the change had become most impressive. It was necessary to wear gloves on handling or even approaching her, for the slightest tactile, visual or vibratory stimulus now sufficed to produce a marked exhibition of rage with attack. Her behavior, like that of *cat 22*, contained some elements of a fear reaction; often when approached she rolled onto her back ready to strike. During the last four months of her survival she remained a very savage animal. On the slightest provocation she displayed anger and launched a directed attack. On these occasions growling, spitting, retraction of ears, tail-lashing, striking and biting were accompanied by piloerection, sweating from toepads and maximal pupillodilatation.

On the basis of gross inspection of the brain at autopsy as well as observation at operation, the removal on both sides in *cat 31* was restricted to pyriform lobe and amygdala; no cortex above the posterior rhinal sulcus was damaged. This cat, a male, was neither ill-tempered nor overtly friendly. Rough handling caused efforts to escape but no signs of anger. His postoperative course was very similar to that of *cat 23*. From the sixth to the tenth week there was a very gradual lowering of his threshold to noxious stimuli. At the end of this period he snarled and spat when gently brushed or loosely restrained. At the same time he developed—and retained—a mild pleasure response to very gentle stroking of his head. By the beginning of the fourth month he had become a savage beast in which a mere touch—except around the head—invariably produced a raging attack. This status remained unchanged for the remainder of the 170 days of his survival. Often when one calmly and slowly began to open the door of his cage he growled, spat, retracted his ears, lashed his tail and struck at the door. As in *cat 23*, his rage reactions included sweating, piloerection and pupillodilatation. He differed from *cats 22* and *23* in seldom showing any sign of fear. In contrast to those animals he never sought to escape when handled and would invariably stand up and strike when threatening gestures were made.

These three cats in which amygdala and pyriform cortex were removed bilaterally developed as low a threshold for the exhibition of intense rage as any animal of our series. This development, however, was a gradual one. The effects of the operation did not become apparent for some time. The change was not due to repetitive rough handling and application of nociceptive stimuli, for considerable intervals elapsed between examinations and our handling of the cats during the first month or two involved as much petting as roughing. Further, many cats of our series that failed to become in any way unpleasant received far more noxious stimulation than did these animals. We cannot supply any explanation of the long delay in the development of ferocity. It does not seem possible to correlate it with secondary degenerations. It is of interest that another animal now under study, with ablations quite similar to those of *cat 31*, began to display excessive anger almost immediately after operation.

DISCUSSION AND SUMMARY

1. A state of extreme refractoriness to rage-provoking stimuli, a condition we term *placidity*, is produced in cats by bilateral removal of neocortex without significant injury to other parts of the forebrain. To obtain placidity it is necessary to spare on one or both sides certain rhinencephalic structures and at least part of that transitional cortex of the midline which forms the cingular gyrus and its extension above and around the rostrum of the corpus callosum. In our placid cats the amygdala, the hippocampal formation and the cortical fields of the pyriform lobe have been left intact. In them too the transitional cortex of the midline had not been damaged operatively, but the condition of the thalami of these animals showed that the afferent projections to the retrosplenial and cingular areas from the anterior group of nuclei had been largely interrupted. On the other hand, a large proportion of the fibers from the anteromedial nucleus to the anterior limbic area remained intact.

2. For any interpretation of the cause of placidity a fact of the utmost importance is that cats deprived not only of neocortex but also of the greater part of the rest of the telencephalon tend to show anger on rather slight provocation. This fact strongly suggests—and comes close to proving—that in the absence of neocortex one or more parts of the forebrain remaining intact in a placid animal continuously exerts a suppressing effect upon the brain stem mechanisms which are executively concerned in the expression of anger or upon their channels of excitation or discharge. This inhibitory influence must be a specific one, for the placid animals showed no paucity of the many nonemotional activities and responses which char-

acterize cats without forebrain. It is therefore unlikely that it is exerted through the bulbar inhibitory mechanism described by Magoun and Rhines (19).

3. Direct evidence that placidity is due to a restraining influence of forebrain origin was secured by converting the placid state to one of ferocity either by removal of the transitional cortex of the midline or by ablation of pyriform lobe, amygdala and hippocampus.

4. When the transitional cortex of the midline was removed on both sides by a procedure which did not cause significant damage to the rest of the brain, the threshold for the elicitation of angry behavior was not altered. When bilateral removal of this cortex was combined with ablation of the neocortex and part of the rhinencephalon of *one* hemisphere, the threshold was lowered only for a short period immediately following the operation. Bilateral removal of Ammon's formation together with overlying neocortex had as its only apparent effect upon the emotional behavior of the cats an augmentation of pleasure reactions. An extraordinary and lasting depression of the threshold of the rage-reactions was produced by restricted bilateral removals that included the amygdaloid nuclear complex and much of the cortex of the pyriform lobe. An unexplained feature of the effect was a latency of several weeks.

5. The results obtained give some impression of the role played by the neocortex in the cerebral control of angry behavior. Since no normal cat ever approximates the degree of emotional unresponsiveness which characterized our placid animals, it follows that the neocortex must normally antagonize the suppressive action of those forebrain structures that are responsible for placidity. This influence may be exerted directly or at some distance "downstream." It is obvious, however, that in the management of expressions of anger the neocortex does more than this. In our cats that became ferocious as a result of bilateral ablations restricted to amygdala and pyriform lobe, rage-reactions could be evoked by stimuli, *e.g.*, visual, that are ineffective in wholly decorticate cats. The effectiveness of such stimulation depends on neocortex. Another obvious result of neocortical influence in these same animals was the accuracy and the calculated timing of their attacks upon the source of stimulation. In the absence of neocortex such attacks are stereotyped and undirected or very poorly directed.

6. The experimental facts summarized in paragraphs 1–5 above do not fit readily into any simple schema of cerebral organization. As a working hypothesis we have tentatively adopted the following propositions: (i) that the area of the amygdala acts as a funnel through which inhibitory influences originating in the transitional cortex of the midline, in the neocortex and in the amygdala itself exert a suppressing action on brain stem mechanisms; and (ii) that the neocortex also exerts a facilitating or excitatory influence which by-passes the region of the amygdala. [Part (i) could of course be replaced by the proposition that the amygdala exerts the sole direct suppressing action and that this is facilitated by impulses from the midline cortex and neocortex.] Thus may be explained the puzzling fact that when either the midline cortex or the pyriform-amygdala region is removed in a cat without neocortex, the remaining part does not maintain the placid state. On the basis of this hypothesis, the failure of a removal restricted to the transitional cortex of the midline to lower the threshold of rage-reactions would be due to continuation of neocortical and "amygdaloid" influences within the "funnel." In the placid cats the neocortical inhibitory influence has been excluded, but so also has the excitatory one; there remains the summed inhibitory influence of midline and amygdala. In the case of removal of the region of the amygdala all three sources of inhibition would be excluded and the excitatory influence of the neocortex would be free to act without check. The appraisal of the worth of any such hypothesis as the one just given is made particularly difficult by lack of knowledge of the efferent connections of the transitional cortex of the midline and of the final destination of fibers in and from the region of the amygdala. On the basis of the important results of Wheatley (31), it might be supposed that the inhibitory influences of our "funnel" extend to the region of the ventromedial hypothalamic nuclei.

7. The results of previous work that bears on our present experimental results have been discussed or mentioned in the introduction. We have not obtained any evidence to support the view that removal of forebrain structures, either neocortical or rhinencephalic, situated rostral to the level of the optic chiasm produces any lowering of the threshold of rage-reactions. Our results suggest that if this part of the brain exerts a suppressing influence on the readiness of a cat to express rage it must

contribute also an opposite and nearly equal effect. Our results are in agreement with Spiegel, Miller and Oppenheimer's finding (29) in acute experiments on cats that bilateral destruction of the amygdaloid nuclei leads to marked outbursts of rage behavior. In very striking experiments by Bucy and Klüver (8, 15) on monkeys yielded results that seem quite incompatible with many of ours. By bilateral removal of the temporal lobes, the greater part of the hippocampus, the uncus and the amygdala, they greatly reduced the anger and fear-reactions of the normally wild and intractable *Macaca mulatta*. Our results indicate that in a gentle and friendly normal cat such an operation leads to savageness. At present we have no useful suggestion to offer in explanation of this extraordinary discrepancy.

DISCUSSION

DR. PAUL C. BUCY (Chicago): Dr. Bard, first I should like you to know that I appreciate the clear-cut nature of these experiments. There can be no doubt about the observations. I must admit, however, that I am at a complete loss as to how to correlate your findings with and to interpret them in the light of our observations on the monkey. In our experience we observed the type of change after removal of the temporal lobes, including the rhinencephalon which you saw after removing the other part of the brain, leaving the cingular gyrus and the rhinencephalon intact. In other words, the two series of experiments, yours on the cat and ours on the monkey, would seem to entirely contradict each other. Can you explain this apparent discrepancy?

DR. MARGARET A. KENNARD (New York): Following Dr. Bucy's remarks, Dr. Crawshaw and I last spring took off the temporal lobes in cats bilaterally. That work is not yet finished. I cannot tell you how much of the rhinencephalon has been destroyed, but those cats with all of the temporal lobe tips removed show the same kind of disturbance as Dr. Bucy's monkeys; they are placid animals rather than excitable ones.

DR. RICHARD M. BRICKNER (New York, N.Y.): I have a question. Were there any other experiments made on any other basic kinds of feeling, such as fear, hunger, thirst or sex activity? And Dr. Penfield asked me to put the question of whether any observations were made on smell.

PRESIDENT FULTON: Dr. W. J. Turner asks, "In *cat 4*, how long did the rage response exist after cessation of stimulation?"

DR. PHILIP BARD (Baltimore, Maryland) [Closing discussion]: I haven't any explanation, Dr. Bucy. The problem has worried us a great deal. We have here, of course, the exact opposite of what one would expect on the basis of using Papez' proposition as a hypothesis. If the midline cortex and rhinencephalic structures are important in the sense he made them important by his proposition, then we would expect to get exactly the opposite results, because, according to him, they are structures involved in emotional experience and expression. We have a number of animals in which, after making a relatively small removal of temporal cortex, we have gone in and taken out all of Ammon's formation on both sides. We have studied those animals over several months and have seen no change as regards their rage behavior or their threshold, but we have seen in them what appears to be an increment in their pleasure actions. They appear to be much more desirous of being petted; they show the feline responses to agreeable stimuli in considerable elaboration.

I think that in our experience we have never removed just the "tip" of the temporal lobe, but in the past a number of times I have removed what might, in the cat, be called the entire temporal lobe without noticing changes.

Dr. Brickner asked a question as to whether we had studied or paid any attention to other affective responses. Quite a long time ago Dr. Rioch and I reported on four cats, and in three of them loud noises—especially tones of high pitch—were capable of giving a reaction which was identical with that of a terrified cat. In the present group of cats we have not been able to reproduce that response, certainly not to the degree that I have seen it previously.

We have, in the case of several of the animals that were females, attempted to study their responses to estrogenic materials—in other words, we have put them in heat to observe estrous behavior. It can be obtained in a wholly decorticated cat.

REFERENCES

1. Bard, P. *Amer. J. Physiol.*, 1928, **84**, 490-515.
2. Bard, P. *Psychol. Rev.*, 1934, **41**, 309-329, 424-449.
3. Bard, P. *Res. Publ. Ass. nerv. ment. Dis.*, 1939, **19**, 190-218.
4. Bard, P. *Res. Publ. Ass. nerv. ment. Dis.*, 1940, **20**, 551-579.
5. Bard, P., & Rioch, D. McK. *Johns Hopk. Hosp. Bull.*, 1937, **60**, 73-147.
6. Bazett, H. C., & Penfield, W. G. *Brain*, 1922, **45**, 185-265.
7. Bromiley, R. B. *J. comp. physiol. Psychol.*, 1948, **41**, 102-110.
8. Bucy, P. C., & Klüver, H. *Arch. Neurol. Psychiat.*, Chicago, 1940, **44**, 1142-1146.
9. Dusser de Barenne, J. G. *Arch. néerl. Physiol.*, 1920, **4**, 31-123.
10. Fulton, J. F., & Ingraham, F. D. *J. Physiol.*, 1929, **67**, xxvii.
11. Goltz, F. *Pflüg. Arch. ges. Physiol.*, 1892, **51**, 570-614.
12. Keller, A. D. *Amer. J. Physiol.*, 1932, **100**, 576-586.
13. Kelly, A. H., Beaton, L. E., & Magoun, H. W. *J. Neurophysiol.*, 1946, **9**, 181-189.

14. Kennard, M. A. *J. Neuropath. exp. Neurol.*, 1945, **4**, 295-304.
15. Klüver, H., & Bucy, P. C. *Arch. Neurol. Psychiat.*, *Chicago*, 1939, **42**, 979-1000.
16. Macht, M. B., & Bard, P. *Fed. Proc.* 1942, **1**, 55-56.
17. Magoun, H. W., Atlas, D., Ingersoll, E. H., & Ranson, S. W. *J. Neurol. Psychopath.*, 1937, **17**, 241-255.
18. Magoun, H. W., & Ranson, S. W. *J. Neurophysiol.*, 1938, **1**, 39-44.
19. Magoun, H. W., & Rhines, R. *J. Neurophysiol.*, 1946, **9**, 165-171.
20. Murphy, J. P., & Gellhorn, E. *J. Neurophysiol.*, 1945, **8**, 431-448.
21. Papez, J. W. *Arch. Neurol. Psychiat.*, *Chicago*, 1937, **38**, 725-743.
22. Pinkston, J. O., Bard, P., & Rioch, D. McK. *Amer. J. Physiol.*, 1934, **109**, 515-531.
23. Ranson, S. W. *Trans. Coll. Phys.*, *Phila.*, 1934, **2**, 222-242.
24. Ranson, S. W. *Harvey Lect.*, 1936-1937, **32**, 92-121.
25. Rhines, R., & Magoun, H. W. *J. Neurophysiol.*, 1946, **9**, 219-229.
26. Rose, J. E., & Woolsey, C. N. Structure and relations of limbic cortex and anterior thalamic nuclei in rabbit and cat. *J. comp. Neurol.*, [1948, **89**, 279-348].
27. Rose, J. E., Woolsey, C. N., & Jarcho, L. W. *Fed. Proc.*, 1947, **6**, 193.
28. Rothmann, H. *Z. ges. Neurol. Psychiat.*, 1923, **87**, 247-313.
29. Spiegel, E. A., Miller, H. R., & Oppenheimer, M. J. *Trans. Amer. neurol. Ass.*, 1940, **66**, 127-131.
30. Spiegel, E. A., Miller, H. R., & Oppenheimer, M. J. *J. Neurophysiol.*, 1940, **3**, 538-548.
31. Wheatley, M. D. *Arch. Neurol. Psychiat.*, *Chicago*, 1944, **52**, 269-316.

KEY TO ABBREVIATIONS USED IN FIGURES

A	Aqueduct of sylvius	DB	Diagonal band of Broca
AC	Anterior commissure	EC	Entorhinal cortex
AD	Anterodorsal nucleus of the thalamus	F	Fornix
		LC	Cingular (limbic) cortex
AL	Anterior limbic cortex	LG	Lateral geniculate body
AM	Anteromedial nucleus of the thalamus	LV	Lateral ventricle
		M	Mammillary nuclei
AMG	Amygdaloid nuclear complex	MV	Medioventral nucleus of the thalamus
Aud.C	Auditory cortex	OC	Optic chiasm
AV	Anteroventral nucleus of the thalamus	Ol.T	Olfactory tubercle
		OT	Optic tract
C Am.	Cornu ammonis	Par	Paraventricular nucleus of the thalamus
CC	Corpus callosum		
CN	Caudate nucleus	PC	Pyriform cortex
Cr.S	Cruciate sulcus	PG	Pituitary gland
CS	Splenial (cingular) sulcus	PPC	Prepyriform cortical fields

Pt	Paratenial nucleus of the thalamus	SP	Septum pellucidum
RS	Anterior or posterior rhinal sulcus	SS	Suprasylvian sulcus
		Th	Thalamus
		tth	Tenia thalami
SC	Superior colliculus	III	Third ventricle

[ADDENDA FROM THE ORIGINAL PRINTING OF THIS ARTICLE: *Department of Physiology, School of Medicine, The Johns Hopkins University, Baltimore, Maryland. Aided by grants from the Josiah Macy, Jr. Foundation and from the United States Public Health Service.*]

BEHAVIORAL CHANGES FOLLOWING RHINENCEPHALIC INJURY IN CAT ※ *Leon Schreiner and Arthur Kling*

INTRODUCTION

EVIDENCE ACCUMULATED from stimulation and ablation studies indicates that certain parts of the brain are intimately associated with the synthesis and elaboration of emotional behavior (12). One area, which in recent years has been given increasing attention, is that portion of the rhinencephalon containing the amygdaloid nuclei (*e.g.*, 21, 16, 27, 5, 18, 20, 13, 3). In several publications, Klüver and Bucy (14, 15, 16) reported pronounced diminution of aggressive behavior, loss of fear reactions, increased sexual activity, and strong oral tendencies in untamed monkeys after bilateral injury of the amygdala, hippocampus, and adjacent portions of the temporal lobe. After similar lesions, dogs (22) and rats (2, 3) are friendly and display a marked reduction in spontaneous motor activity.

In cats, however, Spiegel, Miller and Oppenheimer (27) ob-

REPRINTED FROM THE *Journal of Neurophysiology*, 16:643-659. COPYRIGHT © 1953 BY THE AMERICAN PHYSIOLOGICAL SOCIETY.

served increased motor activity, polypnea, and rage reactions immediately after destruction of the amygdaloid nuclei, pyriform cortex, and adjacent structures. Bard and Mountcastle (5) observed relatively permanent rage and savageness which appeared several months after placement of similar lesions. On the other hand, Anand and Brobeck (3) recently stated, ". . . cats having localized destruction of the lateral and medial amygdaloid nuclei did not develop any rage reactions." In a study of the effects of central nervous system lesions upon the emotional behavior of various species of animals, we have observed 20 cats for periods of 4 to 14 months after injury of the pyriform cortex, amygdaloid nuclei, and adjacent structures—the results of which are presented in this communication.

Methods

Fifteen male and five female adult stock cats were utilized as experimental animals. The duration of the preoperative observation periods varied from several days to a few months during which time the laboratory behavior of each animal was repeatedly observed and recorded. Such preoperative data on each subject included general cage behavior, reactivity to routine animal care, behavior when in the presence of other animals (mice, agoutis, cats, dogs, and monkeys), responses to stroking and petting, and the degree of aggressive behavior induced by infrequent application of noxious stimuli. These stimuli included threatening the animals, cuffing them about the head, pinching their ears or paws, and suspending them in mid-air by their tails or one lower extremity.

All surgery was performed aseptically in one stage under sodium nembutal anesthesia. Through an extensive mid-line incision, large bilateral temporal bone flaps were mobilized. The temporal muscle was gently separated from its attachment to the calvarium and the remaining portion of the temporal bone was removed down to, or below, the upper border of the zygomatic arch. At this level, removal of the skull was then continued rostrally and medially to invade the bony part of the eye socket. The dura was incised in an elliptical fashion, bringing into view the entire lateral surface of the temporal lobe and the posterior aspect of the lateral orbitofrontal cortex. With gentle retraction of the temporal lobe, the olfactory stalk, middle cerebral artery, rostral pyriform cortex, and the rhinal sulcus were visualized.

Lesions were made by aspiration. Glass suction tips of appropriate curvature, bore, and design were introduced and careful aspiration of the pyriform lobes containing the amygdaloid complex was accomplished. The rostral boundaries of the lesions were designed to extend up to the junction of the olfactory stalk with the rostral pyriform cortex, at which level the middle cerebral artery is seen to cross. Care was taken to avoid undue manipulation of—or injury to—these vessels. In progressing caudally with the resection, utilizing the rhinal sulcus and its vessels as the lateral boundary, the optic tracts were identified and all adjacent paleocortical tissue was aspirated. In uncovering the optic tracts, the hippocampal tips were carefully exposed and avoided. This permitted carrying the resection further caudally and medially to ablate the posterior extensions of the amygdala and pyriform cortex. After satisfactory hemostasis was obtained, the dura and bone flaps were replaced. Interrupted silk sutures were used to approximate deep tissue layers. The wound edges were opposed by the use of a continuous silk suture placed in the subcuticular layers of the skin.

In the immediate postoperative period, normal saline and antibiotics were administered parenterally. Until such time as the animals were able to eat and drink voluntarily, they received daily spoon feedings of meat and were given milk via gastric lavage. In the chronic period, the general behavior of each animal was observed and evaluated in a manner similar to that carried out preoperatively. Several months after placement of the rhinencephalic lesions, seven preparations were castrated and one male preparation sustained a lesion of the hypothalamus largely limited to the ventromedial nuclei.

At the termination of the observation periods, the brain of each animal was serially sectioned at 50μ thickness. Every tenth and eleventh section was mounted, thus giving two paralleled series, one of which was stained with thionin and the other by the Weil method.

RESULTS

After observing and evaluating the preoperative behavior of each cat, it was apparent that the affective behavior displayed by animals utilized in this study ranged from temperamental, easily irritated, low rage threshold cats, to those which were friendly, exhibited favorable responses to gentle handling, and had high thresholds for the elicitation of rage. Aside from some individual variations which will be described, the behavioral changes observed in each animal after bilateral injury of the pyriform cortex, amygdala, and adjacent structures (Figs. 1, 2) appeared to follow a general pattern. We shall, therefore, present a chronological description of these changes as they developed in the postoperative period. Certain of the more striking alterations in affective behavior and sexual activity will be described in greater detail.

Recovery from anesthesia was quite uneventful. The animals remained quiet and exhibited no spontaneous outbursts of motor activity. When handled, they displayed no outward evi-

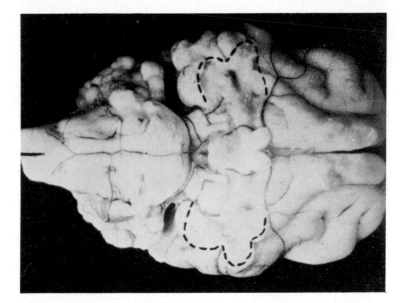

Fig. 1. Ventral view of brain of cat 16. The lateral extent of each lesion is indicated by broken lines.

dence of increased sympathetic discharge, did not hiss, spit, struggle, or offer any other signs of irritation.

During the first postoperative week, the preparations were quite lethargic and unresponsive to surrounding laboratory activity. They typically assumed a posture which can best be described as sphinx-like (sitting position, back arched, neck semi-flexed, head immobile, and eyes half-closed). They were very passive to handling and offered little or no resistance to restraint for purposes of forced feeding and daily intramuscular administration of penicillin. In the second postoperative week, most animals were eating voluntarily, resumed their grooming habits, and displayed a gradual increase in spontaneous motor activity.

Throughout the succeeding observation periods of 4 to 14 months, the preparations displayed further changes in patterns of behavior which, in the main, persisted for the duration of their survivals. This modified behavior, the salient components of which appeared to be closely interrelated and made their appearance either simultaneously or in rapid succession, in-

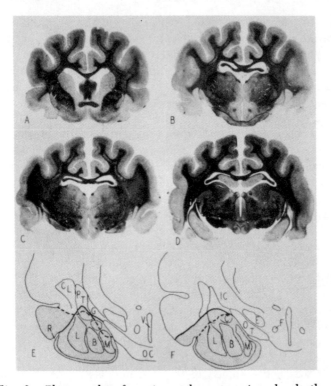

Fig. 2. Photographs of sections taken at various levels through brain of cat 54 (male). Section A—immediately rostral to lesions; sections B and C—through greatest extent of lesions; section D— through caudal aspect of lesions. Diagrams (E and F) illustrate extent of lesions in sections B and C, respectively. Stippled areas below heavy solid lines represent lesions on left side. Stippled areas below heavy broken lines represent lesions on right side. Abbreviations for Figs. 2 and 3 are as follows: B—basal amygdaloid nuclei, C—central amygdaloid nuclei, CL—claustrum, E—entopeduncular nucleus, F— fornix, G—globus pallidus, IC—internal capsule, L—lateral amygdaloid nuclei, M—medial amygdaloid nuclei, OC—optic chiasm, OT— optic tract, PT—putamen, R—rhinal sulcus, V—third ventricle.

cluded increased motor activity in response to visual stimuli, exaggerated oral and vocal behavior, relative docility, and a state of hypersexuality.

The preparations appeared to be overly alert and exhibited extreme interest in all activity occurring in the laboratory. They frequently paced about and rubbed their head and flanks against the sides of the cages. The females, in particular, but also the males to a somewhat lesser extent, engaged in maneuvers which involved rolling onto their sides or backs, squirming, and playfully pawing feeding bowls, cage tags, the observer's hand, and other objects placed at their disposal. Meowing accompanied such activity and the females occasionally vocalized in a fashion strikingly similar to the estral call and to other vocalization associated with mating. This altered vocal behavior and cage activity was unrelated to feeding time and could be most clearly demonstrated when the experimenters petted or otherwise handled an uncaged animal in full view of the preparations. During such instances, they would immediately move to the front of their cages, vocalize, tread, sniff, lick, rub their heads against the cage doors, focus their attention upon the uncaged animal and its caretaker, and closely follow the activities of each.

On removing the preparations from their cages and allowing them freedom of activity upon the laboratory floor, they appeared to be restlessly active and were attracted to all objects within their fields of vision whether animate or inanimate, noxious or pleasurable. These objects, such as apparatus, debris, bits of food, droplets of moisture, flies, dogs, monkeys, etc., were usually slowly approached, closely observed, sniffed, and frequently pawed or orally investigated. Interest in inanimate objects was not sustained in that the animals moved from one to another in a rather compulsive manner. Moving visual stimuli were particularly attractive to them. In the presence of various species of animals (cats, dogs, agoutis, and monkeys), the operated cats became attentive, restless, and displayed a marked tendency toward physical contact. These activities, however, appeared to represent some components of behavior which together constitute expressions of heightened sexual interests and activities as described in a later section.

Throughout their survival periods, the feeding habits of many preparations contained certain elements of interest. Many were rather slow in resuming spontaneous eating and drinking (5–20 days). In general, the animals were delicate eaters and exhibited a good deal of sniffing and licking during the ingestion of their daily ration. On several occasions, a number of preparations were seen to take into their mouths meat containing methyl salicylate which, however, was promptly ejected. On occasions this procedure was repeated several times by the same animal over a short period of time. Of special interest was the repeated ingestion of feces by one of the operated females—a behavioral trait which is unusual among cats.

At intervals, during their postoperative survival periods, the preparations were given access to a mouse placed within their individual cages. In each instance, over a one-half-hour test period, none of the cats seized or killed its prey. Indeed, their activities in this situation were somewhat the opposite—namely, to pay no attention, retreat, or thoroughly investigate the mouse in a playful fashion which included sniffing, pawing, and licking.

Changes in affective behavior. After placement of the rhin-encephalic lesions, the changes in affective behavior of all animals took on a general pattern characterized principally by an early and definite shift toward the side of greater docility. This change was demonstrated primarily by failure of the preparations to exhibit fear, escape activity, or "normal" defensive and aggressive behavior when placed in unrestricted association with unfriendly animals of other species (mice, agoutis, dogs, and monkeys). Secondly, the preparations displayed elevated thresholds for the elicitation of anger by the application of noxious tactile stimuli and a concomitant augmentation of pleasure responses to petting. After the first postoperative month, however, 16 of the preparations developed unmistakable and pronounced increases in sexual activity as described in the next section. *Thus, in the remaining observation periods, the affective behavior of these animals, of necessity, was evaluated upon this background of continuous emotional excitement—and not as an isolated entity.* With the appearance of increased sexual activity, the affective behavior of 14 of the 16 preparations underwent further modifications which were sufficiently similar in each animal to warrant their description as a group.

The early postoperative elevation in rage thresholds, as determined by the application of noxious tactile stimuli, gradually receded to a level comparable to that present in each animal prior to placement of the lesions. Pinching their ears or suspending them in mid-air by their tails brought forth rage responses which were convincing in nature. Their reactivity to such handling subsided soon after cessation of the stimulus and had little effect upon subsequent behavior.

In these same 14 preparations, the early outward expression of increased pleasure responses to gentle handling likewise became less pronounced after the appearance of increased sexual interests. Stroking or petting them almost invariably brought forth activities associated with sex play. At such times, they became restless, vocalized, and carried out jerky movements with their heads, bodies, and tails. In addition, the preparations would repeatedly and harmlessly grasp the observer's fingers, hand, or sleeve with their teeth in a manner strikingly similar to the neck grasp taken by male cats during copulation. Therefore, their attitudes toward pleasurable stimuli were difficult, if not impossible, to evaluate because of heightened sexual interests which dominated their behavior at all times. It was clear, however, that the early postoperative increase in pleasure responses to gentle handling, as well as the elevated thresholds for the elicitation of anger in response to noxious tactile stimuli, definitely diminished with the appearance of increased sexual activity.

One aspect of early postoperative behavior which remained unaltered was the marked docility exhibited by the operated cats toward mice, dogs, and monkeys. At no time during their survival periods did the 14 preparations display the aggressive behavior shown by them when placed in this situation preoperatively. Indeed, their postoperative conduct was almost entirely concerned with sexual advances and contained no evidence of irritability, aggressive behavior, or escape activity. On this basis, therefore, we conclude that the affective behavior of these 14 preparations remained permanently altered toward the side of greater docility.

The changes in affective behavior of 2 of the 16 preparations, which developed marked increases in sexual activity, deviated to some extent from those described above. These animals were young females. During the first postoperative month, like the other preparations, they were playful, docile, and friendly. After the onset of increased sexual activity and for the remainder of their observation periods, they became increasingly irritable and refractory to handling. At times they could be approached and petted, to which they gave favorable responses including pawing and licking the observer's hand. Lightly pinching their ears or tails resulted in explosive rage activity which was maximal in character. Near the end of their observation periods, the approach of the observer would cause them to retreat to the rear of their cages, growl, and assume the crouched "fighting" position. During this period, protective precautions were necessary in

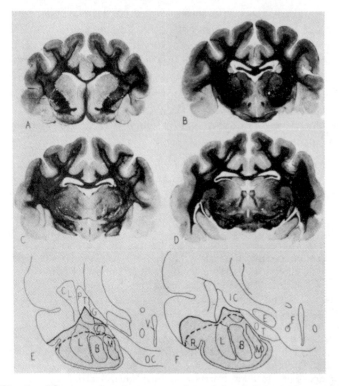

Fig. 3. Photographs of sections taken through brain of cat 1 (female). See legend of Fig. 2 for abbreviations and additional description.

removing them from their cages since such handling usually resulted in the animals biting and striking the observer's gloves with the forepaws. Serial sections of the brains of these two animals (*e.g.*, Fig. 3) revealed extensive destruction of the amygdala and adjacent pyriform cortex similar in extent to that present in the other 18 preparations.

Throughout the survival periods of the remaining four preparations (three males and one female), which displayed only minimal increases in sexual activity, the change in affective behavior was one of marked docility. These animals actively sought petting even to the extent of rising up on their hind legs in order to rub their heads against the observer's hand which was held a good distance above the laboratory floor. With further handling, they would roll over onto their sides or backs, playfully paw the observer's hands, and repeatedly sniff, lick, and gently grasp his fingers or hand with their teeth. Such friendly responses toward the observer and similar conduct toward dogs and monkeys contained patterns of behavior usually associated with feline sex play. In addition to the above described changes in affect, these four preparations maintained high thresholds for the elicitation of anger, the most pronounced of which is described in the following protocol.

Preoperatively, cat 10, a mature white male, was quite demonstrative in that he displayed good pleasure responses to petting. However, when pinched, spanked, or otherwise irritated, he was quick to show signs of anger which were both defensive and aggressive in nature. Beginning on the first postoperative day and continuing for a 90-day period, this animal was subjected to daily pinching, spanking, slapping, and suspension in mid-air by the tail or one ear. In the early postoperative period, he was lethargic and displayed very little reactivity to such stimuli. In the succeeding period of approximately 83 days, the animal's reactivity during the daily episodes of noxious treatment became more aggressive in character, changing from the initial meowing, squirming, and escape activity, to spitting, hissing, biting, and striking with the forepaws. At the end of the three-month stimulation period, the character and intensity of his reactivity to noxious stimuli was no more forceful than observed preoperatively. The aftereffects of such handling were of short duration. At no time was it necessary to take protective precautions in removing him from his cage. The animal at all times accepted and reacted favorably to petting regardless of whether or not such handling was immediately preceded by noxious stimulation. Throughout the three-month stimulation period, when repeatedly placed in association with rather unfriendly dogs and monkeys, he displayed no fear, escape activity, or aggressive behavior. The animal remained in a state of good health and nutrition throughout the five-month observation period.

Serial sections of the brain of this animal revealed extensive destruction of the pyriform cortex, tip of the hippocampus, and amygdala bilaterally. The photomicrograph of a section taken through the greatest extent of the lesions is seen in Fig. 4D. Except for somewhat less involvement of the hippocampal tips, the lesions in the other three animals of this group were comparable to those present in cat 10.

Sexual activity. In considering the various components of behavior related to and comprising sexual activity of cats housed in an experimental laboratory, it became apparent that preparations sustaining injury of the amygdala displayed varieties of sex behavior which deviated sufficiently from that seen in unoperated cats to warrant description in some detail. This altered

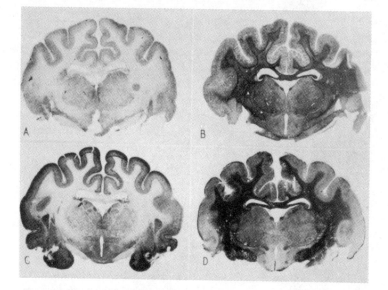

Fig. 4. *A*—photograph of section taken through the greatest extent of rhinencephalic and hypothalamic lesions in cat 9. The amygdaloid nuclei are extensively destroyed and hypothalamic lesion involves greater portion of each ventromedial nucleus. *B*—lesions in brain of cat 44 which, in addition to destroying amygdaloid nuclei, resulted in massive destruction of basal ganglia. *C*—lesions in brain of cat 4 which destroyed tissue on either bank of rhinal sulcus, sparing medial aspect of each pyriform lobe. *D*—photograph of section taken through the greatest extent of lesions in cat 10.

behavior usually became apparent in the first or second postoperative month, persisted in most preparations for the duration of their observation periods, was observed in both sexes, and contained elements which when considered together, constitute a state of hypersexuality.

Beginning in the second postoperative week, the preparations exhibited excessive vocalization which, in many instances, had characteristics strikingly similar to that elicited by cats during the mating season. During these periods of vocalization, the preparations appeared to be very restless and overly alert. Their attention and activities appeared to be directed toward movements in the room and became most intense when an uncaged animal and its caretaker were in view. In such instances, treading with the forelimbs and jerky movements of the head, body, and tail were particularly apparent in the male preparations.

Other postoperative behavioral traits which appeared to be related in some manner to sexual behavior was an increase in oral and investigative activity. As previously described, many preparations were frequently seen to sniff, lick, and paw the bottoms, sides, tops, and contents of their cages for long periods of time even though they were housed in the same quarters for the duration of the observation periods. Stroking and petting the preparations resulted in their rolling on their sides, squirming, pawing the observer's hands, and in a playful non-injurious manner repeatedly grasping the observer's fingers or wrists in a fashion similar to that done by the male cat when taking the copulatory neck grasp. In addition, such handling of the females frequently brought forth arching of their tails, raising of the hind quarters, and flexion of the forelimbs. Three of the five females would assume this position and remain tolerant during the placement of a glass rod into their vaginae. Male preparations tolerated manipulation of their genitalia which in some instances resulted in penile erection.

On placing an operated female upon the laboratory floor in full view of 12 of the 15 operated males, they would come to the front of their cages, direct their attention toward the uncaged animal, vocalize, carry out treading movements, and display marked restlessness. Upon opening the door of the cage containing any one of the males, he would immediately approach the previously uncaged animal, take the neck grasp, mount, and carry out pelvic thrusts. In this situation, the conduct of the operated females was one of tolerance and moderate receptivity characterized by assuming a crouched position with flexion of the forelimbs and intermittent elevation of the pelvis. If attempts were made to separate the animals by grasping the male by the loose skin of the shoulders, he gave little attention to the observer and tenaciously hung onto his partner even when both animals were suspended in mid-air. During intervals in which the male was not mounted, the females would indulge in courtship maneuvers which included crawling under the males and licking them about the head. The male preparations seldom if ever refused to display copulatory activity for prolonged periods several times per day or daily for the duration of their observation periods.

Placing together any two of 12 operated males brought forth repeated attempts by each animal to mount the other. After a short interval of maneuvering, one perparation would assume the dominant position, take the neck grasp, and carry out pelvic thrusts. The male in the recessive position was tolerant in that he would remain in a quiet, crouched, and motionless position. With further sex play, the relative positions of the animals would become reversed.

From the foregoing description, it is clear that the male preparations did not restrict their sexual activities solely to receptive females nor did they favor the female in preference to males. Indeed, on numerous occasions, operated males engaged in heterosexual activity were seen to leave the female in order to mount, take the neck grasp, and carry out pelvic thrusts upon another male standing nearby. Similar sexual advances were made toward four-week old kittens.

Aside from the above described sexual activities carried out by the male preparations, certain elements of behavior which are integral parts of the copulatory act were intensified and deviated sufficiently from those displayed by the unoperated cat to regard them as being abnormal in character. Placing together four or more males brought forth various activities in which sex play was the dominant pattern of behavior. On such occasions, one of the males was immediately mounted. In rapid succession, the remaining males would, in turn, mount the already mounted animals—after which each would take the neck grasp and execute pelvic thrusts upon his partner below. Such activities presented bizarre scenes of continued attempts at "tandem copulation" in which all members of the group participated (Fig. 5).

Aberrations in sex behavior of the male preparations were not limited to members of their own species. Throughout their survival periods, when given the opportunity, they would repeatedly take the neck grasp, mount, and carry out pelvic thrusts upon a small and rather friendly dog (Fig. 5). In this situation, the cats exhibited no outward evidence of fear and did not withdraw or attack the dog during periods in which the latter became irritable and somewhat uncooperative. Identical conduct was exhibited by these cats when repeatedly placed in unrestricted association with a female rhesus monkey, an amygdalectomized agouti, and an old hen (Fig. 5).

Additional observations. Four months after injury of the amyg-

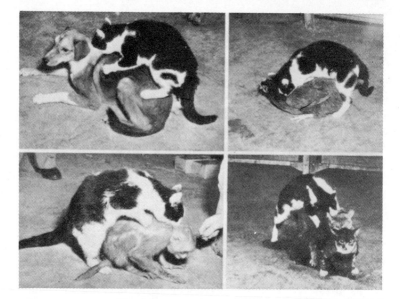

Fig. 5. Illustrations of various phases of sexual activity displayed by male preparations. Photos on right side were prepared from 16 mm. color film. Lower right photo illustrates attempts at "tandem copulation" among four male preparations. See text for additional descriptions.

daloid nuclei, one male preparation sustained lesions of the hypothalamus (Fig. 4A) largely limited to the ventromedial nuclei (29). The previously existing increased motor activity in response to visual stimuli, exaggerated oral behavior, frequent vocalization, and relative docility were abolished. Within ten days this animal became unfriendly, vigorously attacked other animals, resisted all attempts at handling, and was thrown into a fit of rage at the slightest provocation. In addition, the heightened sexual activity, which was particularly pronounced in this animal, had disappeared. Solicitous sexual advances by receptive females were also promptly terminated by vicious attacks with teeth and claws.

Near the end of the observation periods, 7 of the 12 cats which displayed the previously described hypersexuality were castrated. These preparations continued to attempt copulation with dogs, monkeys, and chickens for several days. However, within one week, all signs of such activity had disappeared and were never again observed. These preparations retained their friendliness toward other animals and displayed gradual increases in pleasure responses to gentle handling.

Several additional males were castrated either before or at the time of placement of amygdala lesions. For the duration of their survivals, they displayed little or no aggressive behavior toward other animals of various species, reacted very favorably to stroking and petting, and maintained high "rage" thresholds to tactile noxious stimuli. None of these preparations was ever seen to enter into copulatory activity with receptive females. Likewise, they made no sexual advances toward male cats or animals of other species.

Preparations with lesions either restricted to the temporal cortex or combined with hippocampal injury, and others sustaining destruction of cortical tissue on either bank of the rhinal sulcus (Fig. 4C), displayed little change in behavior except for some increase in pleasure responses to stroking and petting.

Two docile, young, anestrus females were spayed—after which they were observed for several weeks. During this period, no appreciable change in affective behavior could be detected. They were then given daily oral doses of 0.5 mg. diethyl-stilbesterol (U.S.P.) for a period of two weeks or more. After several days' medication, they became less friendly but could be handled if gently approached. However, the slightest noxious tactile or threatening stimulus would cause them to attack the observer vigorously with maximal intensity. After cessation of the medication, the preparations gradually regained their initial postoperative behavior.

Lesions. Each of the 20 preparations sustained extensive bilateral injury of the amygdaloid nuclei and overlying pyriform cortex (*e.g.*, Figs. 1, 2, 3, 4). In all cases, however, the diffuse rostral extension of each amygdaloid complex (anterior amygdaloid area) was partly intact. Similarly, in some preparations, the most caudal aspects of the main nuclear masses could be identified. In a few preparations, intact cells comprising remnants of various nuclear groups were present in sections taken through the main body of the amygdaloid complex (*e.g.*, Fig. 3).

In 2 of the 4 animals which displayed minimal increases in sexual activity, destruction of the amygdala (*e.g.*, Fig. 4D) was no less extensive than that present in the other 16 preparations. In the remaining 2 animals of this group, deep parts of the lateral, basal, medial, and central nuclei were spared. The presence of these small tags of amygdala tissue could not be clearly correlated with the variations in sexual activity observed in the postoperative periods. It was clear, however, that lesions involving only the dorso-lateral aspect of each pyriform lobe (Fig. 4C) did not produce the dramatic changes in behavior which were observed in those preparations in which the lesions almost completely destroyed the amygdaloid complex bilaterally.

The majority of the preparations sustained injury of the lentiform nucleus and claustrum. In 6 animals, however, involvement of these structures was extremely limited or absent. On the other hand, massive injury of the claustrum and lentiform nucleus was present in a few preparations. Again, no definite correlation could be established between the extent of involvement of these structures and the presence or intensity of behavioral changes observed in the postoperative periods. However, it was apparent that preparations sustaining considerable injury of the claustrum and lentiform nucleus had rather prolonged post-surgical recovery periods, during which time transient poverty of spontaneous motor activity was particularly pronounced. The added injury had little effect upon the hypersexuality and relative docility, precipitated by injury of the amygdala, as exemplified by the behaviorally typical cat 44 in which a large bilateral lesion of the lentiform nucleus was present (Fig. 4B). In most preparations, involvement of the tip of the hippocampus was minimal or absent.

The neocortex adjacent to the rhinal sulcus was injured in the majority of the 20 preparations. Except for some increase in friendliness toward the observers, no pronounced changes in behavior were observed in control preparations sustaining lesions limited either to the neocortex or combined with injury of superficial portions of the pyriform lobes (Fig. 4C).

DISCUSSION

In this study, the salient features of altered feline behavior observed after bilateral one-stage destruction of the amygdala and adjacent pyriform cortex were: (i) over-interest and increased motor activity in response to visual stimuli; (ii) exaggerated oral and vocal behavior; (iii) relative docility; and (iv) a state of hypersexuality. Although these changes are here presented individually, it is understood that—in effect—they are closely interrelated and act together to exert their most obvious influences upon affective behavior and sexual activity. These, in turn, are intimately associated and comprise important basic components of general feline behavior which, in our preparations, remained permanently deranged for the duration of the observation periods.

After placement of the lesions, the changes in affective behavior consisted of a definite shift toward greater docility which remained extreme for several weeks, then gradually became less pronounced with the onset of increased sexual activity. In addition to the early increase in pleasure responses to petting and elevated rage thresholds to noxious stimuli, our basis for considering this change in affect to be a durable post-surgical finding is primarily derived from the failure of the preparations to exhibit fear, escape activity, or aggressive behavior when repeatedly placed in close association with mice, agoutis, dogs, and monkeys. In most instances, such stimuli evoke strong emotional responses in unoperated alley cats.

Perhaps the most striking behavioral change was the precipitation of a state of hypersexuality. That this change was not a seasonal finding is attested to by the fact that the animals were operated at various times throughout the year and the resultant increase in sexual activity persisted unabated for the duration of the observation periods which ranged from 4 to 14 months. In this phase of their altered behavior, it is significant that 12 of 15 male preparations would mount, take the neck grasp, and carry out pelvic thrusts upon the male as readily as upon female members of their species, were repeatedly seen to attempt "tandem copulation" among themselves, and carried out all phases of copulatory activity (short of intromission) with agoutis, dogs, monkeys, and chickens (Fig. 5).

Additional animals sustaining lesions designed to destroy tissue on either bank of the rhinal sulcus, sparing the medial two-thirds of each pyriform lobe (Fig. 4C), and others with extensive lesions restricted either to the temporal lobes or combined with lesions of the hippocampus, did not display changes in behavior typical of the "post-amygdalectomy syndrome" as here described.

The affective behavior of 2 young females with typical lesions deviated from the general picture only in that their thresholds for irritability receded to levels definitely below those present before surgery. In this respect, the findings in these two animals are in accord with those reported by Bard and Mountcastle (5) in several cats with similar lesions. In our animals, however, this change in affect was associated with the appearance of increased sexual activity which, together with the gradual increase in irritability, reached maximum intensity in the second postoperative month. No obvious explanation for the deviation in affective behavior of these 2 preparations from that observed in the other 18 animals could be derived from gross and microscopic studies of their lesions. It becomes increasingly significant, therefore, that with the onset of hypersexuality, the increased irritability observed in these 2 females was similar to that observed in 2 spayed but otherwise normal females who received massive daily doses of diethyl-stilbesterol. It might thus be suggested that the increased irritability displayed by the 2 amygdalectomized females might, in part, represent a by-product of their hyper-sexual states. Other factors which might contribute to these variations are the age of the animals when exposed to experi-mentation as well as their previous social and sexual experiences. We are unable to correlate such factors with postoperative be-havior since all subjects were stock cats whose life histories previous to entrance into the laboratory were unknown.

The findings here reported in the cat are strikingly similar to those observed in primates (14, 15, 20), carnivores (22, 3), and rodents (2, 3). In our laboratory, observations on agoutis (Dasyprocta agouti, a large Central-American rodent), lynxes (Lynx rufus) and monkeys (macaques, mangabeys, and ver-vets) with similar lesions are in agreement with the above cited studies as well as those here reported in the cat. However, there does appear to be some variation in magnitude of certain of the behavioral changes common to the different species with comparable lesions. The agoutis, lynxes, and monkeys sustained a greater reduction in aggressive behavior than did the cats. Oral behavior was more marked in the agoutis and monkeys, whereas hypersexuality was unquestionably more pronounced in the cats. These variations cannot be explained by the data now at hand. It is improbable that they depend entirely upon differ-ences in the size and location of the lesions. Factors which might be of greater significance are the relative position of each species in the phylogenetic scale of central nervous system develop-ment and the marked differences in temperament and sexual habits exhibited by them in their natural environments as well as when placed in captivity. A more complete report of these findings in the various species will be presented in a separate communication (24).

These data and those of others (15, 20, 21, 13, 3, 17, 18, 26) further substantiate Papez' views concerning the relationship of the rhinencephalon to the expression of emotion (19) in that this phylogenetically old structure, when injured, modifies in a similar manner certain basic patterns of behavior common to several species of animals with varying degrees of encephalization ranging from the more simple rodent, through carnivores, to and including the relatively more complex primate. In addition, changes in affective behavior and sexual activity have been described in humans with lesions in the rhinencephalon (6, 28).

Experiments now under way are directed toward further analysis of factors underlying these general changes in behavior. Preliminary observations in the cat (25) indicate that castration, either before or at the time of amygdala injury, prevents the development of hypersexuality which normally follows placement of such lesions. Similarly, after the full-blown picture of hypersexuality (as here described) is present, castration results in its abolition.

An interesting aspect of this study was the conversion of a hypersexual, docile cat (post-amygdalectomy) to a savage, hyposexual preparation by subsequent destruction of the hypothalamic ventromedial nuclei. Since these nuclei receive an afferent input from both the amygdaloid complex (1) and the frontal lobes (10), they are ideally situated to influence affective behavior (29) and sexual activity (4, 7, 8, 9, 11) which in themselves appear to be closely interrelated.

These findings pose the question of whether certain of the changes in affective behavior and sexual activity, precipitated by injury of the amygdaloid complex, are due to a post-surgical state of altered endocrine activity. The available evidence is insufficient to warrant little more than a few speculative statements. As shown in this study, injury of the amygdala results in an early and definite shift in affective behavior toward the side of greater docility. This change might be a direct consequence of interrupting neural systems involved in the regulation of affective behavior. In the chronic period (usually within 30–60 days), however, the preparations develop an increase in sexual activity which persists unabated and contains elements which are not present in the sex patterns of unoperated cats. With the appearance of hypersexual activity, further changes in affective behavior occur which can be most simply described as a gradual loss of the early postoperative increased docility. Because of the delayed appearance of these behavioral changes, they can hardly be attributed to a direct effect of the surgical lesions upon the neural substrata of emotional behavior since castration results in a rather sudden abolition of hypersexual activity and a gradual increase in docility. It would not seem inconceivable then that the amygdaloid complex, in the cat, regulates to some extent certain endocrine mechanisms which in turn influence affective behavior and sexual activity. Abolishing or otherwise altering these neural influences upon such endocrine mechanisms, by injury of the amygdala, might thus serve in part to explain the delayed changes in affective behavior and sexual activity reported by numerous other workers as well as those presented in this communication.

The changes in affective behavior and sexual activity in the cat as here described, as well as similar results in agoutis, lynxes, and monkeys with comparable lesions, were recorded cinematographically and utilized in the production of a 16 mm. sound color movie—U. S. Army M. F. 8–7935 (23).

SUMMARY

The salient features of altered behavior observed in cats after bilateral injury of the amygdaloid nuclei and adjacent structures are described. These include (i) over-interest and increased motor activity in response to visual stimuli; (ii) exaggerated oral and vocal behavior; (iii) relative docility; and (iv) a state of hypersexuality.

Addendum. After submitting this work for publication, an excellent paper by Dr. Henri Gastaut (Corrélations entre le système nerveux végétatif et le système de la vie de relation: Dans le rhinencéphale. *J. Physiol. Path. gén.,* 1952, **44**:431–470) came to our attention. Alterations in feline affective and sexual behavior, as observed by Dr. Gastaut, are strikingly similar to those reported in the present communication.

REFERENCES

1. Adey, W. R., & Meyer, M. Hippocampal and hypothalamic connexions of the temporal lobe in the monkey. *Brain,* 1952, **75,** 358-383.

2. Anand, B. K., & Brobeck, J. R. Hypothalamic control of food intake in rats. *Yale J. Biol. Med.*, 1951, **24**, 123-140.

3. Anand, B. K., & Brobeck, J. R. Food intake and spontaneous activity of rats with lesions in the amygdaloid nuclei. *J. Neurophysiol.*, 1952, **15**, 421-430.

4. Bard, P. The hypothalamus and sexual behavior. *Res. Publ. Ass. nerv. ment. Dis.*, 1940, **20**, 551-579.

5. Bard, P., & Mountcastle, V. B. Some forebrain mechanisms involved in expression of rage with special reference to suppression of angry behavior. *Res. Publ. Ass. nerv. ment. Dis.*, 1948, **27**, 362-404.

6. Bronstein, B. Zur Physiologie und Pathologie des Rhinencephalon. *Schweiz. Arch. Neurol. Psychiat.*, 1951, **57**, 264-273.

7. Brookhart, J. M., & Day, F. L. Reduction of sexual behavior in male guinea pigs by hypothalamic lesions., *Amer. J. Physiol.*, 1941, **133**, 551-554.

8. Brookhart, J. M., Dey, F. L., & Ransom, S. W. Failure of ovarian hormones to cause mating reactions in spayed guinea pigs with hypothalamic lesions. *Proc. Soc. exp. Biol., New York*, 1940, **44**, 61-64.

9. Brookhart, J. M., Dey, F. L., & Ransom, S. W. The abolition of mating behavior by hypothalamic lesions in guinea pigs. *Endocrinol.*, 1941, **28**, 561-565.

10. Clark, W. E. LeGros, & Meyer, Margaret. Anatomical relationships between the cerebral cortex and the hypothalamus. *Brit. med. Bull.*, 1950, **6**, 341-344.

11. Dey, F. L., Fisher, C., Berry, C. M., & Ranson, S. W. Disturbances in reproductive functions caused by hypothalamic lesions in female guinea pigs. *Amer. J. Physiol.*, 1940, **129**, 39-46.

12. Fulton, J. F. *Frontal lobotomy and affective behavior.* New York: W. W. Norton, 1951.

13. Kaada. B. R. Somato-motor, autonomic and electrocorticographic responses to electrical stimulation of 'rhinencephalic' and other structures in primates, cat and dog. *Acta Physiol. scand.*, 1951, **23**, (Suppl. 24) i-vi.

14. Klüver, H., & Bucy, P. C. "Psychic blindness" and other symptoms following bilateral temporal lobectomy in Rhesus monkeys. *Amer. J. Physiol.*, 1937, **119**, 352-253.

15. Klüver, H., & Bucy, P. C. An analysis of certain effects of bilateral temporal lobectomy in the rhesus monkey, with special reference to "psychic blindness." *J. Psychol.*, 1938, **5**, 33-54.

16. Klüver, H., & Bucy, P. C. Preliminary analysis of functions of the temporal lobes in monkeys. *Arch Neurol. Psychiat., Chicago*, 1939, **42**, 979-1000.

17. MacLean. P. D. Psychomomatic disease and the "visceral brain." *Psychosom. Med.*, 1949, **11**, 338-353.

18. MacLean, P. D., & Delgado, J. M. R. Electrical and chemical stimulation of fronto-temporal portion of limbic system in the waking animal. *EEG clin. Neurophysiol.*, 1953, **5**, 91-100.

19. Papez, J. W. A proposed mechanism of emotion. *Arch. Neurol. Psychiat., Chicago,* 1937, **38**, 725-743.
20. Pribram, K. H., & Bagshaw, M. H. Further analysis of the temporal lobe syndrome utilizing fronto-temporal ablations. *J. comp. Neurol.,* 1953, **99**, 347-375.
21. Rioch, D. McK., & Brenner, C. Experiments on the striatum and rhinencephalon. *J. comp. Neurol.,* 1938, **68**, 491-507.
22. Rosvold, H. E., Fuller, J. L., & Pribram, K. H. Ablations of pyriform, amygdala, hippocampal complex in genetically pure strain cocker spaniels, in press. [Published as: Fuller, J. L., Rosvold, H. E., & Pribram, K. H. The effect on affective and cognitive behavior in the dog of lesions of the pyriform-amygdala-hippocampal complex. *J. comp. physiol. Psychol.,* 1957, **50**, 89–96.]
23. Schreiner, L., & Kling, A. Behavioral changes following paleocortical injury in rodents, carnivores, and primates. *Medical Film U.S. Army* 8-7935.
24. Schreiner, L., & Kling, A. Behavioral changes following paleocortical injury in rodents, carnivores, and primates. *Amer. J. Physiol.,* 1952, **171**, 765.
25. Schreiner, L., & Kling, A. Effects of castration on hypersexuality induced by injury of the rhinencephalon in the cat. *Arch. Neurol. Psychiat., Chicago,* 1954, **72**, 180–186.
26. Schreiner, L., Rioch, D. M., Pechtel, C., & Masserman, J. H. Behavioral changes following thalamic injury in cat. *J. Neurophysiol.,* 1953, **16**, 234-246.
27. Spiegel, E. A., Miller, H. R., & Oppenheimer, M. J. Forebrain and rage reactions. *J. Neurophysiol.,* 1940, **3**, 538-547.
28. Vonderahe, A. R. The anatomic substratum of emotion. *New Scholasticum,* 1944, **18**, 76-95.
29. Wheatley, M. D. The hypothalamus and affective behavior in cats: A study of the effects of experimental lesions, with anatomic correlations. *Arch. Neurol. Psychiat., Chicago,* 1944, **52**, 296-316.

[ADDENDA FROM THE ORIGINAL PRINTING OF THIS ARTICLE: *Received for publication, February 5, 1953.* IN REFERENCE TO THE AUTHORS: *Neuropsychiatry Division, Walter Reed Army Medical Center, Washington 12, D. C.* IN REFERENCE TO SCHREINER: *Present address: Mayo Clinic, Rochester, Minnesota.* IN REFERENCE TO KLING: *Present address: The Medical School, University of Utrecht, Holland.*]

PSYCHOSOMATIC DISEASE AND THE "VISCERAL BRAIN": RECENT DEVELOPMENTS BEARING ON THE PAPEZ THEORY OF EMOTION ❈ *Paul D. MacLean*

IN MOST OF THOSE DISEASES where emotional states are thought to be etiologically related to focal or systemic lesions, it is generally assumed that the pathologic process is mediated by the autonomic nervous system and the humoral mechanisms under its control. There is considerable experimental and clinical evidence to support such an assumption. But little information has accumulated to indicate by what mechanism the emotions can so act on autonomic centers as to lead to diseases as diverse as essential hypertension, peptic ulcer, asthma, etc.

The first part of this paper will be devoted to a review of certain neuroanatomic and neurophysiologic evidence now at hand that contributes to the understanding of emotional mechanisms and points to a variety of ways by which the affective qualities of experience could act on autonomic centers. In the subsequent

REPRINTED FROM *Psychosomatic Medicine,* 11:338-353. COPYRIGHT © 1949 BY THE AMERICAN PSYCHOSOMATIC SOCIETY, INC.

section it will be suggested how this evidence perhaps ties in with some of the current psychodynamic formulations regarding those psychosomatic diseases where lesions are present.

The problem pertaining to emotional mechanisms is basically one of communication in the central nervous system. It may be assumed that messages from both without and within the organism are relayed to the brain by nervous impulses traveling along nerve fibers and possibly by humoral agents carried in the blood stream. Ultimately, however, any correlation of these messages must be a function of a highly integrated body of neurones capable of sorting, selecting, and acting upon various patterns of bioelectrical activity. The indications are that both the experience and the expression of emotion are the resultant of the association and correlation of a wide variety of internal and external stimuli whose messages are transmitted as nervous impulses in cerebral analyzers. The manner in which these impulses can give rise to the subjective feeling of emotion remains a complete mystery. But in the light of what is known about the capacity of small electrical charges to trip large scale mechanisms into action, it is more readily understood how nervous impulses set going the various phenomena associated with emotional expression.

The hypothalamus is considered to be the head ganglion of the autonomic nervous system (31). On the basis of investigations showing the role of the hypothalamus in sham rage (6, 11) it has often been inferred in the literature on psychosomatic medicine that this nerve center is responsible both for the experiencing and expression of emotion. Masserman, however, has amassed considerable evidence to show that whereas the hypothalamus is the main neural center for mediating the expression of emotion, it does not share in the experiencing of emotion (46). Although the thalamus probably participates in a crude awareness of somesthetic sensations (38), the present evidence indicates that only the cerebral cortex is capable of appreciating all the various affective qualities of experience and combining them into such states of feeling as fear, anger, love, and hate (cf. 15, 46, 52, 69).

To emphasize the role of the cerebral cortex in the experiencing of emotion, however, is to require one to stress at the same time its connections with the hypothalamus, the effector mechanism of emotional expression. In the light of this it is an interesting and significant observation that the neopallium, despite its forming most of the cerebral mantle, has (as far as is known at the present time) comparatively little autonomic representation. If one accepts Yakovlev's interpretation that the orbitomesial surface of the frontal lobes belongs to the mesopallium (79, 80),[1] there remains only a relatively small area of the neocortex—namely, the rostral part of the motor cortex—from which autonomic responses can be obtained by appropriate stimulation (31). The anatomic pathways over which these responses are mediated have yet to be ascertained. There are known to be relay circuits from the frontal lobes to the hypothalamus by way of the septal nuclei and medial forebrain bundle (cf. Fig. 2), as well as through the dorsomedial nuclei of the thalamus and the periventricular system (70); but the anatomic details of these fiber connections are still obscure. It is only within the last two years, as the result of further microanatomic studies (50) and physiologic neuronography (74), that there has been any clear indication of *direct* pathways to the hypothalamus.

The difficulty in demonstrating pathways between the neopallium and the hypothalamus is in marked contrast to the ease with which one can point to many and strong connections between the old brain (rhinencephalon) and the hypothalamus, some of which, such as the fornix, are almost the diameter of a pencil (cf. Figs. 1 and 2).

On the strength of this intimate relationship of the phylogenetically older cerebral structures with the hypothalamus, together with certain experimental and clinical considerations, Papez in 1937 published a paper called "A Proposed Mechanism of Emotion" in which the theory was advanced "that the hypothalamus, the anterior thalamic nuclei, the gyrus cinguli, the hippocampus and their interconnections constitute a harmonious mechanism which may elaborate the functions of central emotion, as well as participate in emotional expression" (52).

GENERAL CONSIDERATIONS OF THE PAPEZ THEORY

The theory expressed in this paper has done much to revive interest in the rhinencephalon. As Papez observed, many of the structures he listed as being involved in emotional experience have commonly been "represented as dealing with some phase of

---

[1] Transitional cortex between "old" brain and "new" brain.

the olfactory function." He felt that there was "no clinical or other evidence to support this view."

To be sure, the doubt has long been expressed that the cingulate gyrus should be included as part of the rhinencephalon (19). It has been noted that not only this gyrus, but also the hippocampal system, are present in such forms as the dolphin and the porpoise where the sense of smell is absent.[2] Furthermore, it is remarkable that in man where the olfactory bulbs are small compared with macrosmatic animals, the hippocampal formation and the cingulate gyrus reach their greatest development (9). Recently Brodal, in a review dealing with the hippocampus and related structures, has concluded that only a comparatively small part of the cerebral cortex usually assigned to the rhinencephalon is directly involved in olfaction (9). On the basis of extensive comparative studies, C. Judson Herrick maintained that the rhinencephalon, in addition to mediating the sense of smell, served as a nonspecific activator for all cortical activities, influencing appropriately, in an excitatory or inhibitory capacity, such functions as memory, learning, and affective behaviour (30).

The mechanism of emotion proposed by Papez will require further elaboration during the course of this paper. Briefly, the concept, as first presented in 1937, is formulated as follows (see Fig. 1): "The central emotive process of cortical origin may . . . be conceived as being built up in the hippocampal formation and as being transferred to the mammillary body and thence through the anterior thalamic nuclei to the cortex of the gyrus cinguli. The cortex of the cingular gyrus may be looked on as the receptive region for the experiencing of emotion. . . . Radiation of the emotive process from the gyrus cinguli to other regions in the cerebral cortex would add emotional colouring to psychic processes."

In the light of subsequent experimental findings, Papez's delimitation of this region in the experiencing of emotion strikes one today as a considerable *tour de force*. For, other than the known comparative and neuroanatomy of this region, there was little experimental data to support his thesis, and the clinical evidence was more suggestive than definitive. He emphasized that lesions directly involving or impinging on the anatomic cir-

[2] See 9, 19, 69 for review and further references.

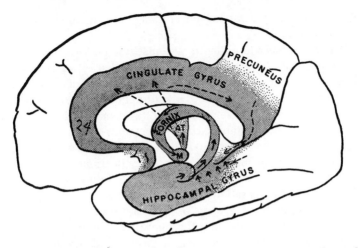

Fig. 1. The shaded area of cortex represents what was formerly known as the limbic lobe of Broca and subsequently termed the rhinencephalon by Turner. It corresponds to what is arbitrarily referred to in this paper as the visceral brain. M, mammillary body; AT, anterior thalamic nucleus.

cuit shown in Figure 1 caused a variety of symptoms that were confined largely to the affective behaviour of the individual. Starting with the hippocampal formation (cf. Figs. 1, 2, and 4), Papez noted that in rabies where the disease appears to have a predilection for the hippocampus and cerebellum, the patient is subject to anxiety, apprehensiveness, and paroxysms of rage or terror. I might add that both the "dreamy state" and epileptic automatisms indicate that the hippocampal formation and associated structures are concerned in emotional experience. Hughlings Jackson, who preferred the term "dreamy state" to "intellectual aura," described the condition as a kind of "double consciousness" or "mental diplopia" (32). It was as though the individual had the sense of being in contact with reality, but at the same time had the *feeling* he was experiencing a dream or something that had happened before (*déja vu*). Jackson associated the dreamy state with "discharges" or lesions in the uncinate region. In the experience of Penfield and Erickson the lesion responsible for the dreamy state has usually been situated deep within or underneath the temporal lobe (58). They have stressed that the sense of reminiscence that occurs with discharges in this region is often "*only the feeling*[3] which normally accompanies the act of remembering."

Patients subject to epileptic automatisms perform bizarre acts for which they have no memory. These seizures, as well as the dreamy state, are frequently associated with a variety of visceral emotional, and other sensory manifestations. There may be a visceral aura such as a sense of smell, taste, epigastric uneasiness, or asphyxia. Chewing and tasting movements, grinding the teeth, etc., may accompany the seizure. The author has seen one case where a feeling of hunger and frequency of urination and bowel movements persisted for a day or more following a seizure. Crude auditory sensations or peculiar visual impressions are sometimes present. A feeling of fear or terror may accompany the visceral aura, or may be the only premonitory symptom. As Jackson noted, "The occurrence of gastric and intestinal symptoms in some cases of uncinate fits with abnormal emotional states is obviously significant" (32). Patients with automatisms are commonly afflicted by severe emotional and psychologic disturbances (nervousness, obsessive thinking, depression, etc.,) between seizures. Since the introduction of electroencephalography it has been shown that in the type of epilepsy under discussion there are abnormal electrical discharges arising in the region of one or both temporal lobes (27, 33). The author, in association with Arellano, has demonstrated, by use of special leads at the base of the brain, that in a majority of the patients studied the origin of such discharges was nearer the electrodes in the vicinity of the basilar part of the rhinencephalon than those recording from the scalp (45a).

Papez cited a number of references to show that preservation of the nervous pathways from the mammillary bodies, through the anterior nuclei of the thalamus to the cingulate gyrus, are necessary to a state of vigilance and wakefulness in both man and animal. By inference, therefore, this circuit would be concerned in affective behaviour. The involvement of the mammillary bodies in Korsakoff's psychosis and Wernicke's syndrome also suggests the significance of this pathway in the elaboration of emotional experience (9). In light of the bearing of emotional factors in essential hypertension, it is pertinent that stimulation in what appears to be the region of the mammillotegmental tract will produce in the cat a great rise in blood pressure (13).

[3] Italics mine.

In reference to the possible emotional function of the cingulate gyrus, Papez noted that tumors of the corpus callosum impinging on it are often associated with changes of the personality, loss of affect, and various degrees of somnolence and stupor. He also referred to one case where a softening of the left paracentral lobule and cingulate gyrus was accompanied by a marked disturbance in the emotional realm.

In view of the part played by smelling and mouthing in sexual activity, it is interesting that these various elements of experience may have the opportunity to be associated in the regions defined by Papez. The precuneus (see Fig. 1) which broadens out posteriorly from the cingulate gyrus is contiguous with the sacral representation in the paracentral lobule. Papez has "noted that in the two sexes the precuneus shows a greater difference in size than any other portion of the cortex, being more highly developed in the male," and has suggested that representation of the sex organs may be localized there (52). Further support for this speculation is suggested by the remarkable case of nymphomania reported by Erickson in 1945 (20). The patient was a 55-year-old woman who for more than ten years complained of a persistent "passionate feeling." Later she developed convulsions. It is notable that perfume was thought to exaggerate her symptoms. At operation she was found to have a hemangioma of the right paracentral lobule which anatomically is just above the cingular gyrus and ahead of the precuneus. Penfield has described a patient with a lesion of the temporal lobe who exhibited sexual ideas as a component of his dreamy state (59).

RECENT DEVELOPMENTS IN NEUROPHYSIOLOGY BEARING ON THE PAPEZ THEORY

Since 1937 there have appeared a number of experimental reports which would lend support to Papez's thesis that the rhinencephalon plays a fundamental role in the affective sphere. Perhaps the most striking observations are those of Klüver and Bucy on a series of monkeys deprived of both temporal lobes (36). It is important to stress that where only one lobe was removed or where bilateral lesions spared the rhinencephalon, the animals failed to show significant changes in their behaviour. The bilaterally lobectomized animals, on the other hand, presented a dramatic picture. Formerly wild and intractable, they became docile and showed neither signs of fear nor anger. They would not fight or retaliate when abused by other monkeys, and obviously would not have survived in a natural habitat. They displayed also what the authors refer to as "psychic blindness," "oral tendencies," and "hypermetamorphosis," a kind of compulsive behaviour. It was as though they could no longer discriminate between objects that were either potentially dangerous or useful to them. The "hissing tongue" of a snake or feces might be selected as readily for examination as a piece of food. Such an animal would go around its cage, and as if by compulsion smell and mouth everything—dirt, feces, nail, food—that captured its attention. Unless the object was edible, it would be immediately dropped. If presented with a nail a hundred times in succession, the animal would smell and mouth it in each instance as though he had not examined it before. Finally, these animals showed striking changes in their sexual behaviour. They appeared hypersexed, masturbated excessively, sought partnership with male or female indiscriminately, and manifested bizarre oral-sexual behaviour.[4] It is interesting that many of these phenomena described by Klüver and Bucy were noted sixty years ago by Brown and Schäfer, who performed similar ablations, but their significance was not appreciated (see 10).

In 1940 Spiegel and co-workers reported a number of acute experiments in which they claimed that appropriate lesions in various parts of the rhinencephalon would produce in cats or dogs the picture of sham rage (70). They emphasized that the lesions must be bilateral. Such lesions when confined to the olfactory tubercles, or the anterior portion of the amygdaloid complex, or to parts of the hippocampus and fornix (see Fig. 2), all led to manifestations of the rage reaction. These findings are reminiscent of those of Fulton and Ingraham, who in 1929 described rage reactions in cats following bilateral, prechiasmal lesions at the base of the brain (25). These lesions probably in-

---

[4] The temporal lobectomy as performed in these experiments spared part of the hippocampal formation posterior to the lesion. This should be kept in mind when the possible correlation of sexual and visceral sensations in this region receives further discussion. The indications are that these animals could still smell and taste; on an anatomic basis it is conceivable that some gustatory, olfactory, and other visceral sensations could have been transmitted from the septal nuclei and parolfactory area to the remaining dentate gyrus and hippocampus by fibers passing over the corpus callosum (see Fig. 2).

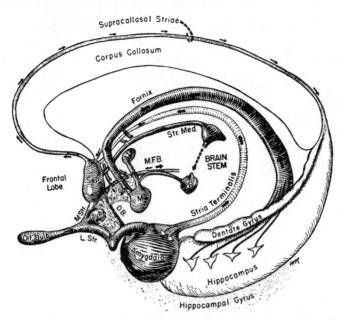

Fig. 2. A schematic representation of the relationship of the main subcortical structures and connections of the rhinencephalon, drawn as though all of them could be seen from the medial aspect of the right hemisphere, with the intervening tissue dissolved away. The composite was suggested by illustrations from W. J. S. Krieg's *Functional Neuroanatomy* (Philadelphia: Blakiston, 553 pp.), but for diagrammatic purposes some of the added or altered connections have been given an arbitrary course. Abbreviations: A.T., anterior nucleus of thalamus; D.B., diagonal band of Broca; H., habenula (a part of the epithalamus); I.P., interpeduncular nucleus; L. Str., lateral olfactory stria; M., mammillary body (a part of the posterior hypothalamus); M.F.B., medial forebrain bundle; M. Str., medial olfactory stria; Olf. Bulb, olfactory bulb; Sep., region of the septal nuclei; Str. Med., stria medullaris; Tub., olfactory tubercle (head of the caudate immediately underneath).

volved rhinencephalic structures in the region of the olfactory tubercles. Bard and Mountcastle, in chronic preparations on cats, have confirmed the findings of Spiegel, Miller, and Oppenheimer in reference to the amygdala (7). In contrast to the observations of Klüver and Bucy on the monkey, however, these investigators report that bilateral temporal lobectomy in the cat "leads to savageness."[5] They have noted that a removal of the entire

[5] Perhaps less of the hippocampal formation was removed in these experiments.

neocortex results in a state of "placidity" provided rhinencephalic structures are not significantly damaged. It is their opinion that the amygdala acts as a "funnel" through which inhibitory influences originating in the cingular gyrus, the neocortex, and the amygdala itself, exert a suppressing action on brain stem mechanisms.

As regards hypertension it is pertinent to note that stimulation of the anterior perforated space, which is posterior to the olfactory tubercle, will cause "sharp rises" in the blood pressure of the monkey (65). In the same animal stimulation in the region of the hippocampal gyrus produces vocalization and vagal-like vasomotor changes that last well beyond the cessation of the stimulus (67). In one instance Chapman, Livingston, and Poppen have had the opportunity to stimulate the region of the temporal pole in man and found there resulted a considerable rise of both ·the systolic and diastolic blood pressure (12).

Recently the cingulate gyrus has been subject to extensive experimental investigation. The results of experiments on the dog (37) and the monkey (69, 75) have been fairly consistent and establish this part of the brain as an important autonomic center. In light of the bearing of emotion on asthma, it should be noted that the anterior part (area 24) of the cingular gyrus can exert a powerful vagal effect on respiration. A considerable rise of blood pressure can also be obtained by appropriate stimulation of this area. Besides its influence on visceral activity, area 24 can exert a profound effect on the electrical activity of the brain as well as the body musculature (5, 69, 75): According to McCulloch, area 24 sends impulses by way of the caudate to the thalamus which block spontaneous thalamocortical activity and cause a suppression of electrical activity of the cortex (49). And Ward has presented evidence to show that area 24 is able, through its connections with the reticular substance in the brain stem, to inhibit all motor activity (75). These mechanisms suggest a possible explanation of how intense emotion could paralyze both thought and action. Finally, ablation of area 24 in the macaque is said to cause a loss of fear of man and other changes of affective behaviour peculiar to the monkey (68, 75).

It is now recognized that a great number of autonomic responses can be obtained from the orbitomesial surface of the frontal lobes (4, 41). Yakovlev maintains that this part of the brain is as much a part of the mesopallium as the cingulate gyrus, and along with the latter "may be looked upon as part of the highest representation of visceral functions" (80). Appropriate stimulation of this area will cause inhibition of respiration, rise of blood pressure, and decrease in tonus of the gastric musculature (4). Livingston, Chapman, Livingston, and Kraintz have recorded a considerable rise of the blood pressure in man after stimulation at a critical frequency in this region (42). Finally, it is highly significant that stimulation of this area (as well as the posterior hypothalamus and other points along the sympathetic chain to the kidney) will produce a blanching, and hence ischemia, of the renal cortex (16). If emotion found chronic expression over these pathways, it is conceivable how the renin enzyme system could be so activated as to lead to persistent hypertension.

The island of Reil, which lies buried beneath the frontal and temporal lobes, is also intimately associated with the rhinencephalon. But all one can emphasize here is how little is known about the comparative neurology, neuroanatomy, and physiology of this region. Penfield has indicated in recent lectures that the insula is concerned with gastrointestinal sensation and function. Experiments are now under way at the Laboratory of Physiology at Yale which suggest that the orbitomesial surface of the frontal lobes, the anterior insula, the temporal pole, and the pyriform-amygdaloid complex are mutually related in their bearing on autonomic activity and emotional behaviour (26, 35; see also 48).

POSSIBLE ANATOMIC, PHYSIOLOGIC, AND PSYCHOLOGIC CORRELATES

The recognition that the cerebrum is an outgrowth of the olfactory brain is obtrusive evidence of the part played by the sense of smell in the evolutionary development of the vertebrate (29). Smell not only has a fundamental role in obtaining food, but warns the animal of enemies; it participates in the sexual functions of mating and copulation (30). In primitive forms where life seems to be a matter of incorporating or being incorporated, it is the medial olfactory tract leading to correlation centers for smell, taste, and sensations from the mouth and viscera that shows the greatest development in size (3) (cf. Fig. 2). Smell therefore might be thought of as an oral sense, or more broadly as a visceral sense. In the course of phylogeny, as other senses exert a greater influence in directing the movements of the animal, the lateral olfactory tract leading to the "olfacto-so-matic"[6] correlation center in the pyriform lobe[7] becomes larger than the medial tract (3, 34). Although, in the ascension to higher forms, the rhinencephalon yields more and more control over the animal's movements to the neocortex, its persistent, strong connections with lower autonomic centers suggests that it continues to dominate in the realm of visceral activity. Hence the rhinencephalon might be justifiably considered a visceral brain, and will be so referred to in the remainder of this paper to distinguish it from the neocortex which holds sway over the body musculature and subserves the functions of the intellect.

In primitive forms the visceral brain provides the highest correlation center for ordering the affective behaviour of the animal in such basic drives as obtaining and assimilating food, fleeing from or orally disposing of an enemy, reproducing, and so forth. From anatomic and physiologic considerations previously referred to as well as those about to be mentioned, it might be inferred that the visceral brain continues to subserve such functions in higher forms, including man. Some of the neuroanatomy of the visceral brain that may have to do with the correlation of feeding and sexual activities and their bearing on affective states will be dealt with presently in more detail. As a preliminary, it will serve to point up the problems discussed in this paper if it is first indicated how the primitive brain perhaps ties in with behaviour that has been so often described as primitive, or infantile, in patients with psychosomatic illness (40, 45, 64). Psychiatrists have resorted to these adjectives probably because so much of the information obtained from these patients has to do with material which in a Freudian sense is assigned to the oral and oral-anal level, or, as one might say all inclusively, the visceral level. In practically all the psychosomatic diseases such as hypertension, peptic ulcer, asthma, ulcerative colitis, that have been subject to fairly extensive psychiatric investigation, great emphasis has been placed on the "oral" needs, the "oral" dependencies, the "oral" drives, etc., of the patient (71, 76). These oral factors have been related to rage, hostility, fear, insecurity,

---

[6] A term used in comparative neurology. Somatic, in this instance, refers to the body exclusive of the viscera.

[7] Refers to the forward pear-shaped expansion of the hippocampal gyrus.

resentment, grief, and a variety of other emotional states. In certain circumstances, for example, eating food[8] may be the symbolic representation of psychologic phenomena as diverse as (a) the hostile desire to eradicate an inimical person, (b) the need for love, (c) fear of some deprivation or punishment, (d) the grief of separation, etc. It will be useful to refer subsequently to the *excessive* oral manifestations of hostility and anger as "visceral aggression"; of insecurity and fear, as "visceral fear"; of a feeling of dependence, as "visceral need," etc. It is to be noted that many of the seemingly paradoxical and ridiculous implications of the term "oral" result from a situation, most clearly manifest in children or primitive peoples, where there is a failure or inability to discriminate between the internal and external perceptions that make up the affective qualities of experience (77). Visceral feelings are blended or fused with that the individual sees, hears, or otherwise senses, in such a way that the outside world is often experienced and dealt with as though it were incorporated. Thus the child looking at a leaf may say, "It tastes green" (cf. 77). Or the primitive may attribute a feeling of anguish to a squirming animal in his stomach. On the basis of interview material it is claimed that the patient with psychosomatic illness deals with the affective qualities of experience very much as a child or a primitive. In regard to interpersonal relationships, for example, such a patient may give evidence of a symbolic sort that he either identifies with, or seeks to master, other individuals by a process of incorporation. Hence his emotional life often becomes a matter if "inviscerating" or "exviscerating." It is as though such a person never "learned to walk" emotionally. A few of the psychodynamic formulations relating to psychosomatic disease will be touched on in the concluding pages.

The best way to comprehend the anatomy of the visceral brain and to derive a relatively clear picture of its tangle of connections with the hypothalamus and lower centers (cf. Fig. 2) is to consider it from the standpoint of comparative neurology. Space does not permit, however, a tracing of its history from the stage in primitive vertebrates where it is so diffusely connected with the epithalamus and hypothalamus as to be indistinguishable, to the point of development in man where the exuberant growth of the neocortex relegates it backward and downward into the

---

[8] Or indulgence in drugs, alcohol, etc.

mesial and basal parts of the cerebrum (3). Anatomic emphasis therefore will be given to such of its structures as may have a bearing on the correlation of emotional experience.

Bucy and Klüver have remarked that "of all the areas of the cortex the temporal is anatomically the one to which the term 'association area' is most suited" (10). But it is generally not recognized that such a statement applies particularly to the hippocampal formation[9] in the basal parts of the temporal lobes. Here, as we shall subsequently see, the possibility exists for correlating not only olfactory, gustatory, and other visceral sensations, but auditory, visual, somesthetic, and, perhaps sexual, sensations as well (57). And once correlated in the hippocampal gyrus, the impressions can be discharged through the motor cortex of the hippocampus, or the nuclei of the amygdala.

The motor cortex of the hippocampus is infolded longitudinally into the inferior horn of the lateral ventricle, presumably as the result of expanding cortex around it (3). The dentate gyrus, which suggests a receptive type of cortex and which may serve as a visceral correlation center,[10] lies along most of the medial side of the hippocampus and discharges its impressions into it. The hippocampal gyrus, which also has attributes of a sensory type of cortex is contiguous with the entire lateral aspect of the hippocampus, and projects to the motor cells of the latter through the transitional region known as the subiculum. Its anterior portion is intimately associated with the amygdala (cf. Figs. 2 and 4).

According to Lorente de Nó, Cajal was the first to note that in addition to the angular bundle from the olfactory area, the subiculum of the hippocampal gyrus receives two other large contributions—one from the cingulum and one from the supracallosal striae. I had the opportunity to see Dr. Papez dissect out these and other association tracts of the rhinencephalon and the temporal lobes. In gross dissection the cingulum is a most im-

[9] The designation "hippocampal formation" is used in this paper to include the hippocampal and dentate gyri, the hippocampus, and the amygdala (cf. Fig. 4).

[10] The dentate gyrus is the only part of the hippocampal formation absent in anosmatic animals. Comparative neurology suggests that it is the first cortical association area for smell, taste, and sensations from the mouth and viscera. It receives afferents from the primitive smell-taste-visceral nuclei in the septal region by way of the longitudinal striae running over the corpus callosum (cf. Figs. 2 and 3), as well as afferents from the hippocampal gyrus.

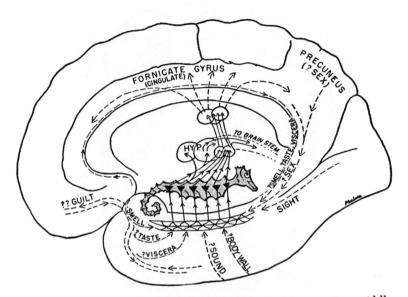

Fig. 3. Explanation in text. HYP, indicating the anterior, middle, and posterior divisions of the hypothalamus. Directly above are the three subdivisions of the right anterior nucleus of the thalamus.

pressive bundle. It is possible that fibers passing in it could interconnect the hippocampal formation with the whole length of the cingulate gyrus. If the Papez theory is correct, the cingulum could carry sexual impressions, among others, to the hippocampal region. The supracallosal striae possibly convey visceral sensations from the primitive smell-taste-visceral nuclei in the septal region (3) (cf. Figs. 2 and 3).

Dr. Papez indicated that there is ample opportunity for auditory and somesthetic sensations to pass by way of association fibers to the hippocampal gyrus. He also pointed out fibers coming by way of the lingual gyrus from the part of the visual cortex where the periphery of the retina is represented. He noted that it is objects that move in the periphery of our vision that most startle and alarm us.[11]

[11] Is it possible that here may be a partial neuroanatomic explanation for such psychologic phenomena as anxiety and delirium frequently occurring in the sick with the onset of darkness; the mental state of the paranoid who *feels* he is being attacked from the periphery; or more generally the fear and apprehension that is commonly associated with the unseen both in the present and the future?

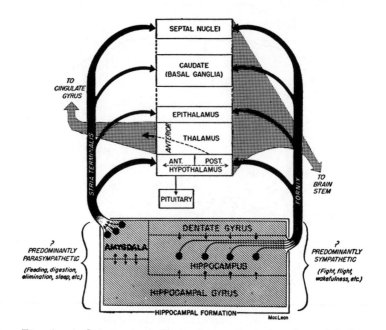

Fig. 4. A diagram to indicate the anatomical and possible functional relationships of various parts of the hippocampal formation. The latter designation is used in this paper to include the hippocampal and dentate gyri, the hippocampus and the amygdala.

The anatomic pathways by which olfactory impulses are carried to the hippocampal formation have been fairly well established (14, 23, 43, 44, 61, 62). It is not at all clear, however, how the other visceral sensations, which patients with lesions involving the deep or under part of the temporal lobes experience, reach this area. Ruch and Patton have claimed from experiments in the monkey that the para-insular cortex of the operculum has primacy as a taste center (63), but the possibility exists that taste, as well as smell and other visceral sensations, have multiple cortical representation. The comparative neurologists suggest that taste and other visceral sensations from the septal region could reach the hippocampal formation by way of the diagonal band of Broca and the amygdala, or the supracallosal striae (3, 34) (see Fig. 2). Dr. Papez has evidence that area 38 on the tip of the temporal lobe may receive a visceral projection of vagal origin by way of the central medial and central nuclei of the thalamus, the inferior thalamic peduncle, and the amygdala (54, 55, 56).

Figure 3 is a highly schematic diagram to demonstrate the number of sensory systems streaming into this region. The hippocampus has been externalized in the form of the little sea horse, after which it got its name from Arantius who first described it in 1587 (37). The layer of large pyramid cells in the hippocampus suggests a keyboard on which the various elements of the sensorium can play. In the diagram the arch of the fornix has been straightened out to clarify the direction of impulses going to the hypothalamus, anterior nuclei of the thalamus, and the cingular gyrus. Most of the fibers in the fornix are said to terminate in the mammillary bodies (2); but other parts of the hypothalamus and rhinencephalon, as well as the epithalamus and basal ganglia, also receive contributions (cf. Fig. 4). The diagram emphasizes that the hippocampal gyrus may serve as affectoceptor cortex and the hippocampus as affectomotor cortex, somewhat analogous to the somatic sensory and motor gyri of the neocortex. The lobulations on the hippocampus, which suggested the body segments of the sea horse to Arantius, conceivably might represent parcellations of different functions (57). Perhaps some day an "animunculus" will be drawn for this region.

It has not been possible to include the amygdala in the diagram in Figure 3. As previously stated, this structure is intimately associated with the anterior part of the hippocampal gyrus (cf. Figs. 2 and 4). It is often emphasized that the olfactory fibers, unlike those of other sensory systems, have no known primary projection to the thalamus. When one regards the amygdala from the standpoint of its phylogeny and anatomy (3, 14, 34, 72), however, it is evident that it is a thalamus-like relay station for olfactory stimuli (as well, probably, as other visceral impressions) to the archipallium. One therefore might as justifiably refer to it as an olfactory thalamus as to designate the conventionally known thalamus the optic thalamus. The efferent fibers from the nuclei of the amygdala project in large measure to the region of the septum and the anterior hypothalamus (22, 34, 72).[12] It is notable that these latter regions have been implicated in such highly coordinated viscerosomatic acts as defeca-

[12] Especially the pre-optic nuclei.

tion, urination, etc. Since the amygdala seems to project predominantly to the parasympathetic centers of the hypothalamus, and the hippocampus to the sympathetic, is it possible that these respective parts of the visceral brain are mutually antagonistic? Might the sham rage associated with bilateral lesions of the amygdala result in part from the release of the hippocampus and the posterior hypothalamus to sympathetic discharge? The possibly antagonistic relationship between the amygdala and hippocampus has been indicated in Figure 4.

It is important to stress that there is an overlapping of the three main fiber systems coming into the subiculum of the hippocampal gyrus (44). There are also longitudinal fibers associating the hippocampal formation throughout its entire length. In the light of these observations, there is a possible neuroanatomic mechanism to explain some of the seemingly paradoxical overlapping (or synaesthesia) of the various qualities contributing to emotional experience. The overlapping of oral and sexual behaviour, for instance, must be more than a fortuitous circumstance. In this part of the brain it is possible to conceive how sexual incitations could stimulate a crude, diffuse feeling of visceral yearning that would make the individual seek to mouth and incorporate the object of its desire. According to intensity, the sex-hunger pattern might lead anywhere from gentle kissing to the deviate forms of oral-sexual behaviour, or to such bizarre psychotic manifestations as a woman eating her menses. Likewise, the hunger-rage pattern susceptible to sexual firing might express itself in all gradations from aggressive, sadistic behaviour to sex-murder and mutilation. In regard to the influence of other sensations, it is possible that disturbing impressions from the realm of vision, hearing, etc., could generate appropriately either visceral need, visceral fear, or visceral aggression. To use a crude analogy, it is as though the various elements of the sensorium were gathered together in the hippocampal gyrus and placed on a party line. The ringing of the bell for one party, particularly if persistent and intense, might bring one or more of the other parties to the phone. Much of the gossip going back and forth in this area is what we have commonly come to associate with the id, the beast, or sin in man (e. g., gluttony, lechery, etc.). In the light of this it is interesting that through the large uncinate fasciculus, the frontal lobes "stand guard" over this region. Could it be that feelings of guilt are fomented here? It may have more than little significance that the uncinate fasciculus is apparently involved in lobotomy (51).

In the preceding discussion it has been implicitly assumed that the hippocampal formation provides the kind of analyzer that can derive universals from the particulars of experience and relate them symbolically in the experience of emotion. But in the light of current concepts of servomechanisms, it is pertinent to question whether or not the primitive structure of the hippocampal formation allows such an assumption. In his recent book on *Cybernetics*, Professor Wiener has indicated that a machine having to deal with the recognition and choice of forms may be served by a scanning mechanism in conjunction with a central clocking device (78). McCulloch and Pitts have presented evidence to show that a structure exists in the auditory and visual cortex for scanning, and it was postulated that reverberating thalamocortical circuits provided the necessary clocking device or sweep mechanism (60). Theirs is the first reasonable explanation of how the brain is able to recognize auditory and visual forms. One might further postulate that a sweep circuit exists between the pulvinar and the parieto-occipital[13] cortex and between the dorsomedial nuclei and the frontal cortex, whereby the patterns of electrical activity built up in the sensory areas are carried along the association gyri, somewhat analogous to the moving letters across the light bulbs of a sign board (53).

But when one comes to consider the temporal lobes (exclusive of the auditory area) in the light of such a possible scanning mechanism, one finds a deficiency of the necessary neural apparatus. One of the anatomic enigmas is the apparent absence of projections from the thalamus to the temporal lobes save for the small acoustic area (48, 73). This would indicate that no central clocking device was available to the greater part of the temporal region. As previously noted, however, the amygdala has a thalamus-like relationship with the archipallium. The large lateral nucleus of the amygdala deserves particular attention in regard to the present problem. It develops *pari passu* with association nuclei of the thalamus (57) and reaches its greatest size in man (17). And like the pulvinar and dorsomedial nucleus of the thalamus it receives no projection from sensory systems (34,

[13] Inclusive of a small area of temporal cortex.

72).[14] Since many of its fibers appear to run in the external capsule, it is possible they may be distributed to various parts of the
temporal lobe, including the hippocampal formation. If this were
true, there might exist a potential sweep mechanism for this
cortex.

But regardless of any scanning and sweep mechanism that
may exist, the cortical cytoarchitecture of the hippocampal formation indicates that it would have little efficiency as an
analyzer compared with the neocortex. When Lorente de Nó un-
dertook his studies of the cerebral cortex, he started with this
region because, as he noted, it provides the simplest type of
cortex (43). In the regio entorhinalis of the mouse, for example,
only 30 types of cells can be differentiated as compared with
more than 60 in its most complicated cortical structure. Finally,
it should be emphasized that the cortex of the hippocampal formation has a similar architecture throughout its entire length and
presents the same general picture in all mammals from mouse to
man (44). On the basis of these observations one might infer
that the hippocampal system could hardly deal with information
in more than a crude way, and was possibly too primitive a brain
to analyze language. Yet it might have the capacity to participate in a nonverbal type of symbolism. This would have significant implications as far as symbolism affects the emotional life
of the individual. One might imagine, for example, that though
the visceral brain could never aspire to conceive of the colour
red in terms of a three-letter word or as a specific wave length of
light, it could associate the colour symbolically with such diverse
things as blood, fainting, fighting, flowers, etc. Therefore if the
visceral brain were the kind of brain that could tie up symbolically a number of unrelated phenomena, and at the same
time lack the analyzing ability of the word brain to make a nice
discrimination of their differences, it is possible to conceive how
it might become foolishly involved in a variety of ridiculous correlations leading to phobias, obsessive-compulsive behaviour,
etc. Lacking the help and control of the neocortex, its impressions would be discharged without modification into the
hypothalamus and lower centers. Considered in the light of
Freudian psychology, the visceral brain would have many of the

[14] There is the possibility, however, that part of this nucleus may receive
a visceral contribution by way of the inferior thalamic peduncle (54,
55, 56).

attributes of the unconscious id. One might argue, however, *that the visceral brain is not at all unconscious (possibly not even in certain stages of sleep[15]), but rather eludes the grasp of the intellect because its animalistic and primitive structure makes it impossible to communicate in verbal terms.* Perhaps it were more proper to say, therefore, it was an animalistic and illiterate brain.

If the visceral brain functioned in the realm of emotion in the manner described, certain puzzling aspects of the psychologic status of patients with psychosomatic disease would be more readily understood. It strikes one as paradoxical, for example, that such patients often advance to superior attainments in the intellectual sphere, and at the same time, according to some psychiatrists, show evidence that their emotional life has been arrested at or near the oral level. This would suggest that more attention should be directed toward factors having to do with the emotional development of these individuals during infancy and childhood.

It has been stated that the first directed act the child performs on coming into the world is to smell and root its way to its mother's breast (1). If hungry it cries, and it may be predicated in this instance that both hunger and crying are manifestations of insecurity in its new environment. If its hunger is unsatisfied, the instinctual patterns of response appear limited and stereotyped. It may scream in anger and bite the mother's breast, or if neglected for a long period lapse into a wailing type of cry. Once fed and satisfied, it becomes placid and goes to sleep. During the infantile stage, the majority of its preoccupations continue to be associated with obtaining food and being fed. It would not be unreasonable to suppose therefore that in its emotional development the act of being fed would symbolize for it being loved and cared for; whereas the contrary situation would be associated with feelings of insecurity, resentment, and anger.[16] Once the child begins to sit up and to share in the activities of

[15] The role of the rhinencephalon in sleep presents a fascinating problem when considered in the light of comparative zoology and neurophysiology. Animals without a neocortex appear to sleep at irregular intervals. The basal electroencephalogram in man (involving leads near the basilar rhinencephalon) recorded during early sleep has a different appearance from the tracing obtained in the region of the neocortex, resembling more the waking type of record (*personal observation*). It has been suggested that dreaming is a function of the temporal lobes (58).

[16] It may prove pertinent to the problem under discussion that, according to Flechsig, the process of myelination in the cerebrum commences in

the home, its oral and visceral sensations must obviously fall into greater association with those of the eye, the ear, and the body wall. Stimuli from the genitalia would also be integrated with these other sensations. (Feelings from bladder and bowel, of course, fall into the visceral category.) Although the child might live in an environment where all the requirements for food were satisfied, the harsh voice or look of rejection would have the opportunity in the hippocampal formation to be associated with the oral and visceral sense, and thereby serve as the stimulus to arouse visceral fear, visceral need, or visceral aggression. To cite examples of the great variety of ways anger, resentment, feelings of rejection, etc., reflect themselves in the eating habits of a child, and are therefore symbolically a function of the visceral brain, would not only be time-consuming, but also result in belaboring much that is well known. It should be stressed that the possibility exists for anger or fear to generate hunger as well as a paralysis of the desire to eat. Such a situation, as well as the symbolic content, is often more clearly evident in adults than in children. I might mention, for example, a hypertensive patient, who after a violent quarrel with her sister, proceeded to a restaurant and ate what she described as the biggest meal of her life. It is not unusual for persons with obesity to admit they constantly "nibble" or eat excessively because they feel "nervous," "anxious," or "frustrated."

The question arises in reference to psychosomatic disease whether or not patterns of emotional behaviour leading to *excessive* visceral expression are repeated so often in childhood as to become permanently ingrained in the visceral brain, with the result that they are perpetuated in later life. The combined studies of neuroanatomists and neurophysiologists during the past fifty years have led to a fascinating concept of how transient memory is kept alive in the brain (18, 21, 43, 47, 60, 61, 78).[17]

This in turn may have a bearing on permanent memory. Transient memory is postulated to be a function of the self-reexciting chains of neurones which exist at all levels of the nervous system (43) and which allow the electrical impulses transmitting information of a transitory sort to reverberate in a fixed

---

the eighth month of intrauterine life and involves first the afferent fibers passing to the somesthetic area in the postcentral gyrus and the afferent fibers to the hippocampal formation (see 28, p. 749).

[17] See (8) for a review.

pattern until they are dissipated in the discharge of an effector circuit. It is possible that if a certain electrical pattern of information were to reverberate for a prolonged period or at repeated intervals in a neuronal circuit, the nerve cells (perhaps, say, as the result of enzymatic catalysis in the dendritic processes at specific axone-dendritic junctions) would be permanently "sensitized" to respond to this particular pattern at some future time. Such a mechanism would provide for one variety of enduring memory in a way that is remotely analogous to a wire recorder. These hypothetical considerations suggest how oft-repeated childhood emotional patterns could persist to exert themselves in adult life. They would also indicate the problems facing the psychiatrist in dealing with old memory patterns; to dissipate the impulses of an old memory reverberating in a circuit is not to affect the memory of the cell. But the possibility exists that new patterns of behaviour may be learned that could modify the old.

Only brief reference can be made to some of the psychodynamic formulations that have been made in regard to those psychosomatic diseases where lesions are present. In essential hypertension it has been postulated that the patient suffers "chronic unexpressed rage" because of his inability either to satisfy his "oral" demands (e.g., failure to elicit the love and protection of a dominating parental figure) or his ambitious, independent strivings (66). In patients with peptic ulcer unconscious "oral" dependent needs (e.g., craving for continued maternal care) are said to stand in conflict with the conscious struggle to achieve independence and success (71, 76). Similarly, the asthmatic patient is described as being in an emotional dilemma where lingering "oral" dependence on a parent makes it impossible to fulfill his strong desire for emancipation (24). It has been suggested that asthmatic breathing is a form of wailing or crying which occurs whenever the patient is faced with the crisis of deciding to break the parental tie. The "inclination" to primitive behaviour in patients with ulcerative colitis has been noted by Lindemann (40). It might be generalized that these patients manifest the primitive psychologic state where other individuals are identified with, or mastered by, a process of incorporation. Unsatisfactory identification or unsuccessful mastery because of lingering resentment, anger, etc., may lead to a feeling of visceral turmoil, and defecation becomes the symbolic expression of the desire to extrude and rid from the body the incorporated figure. The part played by symbolic incorporation and defecation in grief reactions of patients with ulcerative colitis has received the attention of Lindemann and his co-workers. In a psychiatric and psychoanalytic study of patients with rheumatoid arthritis Ludwig has observed that these individuals "are unable to express their very strong emotions, but instead react to emotional crises with intense autonomic activity, in a manner which closely resembles the primitive and poorly organized techniques of mastery by destruction and ingestion described in the traumatic neuroses" (45).

It is not the purpose here to defend or criticize these formulations, but rather to indicate that a mechanism (possibly involving dominantly inherited neural patterns) may exist in the visceral brain to account for the phenomena described. It might be imagined that the "rage" of the hypertensive patient, arising out of unsatisfied "oral" demands, has a similar mechanism to the rage-producing hunger in the animal. In both instances the visceral brain might be postulated as participating in the release of the hypothalamus to sympathetic discharge (cf. Fig. 4). But in the hypertensive the conscious need for restraint would exert through the neocortex an inhibition of the somatic expression of rage for which the autonomic responses are brought into play, and so interfere with the physiologic safety valve of muscular activity. On the other hand, the "emotional hunger" of the patient with peptic ulcer might be considered as chronically activating that part of the visceral brain which is linked to the hypothalamic nuclei governing gastric function, with the result that the stomach is being constantly prepared for food (cf. Fig. 4). Similarly one might speculate about possible mechanisms for asthma, ulcerative colitis, and other diseases where the emotions are thought to contribute to the development of lesions.

PSYCHOTHERAPEUTIC CONSIDERATIONS

Preliminary to a few comments on therapy, it should be remarked that one of the striking observations regarding the patient with psychosomatic illness[18] is his apparent intellectual inability to verbalize his emotional feelings. Anatomically it would appear that the intellect could obtain information from the visceral brain directly on the cerebral level by way of the

---

[18] Here again we have reference particularly to that variety of psychosomatic diseases where lesions are present. See introduction.

long and short association fibers, or otherwise be left to determine at second hand from feed-back signals what messages the visceral brain had discharged autonomously to lower centers. In the psychosomatic patient it would almost seem there was little direct exchange between the visceral brain and the word brain, and that emotional feelings built up in the hippocampal formation, instead of being relayed to the intellect for evaluation, found immediate expression through autonomic centers. In other words, emotional feelings, instead of finding expression and discharge in the symbolic use of words and appropriate behaviour, might be conceived as being translated into a kind of "organ language." Such a concept would have a bearing on some of the differences that have been noted between patients with psychoneuroses and those with psychosomatic illness. The former are claimed by the analysts to have an emotional disturbance involving more the genital, rather than the oral, stage of development. Furthermore, they are said to have a greater facility than psychosomatic patients in giving verbal expression to, and "acting out" their emotional feelings. Perhaps this facility affords a reduction of traffic on the autonomic circuits and thereby helps to ward off the development of lesions.

If the psychosomatic patient is inarticulate about his emotional feelings, and if, as indicated, the visceral brain is an animalistic and illiterate brain, one would not expect at the beginning of psychotherapy to accomplish a great deal by verbal methods. Rather, at the onset of therapy, such a situation would suggest an emphasis on those activities of the doctor that have a "disalarming" effect on the patient—such for example as the doctor's kindly manner, his interest, tone of voice, etc. In other words these activities would involve the kind of things that have been hypothesized as having meaning for the visceral brain, and which clinically are regarded as supportive measures. After a good patient-doctor relationship was once established, one might progress gradually to the verbal methods involved in insight therapy.

SUMMARY

A notable deficiency attendant on psychosomatic theory at the present time is the inability to point to a mechanism of emotion that would account for the variety of ways the affective qualities of experience may act on autonomic centers. The first part of this paper reviews certain neurophysiologic and neuroanatomic evidence now at hand that contributes to the understanding of emotional mechanisms. There are indications that the phylogenetically old brain (classically known as the rhinencephalon and arbitrarily referred to in this paper as the "visceral brain") is largely concerned with visceral and emotional functions. This region of the brain appears to be so strategically situated as to be able to correlate every form of internal and external perception. In other words, the possibility exists in this region for bringing into association not only oral (smell, taste, mouth) and visceral sensations, but also impressions from the sex organs, body wall, eye, and ear. And in contrast to the neopallium, the rhinencephalon has many and strong connections with the hypothalamus for discharging its impressions.

These relationships and alleged functions of the rhinencephalon have far-reaching implications for psychiatry. For they indicate that though our intellectual functions are carried on in the newest and most highly developed part of the brain, our affective behaviour continues to be dominated by a relatively crude and primitive system. This situation provides a clue to understanding the difference between what we "feel" and what we "know."

In the remainder of the paper it is suggested how the mechanisms referred to may be related to "oral" and visceral factors that are brought into play in the experience and expression of emotion by the patient with so-called psychosomatic disease.

In view of recent developments in electronics and cybernetics and the light these sciences have shed on neurophysiology, one can no longer be content to think of dynamic psychologic phenomena as existing apart from the restrictions of ordered neural mechanisms.

REFERENCES

1. Aldrich, C. A. Ancient processes in scientific age: Feeding aspects. *Amer. J. dis. Child*, 1942, **64**, 714-722.
2. Allen, W. F. Degeneration in the dog's mammillary body and Ammon's horn following transection of the fornix. *J. comp. Neurol.*, 1944, **80**, 283-291.
3. Ariëns Kappers, C. U., Huber, G. C., & Crosby, E. C. *The comparative anatomy of the nervous system of vertebrates, including man.* New York: Macmillan, 1936. 2 vols.

4. Bailey, P., & Sweet, W. H. Effects on respiration, blood pressure and gastric motility of stimulation of orbital surface of frontal lobe. *J. Neurophysiol.*, 1940, 3, 276-281.

5. Bailey, P., von Bonin, G., Davis, E. W., Garol, H. W., McCulloch, W. S., Roseman, E., & Silveira, A. Functional organization of the medial aspect of the primate cortex. *J. Neurophysiol.*, 1944, 7, 51-55.

6. Bard, P. A diencephalic mechanism for the expression of rage with special reference to the sympathetic nervous system. *Amer. J. Physiol.*, 1928, 84, 490-513.

7. Bard, P., & Mountcastle, V. B. Some forebrain mechanisms involved in expression of rage with special reference to suppression of angry behavior. *Res. Publ. Ass. nerv. ment. Dis.*, 1948, 27, 362-404.

8. Brazier, M. A. B. *Neural nets and integration of behaviour. Perspectives in neuropsychiatry.* London: H. K. Lewis, 1949.

9. Brodal, A. The hippocampus and the sense of smell: A review. *Brain*, 1947, 70, 179-222.

10. Bucy, P. C., & Klüver, H. Anatomic changes secondary to temporal lobectomy. *Arch. Neurol. Psychiat.*, 1940, 44, 1142-1146.

11. Cannon, W. B., & Britton, S. W. Studies on the conditions of activity in endocrine glands. XV. Pseudaffective medulliadrenal secretion. *Amer. J. Physiol.*, 1925, 72, 283-294.

12. Chapman, W. P., Livingston, K. E., & Poppen, J. L. An observation of the effect on blood pressure of electrical stimulation of the tips of temporal lobe in man, [*J. nerv. ment. Dis.*, 1950, 111, 430-439].

13. Chu, H. N., & Loo, Y. T. On vasomotor centers in the forebrain and the midbrain. *Chinese J. Physiol.*, 1937, 11, 295-300.

14. Clark, W. E. L., & Meyer, M. The terminal connexions of the olfactory tract in the rabbit. *Brain*, 1947, 70, 304-328.

15. Cobb, S. *Borderlands of psychiatry.* Cambridge, Mass.: Harvard, 1943.

16. Cort, J. H. Personal communication, in *Res. Publ. Ass. nerv. ment. Dis.*, 1948, 27, 405-417.

17. Crosby, E. C., & Humphrey, T. Studies of the vertebrate telencephalon. II. The nuclear pattern of the anterior olfactory nucleus, tuberculum olfactorium and the amygdaloid complex in adult man. *J. comp. Neurol.*, 1941, 74, 309-352.

18. Dusser de Barenne, J. G., & McCulloch, W. S. The direct functional interrelation of sensory cortex and optic thalamus. *J. Neurophysiol.*, 1938, 1, 176-186.

19. Edinger, L. *The anatomy of the central nervous system of man and vertebrates in general.* (Trans., W. S. Hall) Philadelphia: F. A. Davis, 1899.

20. Erickson, T. C. Erotomania (nymphomania) as an expression of cortical epileptiform discharge. *Arch. Neurol. Psychiat.*, 1945, 53, 226-231.

21. Forbes, A., Cobb, S., & Cattell, H. Electrical studies in mam-

malian reflexes. III. Immediate changes in the flexion reflex after spinal transection. *Amer. J. Physiol.*, 1923, **65**, 30-44.

22. Fox, C. A. The stria terminalis, longitudinal association bundle, and precommissural fornix fibers in the cat. *J. comp. Neurol.*, 1943, **79**, 277-295.

23. Fox, C. A., McKinley, W. A., & Magoun, H. W. An oscillographic study of olfactory system of cats. *J. Neurophysiol.*, 1944, **7**, 1-16.

24. French, T. M., Alexander, F., and others. Psychogenic factors in bronchial asthma. *Psychosom. Med. Monogr.*, No. 2, 1941.

25. Fulton, J. F., & Ingraham, F. D. Emotional disturbances following experimental lesions of the base of the brain (pre-chiasmal). *Amer. J. Physiol.*, 1929, **90**, 253.

26. Fulton, J. F., Pribram, K. H., Stevenson, J. A. F., & Wall, P. D. Interrelations between orbital gyrus, insula, temporal tip, and anterior cingulate. *Trans. Amer. Neurol. Ass.*, 1949, **74**, [175].

27. Gibbs, E. L., Gibbs, F. A., & Fuster, B. Psychomotor epilepsy. *Arch. Neurol. Psychiat.*, 1948, **60**, 331-339.

28. Gray, H. *Anatomy of the human body.* (24th ed.) (Ed., W. H. Lewis) Philadelphia: Lea and Febiger, 1942.

29. Herrick, C. J. A sketch of the origin of the cerebral hemispheres. *J. comp. Neurol.*, 1921, **32**, 429-454.

30. Herrick, C. J. The functions of the olfactory parts of the cerebral cortex. *Proc. Nat. Acad. Sci.*, 1933, **19**, 7-14.

31. Howell's *Textbook of Physiology.* (15th ed.) (Ed., J. F. Fulton) Philadelphia: W. B. Saunders, 1946.

32. Jackson, J. H., & Stewart, P. Epileptic attacks with a warning of a crude sensation of smell and with the intellectual aura (dreamy state) in a patient who had symptoms pointing to gross organic disease of the right temporo-sphenoidal lobe. *Brain*, 1899, **22**, 534-549.

33. Jasper, H., & Kershman, J. Electroencephalographic classification of the epilepsies. *Arch. Neurol. Psychiat.*, 1941, **45**, 903-943.

34. Johnston, J. B. Further contributions to the study of the evolution of the forebrain. *J. comp. Neurol.*, 1923, **35**, 337-481.

35. Kaada, B. R., Pribram, K. H., & Epstein, J. A. Respiratory and vascular responses in monkeys from temporal pole, insula, orbital surface and cingulate gyrus. *J. Neurophysiol.*, 1949, 12, 347-355.

36. Klüver, H., & Bucy, P. C. Preliminary analysis of functions of the temporal lobes in monkeys. *Arch. Neurol. Psychiat.*, 1939, **42**, 979-1000.

37. Kremer, W. F. Autonomic and somatic reactions induced by stimulation of the cingular gyrus in dogs. *J. Neurophysiol.*, 1947, **10**, 371-379.

38. Lashley, K. S. The thalamus and emotion. *Psychol. Rev.*, 1938, **45**, 42-61.

39. Lewis, F. T. The significance of the term hippocampus. *J. comp. Neurol.*, 1923-1924, **35**, 213-230.

40. Lindemann, E. Psychiatric problems in conservative treatment of ulcerative colitis. *Arch. Neurol. Psychiat.*, 1945, **53**, 322-324.
41. Livingston, R. B., Fulton, J. F., Delgado, J. M. R., Sachs, E., Brendler, S. J., & Davis, G. D. Stimulation and regional ablation of orbital surface of frontal lobe. *Res. Publ. nerv. ment. Dis.*, 1948, **27**, 405-420.
42. Livingston, R. B., Chapman, W. P., Livingston, K. E., & Kraintz, L. Stimulation of orbital surface of man prior to frontal lobotomy. *Res. Publ. nerv. ment. Dis.*, 1948, **27**, 421-432.
43. Lorente de Nó, R. Studies on the structure of the cerebral cortex. I. The area entorhinalis. *J. Psychol. Neurol.*, 1933, **45**, 381-438.
44. Lorente de Nó, R. Studies on the structure of the cerebral cortex. II. Continuation of the study of the ammonic system. *J. Psychol. Neurol.*, 1934, **46**, 113-177.
45. Ludwig, A. O. Psychiatric studies in patients with rheumatoid arthritis. [Published as: Emotional factors in patients with rhumatoid arthritis. *Phys. Ther. Rev.*, 1949, **29**, 339-344.]
45a. MacLean, P. D., & Arellano, A. P. Basal lead studies in epileptic automatisms, *EEG clin. Neurophysiol.*, 1950, **2**, [1-16].
46. Masserman, J. H. *Behavior and neurosis: An experimental psychoanalytic approach to psychobiologic principles.* Chicago: Univer. of Chicago, 1943.
47. McCulloch, W. S., & Pitts, W. A logical calculus of the ideas immanent in nervous activity. *Bull. Math. Biophysics*, 1943, **5**, 115-133.
48. McCulloch, W. S. The functional organization of the cerebral cortex. *Physiol. Rev.*, 1944, **24**, 390-407.
49. McCulloch, W. S. Some connections of the frontal lobe established by physiological neuronography. *Res. Publ. Ass. nerv. ment. Dis.*, 1948, **27**, 95-105.
50. Mettler, F. A. Extracortical connections of primate frontal cerebral cortex: corticofugal connections. *J. comp. Neurol.*, 1947, **86**, 119-166.
51. Meyer, A., Brick, E., & McLardy, T. Prefrontal leucotomy: A neuro-anatomical report. *Brain*, 1947, **70**, 18-49.
52. Papez, J. W. A proposed mechanism of emotion. *Arch. Neurol. Psychiat.*, 1937, **38**, 725-743.
53. Papez, J. W. Structures and mechanisms underlying the cerebral functions. *Amer. J. Psychol.*, 1944, **57**, 291-316.
54. Papez, J. W. Fiber tracts of the amygdaloid region in the human brain, from a graphic reconstruction of fiber connections and nuclear masses. *Anat. Rec.*, 1945, **91**, 294.
55. Papez, J. W. *Human growth and development.* Ithaca, N.Y.: Cornell Cooperative Society, 1948.
56. Papez, J. W. Unpublished data.
57. Papez, J. W. Personal communication.
58. Penfield, W., & Erickson, T. C. *Epilepsy and cerebral localization.* Springfield, Ill.: Charles C. Thomas, 1941.

59. Penfield, W. Discussion, in *Arch. Neurol. Psychiat.*, 1945, **53**, 226-231.

60. Pitts, W., & McCulloch, W. S. How we know universals: The perception of auditory and visual forms. *Bull. Math. Biophysics.*, 1947, **9**, 127-147.

61. Ramón y Cajal, S. *Studien über die Hirnrinde des Menschen.* (Trans. from the Spanish, J. Bresler) Leipzig: J. A. Barth, 1900-1906. 5 vols.

62. Ramón y Cajal, S. *Histologie du système nerveux de l'homme et des vertébrés.* (Trans. from the Spanish, L. Azoulay) Paris: A. Maloine, 1909, 1911. 2 vols.

63. Ruch, T., & Patton, H. D. The relation of the deep opercular cortex to taste. *Fed. Proc.*, 1946, **5**, 89-90.

64. Ruesch, J. The infantile personality: The core problem of psychosomatic medicine. *Psychosom. Med.*, 1948, **10**, 134-144.

65. Sachs, E., Jr., & Brendler, S. J. Some effects of stimulation of the orbital surface of the frontal lobe in the dog and monkey. *Fed. Proc.*, 1948, **7**, 107.

66. Saul, L. J. Hostility in cases of essential hypertension. *Psychosom. Med.*, 1939, **1**, 153-161.

67. Smith, W. K. The results of stimulation of the uncus and adjacent portions of the hippocampal gyrus. *Fed. Proc.*, 1944, **3**, 42.

68. Smith, W. K. The results of ablation of the cingular region of the cerebral cortex. *Fed. Proc.*, 1944, **3**, 42-43.

69. Smith, W. K. The functional significance of the rostral cingular cortex as revealed by its response to electrical excitation. *J. Neurophysiol.*, 1945, **8**, 241-255.

70. Spiegel, E. A., Miller, H. R., & Oppenheimer, M. J. Forebrain and rage reactions. *J. Neurophysiol.*, 1940, **3**, 538-548.

71. *Studies in Psychosomatic Medicine.* (Ed., F. Alexander & T. M. French) New York: Ronald Press, 1948.

72. Van der Sprenkel, H. B. Stria terminalis and amygdala in the brain of the opossum (Delphis virginiana). *J. comp. Neurol.*, 1926, **42**, 211-254.

73. Walker, A. E. *The primate thalamus.* Chicago: University of Chicago, 1938.

74. Ward, A. A., Jr., & McCulloch, W. S. The projection of the frontal lobe on the hypothalamus. *J. Neurophysiol.*, 1947, **10**, 309-314.

75. Ward, A. A., Jr. The cingular gyrus: Area 24. *J. Neurophysiol.*, 1948, **11**, 13-23.

76. Weiss, E., & English, O. S. *Psychosomatic medicine.* Philadelphia: W. B. Saunders, 1943.

77. Werner, H. *Comparative psychology of mental development.* New York: Harper, 1940.

78. Wiener, N. *Cybernetics, or control and communication in the animal and the machine.* New York: Wiley, 1948.

79. Yakovlev, P. I. Motility, behavior, and the brain. *J. nerv. ment. Dis.*, 1948, **107**, 313, 335.
80. Yakovlev, P. I. Personal communication, in *Res. Publ. Ass. nerv. ment. Dis.*, 1948, **27**, 405-417.

[ADDENDA FROM THE ORIGINAL PRINTING OF THIS ARTICLE: *Presented before the Staff Meeting of the Psychiatric Service, Massachusetts General Hospital, January 11, 1949. From the Department of Neurology and Psychiatry of the Harvard Medical School and the Psychiatric Service of the Massachusetts General Hospital, Boston. I wish to acknowledge my great indebtedness to Dr. Stanley Cobb for providing the opportunity to carry on these and other studies pertaining to psychosomatic medicine. I also wish to express my sincere appreciation to Dr. James W. Papez for demonstrating to me many of the anatomical structures dealt with in this paper, as well as for permission to refer to certain unpublished data. I want to thank both Dr. Cobb and Dr. Papez for reading this manuscript and offering their valuable criticism.*]

FUNCTIONS
OF THE "OLFACTORY BRAIN"

Karl H. Pribram and Lawrence Kruger

1. DEFINITION OF "RHINENCEPHALON"

RENEWED INTEREST in the "olfactory brain" or "rhinencephalon" has been provoked by the suggestion that in mammals this portion of the brain serves emotional rather than olfactory functions. Recent theoretical and experimental studies have examined various aspects of this suggestion. There has arisen a certain amount of confusion due to discrepancies in results. Furthermore, authors vary in their conceptions of what constitutes "emotion"; and they differ widely in their definitions of which morphological formations are to be subsumed under "rhinencephalon."

Some of the confusion may be traced to differences in results when different techniques are applied; a generalization from the data derived with one technique may not be substantiated by data derived with another technique. Discrepancies of fact may sometimes be resolved by considering the reliability of data (*i.e.*, the number of subjects used; the number of investigations reporting essentially similar results; and significance of the results if statistical techniques are applicable). At other times, the adequacy of the report must be taken into account (*e.g.*, com-

REPRINTED FROM *Annals New York Academy of Sciences,* **58**:109-138.

paring cerebral ablation studies without anatomical verification
of lesions with those where such verification is reported). Usually, discrepancies can be resolved only by further experiments;
ignoring them is least likely to encourage such experiments.

In this review, "emotion" is dealt with as an inference from
behavioral data; speculations regarding emotions based solely
on neuroanatomical data assume a greater knowledge of the
biological variables determining emotion than we possess.

Choice of data is implicit in any survey of this scope and depends on the framework chosen for discussion. Whenever
we are aware of them, such implicit choices will be made explicit. Thus, whether a neural formation might be subsumed
under a definition of "rhinencephalon" depends in part on
whether the reference is "olfactory function," or "emotional behavior," or both, as in this review. This first section deals, therefore, with our definition of the neural formations which are to
be included in the "rhinencephalon."

The term "rhinencephalon" was first used by Kölliker (84) to
denote a group of cerebral structures which, though apparently
cortical, could be easily differentiated from the rest of the cerebral mantle. Meynert (106) had distinguished between cortex
with gray surface and cortex with white surface: the latter constitutes Kölliker's "rhinencephalon" and is found in the "olfactory
lobe," "hippocampus," and "septal region." The conception that
these structures are related to each other and to olfaction came
from studies of comparative and ontogenetic morphology. In sub-
reptilian vertebrates, the entire forebrain is interspersed with a
large mass of fibers originating in the olfactory bulb or anterior
olfactory nucleus (64, 79). In reptiles, although fibers originating
in other systems become more prominent, the forebrain is still
"dominated" by olfactory connections (64). Those neural components of the forebrain which are recognizable in submam-
malian vertebrates can also be distinguished in mammals,
although other, "newer" formations are added. In terms of the
presumed order of their appearance, the divisions of the mammalian brain have been classified as "archipallium" ("hippocampus"), "paleopallium" ("olfactory lobe" and probably "septal
region"), and "neopallium" (64). A body of evidence relating
the size of structures subsumed under archi- and paleopallium
to the size of peripheral olfactory structures has been summarized by Kappers, Huber, and Crosby (79).

Classification invariably runs into difficulty with junctional or transitional categories. Thus, in the case of pallial formations, it is often difficult to distinguish hilar cortex from subcortical masses, *viz.*, in the amygdaloid complex and in the septal region. Another difficulty in classification arises in distinguishing between neocortex and "older" cortex. At the turn of the century, the biological generalization that "ontogeny recapitulates phylogeny" became current (61). Brodmann (29) and the Vogts and their pupils (157) used Nissl's method for selectively staining cell bodies to make ontogenetic comparisons of cortical stratification in an attempt to resolve difficulties in classification. As can be seen from the recent review of these studies by Bailey and von Bonin (15), they were only partially successful. However, their conclusions, in general, support the distinction between new and older cortical formations. The former, which pass through a developmental six-layered stage, were termed "isocortex"; the latter, "allocortex."

There remain, however, large areas of cortex which are not readily placed into one or another of these categories. One such area, the cingulate gyrus, does not pass through a six-layered developmental stage but approximates the appearance of isocortex in the adult. M. Rose (134) suggested the term "mesocortex" to designate this area. A still more useful suggestion is that made by Filimonoff (45) who finds a transitional zone of cortex (both in development and in the adult brain) to separate typical allo- and isocortex along the entire length of the junctional boundary. He designates this transitional cortex (including that of the cingulate gyrus) "juxtallocortex." This suggestion is congruent with the cytoarchitectonic descriptions of von Economo (43) and has been adopted by Bailey and von Bonin. We shall follow them in referring to this cortex as juxtallocortex.[1] In mammals, and especially primates, the increase in the size of isocortical relative to allocortical formations is shared by the increased development of the juxtallocortical transitional areas. Thus, allocortical and juxtallocortical structures form a ring around the hilus of the hemisphere. This ring-like formation was the basis upon which Broca (26) and others, reviewed by Elliot Smith (142), anticipating cytoarchitectural studies, grouped the hilar structures under the term limbic lobe. Support for this

---

[1] However, we do not wish to follow Bailey and von Bonin in classifying juxtallocortex as isocortex.

grouping has come not only from cytoarchitectural comparisons based on Nissl techniques, but also from the studies of Cajal (33) and Lorente de Nó (94, 95) which, using silver staining methods, compared the minute fibro-architecture of these limbic portions of the cerebral mantle with some of those of the lateral cortex. Current interest in the relation of cortex to emotion has encompassed structures which can be discussed only if the definition of "rhinencephalon" includes juxtallocortex as well as allocortex. This review is concerned, therefore, with all cortical formations not *typically* isocortical: *i.e.*, those which do not definitely pass through a six-layer stage in ontogeny. A variety of structures make up the "rhinencephalon" when it is defined in this manner. On morphological grounds, the following units can be distinguished:

1. The *olfactory tubercle* is synonymous with the anterior perforate substance in primates.

2. The *prepyriform cortex* is the area surrounding the lateral olfactory tract. Because of current usage in primate literature, this term is preferred to "anterior pyriform," which is often used to describe the homologous cortex in macrosmatic animals.

3. The *amygdaloid complex* lies caudomedial to the prepyriform cortex and may be subdivided into corticomedial and basolateral groups. The former is also referred to as the periamygdaloid cortex. These terms are preferred to pyriform or posterior pyriform which usually refer to the same structures because occasionally the latter are used to include the entorhinal cortex.

4. The *frontotemporal cortex* is a junctional band of cortex lying between prepyriform and periamygdaloid cortex and orbitofrontal and polar temporal isocortex. Synonymous with orbitoinsulo-temporal cortex, "frontotemporal" is preferred because of brevity.[2]

5. The *area of the diagonal band* is the cortex surrounding the medial olfactory stria.

6. The *septal region* has the same gross anatomical relationship to the area of the diagonal band as the amygdaloid complex has to the prepyriform cortex. The septal area refers to the cortical portion; septal nuclei to the subcortical portion of the region.

7. The *subcallosal area* is a junctional band of cortex lying between the area of the diagonal band and septal nuclei on the one hand, and the mediofrontal isocortex on the other.[2]

---

[2] Evidence regarding the histogenesis of the frontotemporal (unit 4) and

8. *Ammon's formation* is composed of the hippocampus and adjacent structures, the subiculum and fascia dentata (128). The term Ammon's formation is preferred to hippocampal formation because the latter has been used by some to include the hippocampal gyrus. Hippocampal gyrus has in turn been variously used: some authors include only entorhinal cortex; others include isocortex and the amygdaloid complex as well.

9. The *entorhinal cortex* and adjacent *presubiculum* constitute a junctional band of cortex lying between Ammon's formation and temporal isocortex.

10. The *cingulate* and *retrosplenial areas* are a junctional band of cortex lying between the supracallosal hippocampal rudiment (synonym: induseum griseum) and medial frontoparietal isocortex. "Cingulate" is preferred to the term "limbic" because the latter is sometimes used to include the entorhinal cortex and Ammon's formation.

II. CLASSIFICATION OF "RHINENCEPHALIC" SYSTEMS

A. Ontogenetic Histology

These heterogeneous morphological units which have been grouped together "by exclusion" (*i.e.*, by failing to meet the criterion defining isocortex) need not, a priori, serve homogeneous functions. It seems fruitful, therefore, to attempt some classification of these units into systems prior to a discussion of function.

M. Rose (132, 133) has presented thoroughly documented histogenetic studies in an attempt to make such a classification (see Table 1). All cortex is derived from a migration of cells originating from centrally located nuclear masses of the forebrain. Rose pointed out that in some places practically all of the cells partake in this migration while in other places large nuclear masses remain behind. He labeled cortex formed from such "partial" migration as semicortex; it corresponds roughly to paleocortex (as defined phylogenetically). He labeled cortex formed when a "total" migration takes place as totocortex. This term subsumes a variety of structures including all of the isocortex, the cingulate

---

subcallosal juxtallocortex (unit 7) is relatively scanty. These transitional areas are given status apart from isocortex for heuristic reasons. See below pages 217-218 for further discussion.

mesocortex, the entorhinal cortex, and Ammon's formation. The totocortex was subdivided into "split" and "whole" types on the basis of relative contiguity of the migrated strata of cortical cells. Schizocortex (split), as in the entorhinal region, shows a split between the outer and inner layers; holocortex (whole) is found in Ammon's formation, the cingulate region and in isocortex.

TABLE 1.   M. ROSE'S HISTOGENETIC CLASSIFICATION (SIMPLIFIED)

I. Totocortex:
    A. Holocortex: isocortex; cingulate and retrosplenial meso-
        cortex; Ammon's formation.
    B. Schizocortex: entorhinal cortex.
II. Semicortex: olfactory tubercle; area of the diagonal band;
        septal area; prepyriform cortex; periamygdaloid cortex.
III. Bicortex: insular cortex.

The various types of holocortex are distinguished on the basis of the number of cortical layers formed—respectively, two, five, and six. Rose, assuming the claustrum, an incompletely migrated formation, to be part of the overlying insular cortex, had to give special status to this formation ("bicortex"). Beck (18) has criticized the histogenetic findings upon which Rose's classification is based; unfortunately he has so far failed to substitute a more tenable one. Filimonoff (45), on the other hand, although similarly critical of Rose, places emphasis on the aforementioned transitional bands of cortex, and thus provides an alternative basis for classification. In agreement with other cytoarchitectonicists he distinguishes iso- from allocortex on the basis of the early development in the former of six recognizable layers. He places Ammon's formation in a separate allocortical category (archicortex) and suggests that the presubicular and entorhinal areas form a juxtallocortical (periarchicortical) formation which includes not only the usually recognized temporal portion but also supracallosal and retrosplenial portions (Rose's cingulate mesocortex). Thus, in spite of his criticisms of Rose's classification, Filimonoff, on independent grounds, comes to include in related classes (archicortex and periarchicortex) those allocortical structures which Rose had grouped as totocortex.[3] Filimonoff also agrees with other cytoarchitectonicists, including Rose, in grouping together, as semicortex, the olfactory tubercle, diagonal band,

---

[3] The argument with respect to inclusion of the isocortex in this category does not concern this review.

septal area, prepyriform cortex, and periamygdaloid cortex; however, here again he differs as to the basis of classification. Only
with respect to the insular cortex does this difference result in a
change. Because he disagrees with Rose regarding the cortical
nature of the claustrum, Filimonoff is free to classify parts of
insular cortex with parts of the remainder of the cerebral mantle.
A band of transitional cortex abutting semicortical formations
has been described repeatedly (24, 43, 45, 78). This delineation
of a frontotemporal and subcallosal juxtallocortex (perisemicortex) appears useful in subsuming available anatomical and physiological data.

Summary. It is apparent that, although several authors use
separate histogenetic criteria (and only Rose has stated his explicitly), similarities in final classification appear. Two major
divisions of allo- and juxtallocortex may be distinguished. One
includes the olfactory tubercle, area of the diagonal band, septal
area, prepyriform and periamygdaloid cortex, and the surrounding subcallosal and frontotemporal transitional cortex. The other
includes Ammon's formation and its surrounding transitional
cortex: the entorhinal cortex of the temporal lobe, and the peri-
callosal cingulate and retrosplenial cortex. This classification supports the comparative anatomists' distinction between paleo- and
archicortex, but suggests that the newer transitional formations
be classified together with the adjacent older cortex rather than
with the rest of the neocortex. Further evidence supporting the
utility of this classification comes from a study of anatomical relationships *between* these several structures.

B. Axonographic Anatomy

A large body of evidence concerning the interrelationships between the several morphological units which are considered in
this review has been accumulated by observation of stained
"normal" brain sections. Therefore, before turning to the somewhat more reliable and often more specific information derived
from experimental material, an attempt will be made to cover
the extensive literature based on observation of normal tissue.

Fibers are seen leaving the olfactory bulb (which receives the
olfactory fila from the receptor) to course caudally, some terminating in the olfactory tubercle (40, 75, 79), and others crossing to comparable structures in the opposite cerebral hemisphere
via the most rostral fibers of a large tract, the anterior commis-

sure (28). At the level of the olfactory tubercle, the fibers split into two major tracts, a medial and a lateral olfactory stria.

The medial stria can be followed into the subcallosal and septal regions. It appears, however, that these latter structures do not receive fibers directly from the bulb. Fox (46) found that, in the cat, major connections originate *only* from the olfactory tubercle. From the septal region, fibers can be traced to the area of the diagonal band and, perhaps partly through relay in this area, to the amygdaloid complex. Another major outflow of fibers from the septal region apparently reaches the habenular nuclei (of the epithalamus) via the stria medullaris, a conspicuous tract probably formed by fibers from other medial structures (especially amygdaloid complex and anterior hypothalamus). (See review by Brodal (27).)

The lateral olfactory tract can be traced to the prepyriform cortex and to the amygdaloid complex (60, 66, 74, 115, 165). From this complex a large outflow of fibers, the stria terminalis, apparently connects to the septal region and anterior hypothalamus. Connections between the amygdaloid complexes of the two sides have also been described to course in the stria terminalis as well as through the anterior commissure. Some of the fibers of the stria are also said to join the medial forebrain bundle to reach structures in the posterior hypothalamus (46, 79, 165).

The observations relating the other components of the limbic lobe (juxtallocortex and Ammon's formation) to the olfactory afferents are more tenuous. Fibers from the olfactory bulb and anterior olfactory nucleus, via the medial olfactory tract, have been described by a number of authors (46, 60, 66, 74, 79, 165) to reach the anterior end of the supracallosal hippocampal rudiment, a structure believed to be vestigial and distinct from the major portion of Ammon's formation, especially in mammals. Most reports are cautious in their descriptions. Thus, Fox states that fibers appear to "enter into relation" with the hippocampal rudiment. No direct connections between olfactory bulb and cingulate or entorhinal cortex have been claimed.

On the other hand, the interrelations between cingulate and entorhinal cortex and Ammon's formation are better established. Cajal (33) and Lorente de Nó (94, 95) described afferent fibers to Ammon's formation from the cingulate cortex via the cingulum and supracallosal stria and from the entorhinal cortex via "alvear" and "perforant" paths. From Ammon's formation emerges a large tract, the fornix. This tract apparently connects with the septal region and the mammillary body of the posterior hypothalamus (46, 66, 165). Other connections have been described, including the hippocampal commissure which relates the hippocampi of the two hemispheres. In addition, fibers from the mammillary body can be traced via a conspicuous bundle, the tract of Vicq d'Azyr, to the anterior thalamic nuclei—the origin (*vide infra*) of the projections to the cingulate cortex (36).

Summary. From observation in normal stained material of the connections of the allocortical and juxtallocortical formations, three interconnected "systems" can be discerned. The first consists of primary olfactory structures apparently directly related to the olfactory bulb.[4] The second receives fibers from the first and consists primarily of the septal region and the amygdaloid complex. The third "system" consists of cingulate and entorhinal cortex and the structures of Ammon's formation. These appear to be remotely, if at all, related to olfactory afferents. (See excellent review by Brodal (27).) Both the second and third "systems" send afferents to the hypothalamus.

Axonography of normal material thus supports the morphological distinction between those allo- and juxtallocortical areas related to the first and second system (semi- or paleocortical) and those related to third system (archicortical) formations. The distinction between first and second systems on the basis of direct connections with the olfactory bulb would prove useful if substantiated by more reliable techniques, since one of the referents of this review is "olfactory" function. We proceed, therefore, to an examination of experimental anatomical material.

C. Experimental Histology

In many instances, more specific information regarding the interrelationships of these several morphological units has been derived from experimental material. Four staining methods have been employed in tracing the course and termination of fibers originating at the site of an experimental lesion of the brain: the Weigert technique uses hematoxylin to trace neural pathways by

---

[4] In this review, the olfactory bulb is considered analogous to the thalamus. Both bulb and dorsal thalamus (see Rose and Woolsey (121) for review) contain structures which receive the final terminals of afferents from sense organs before relay to cerebral cortex. Thus, the numbering of our system proceeds from the bulb.

their myelin content (interrupted pathways lose their myelin and fail to stain); the Marchi technique employs osmic acid to trace granules of degenerating myelin along interrupted pathways; the Bielshowsky silver method has recently been modified to demonstrate the dissolution of nerve fibers; and modifications of Nissl's thionin or methylene blue stain for cell bodies have been used to show gliosis along degenerating pathways or in related nuclei, and to determine the loss of cells in a structure due to retrograde degeneration when most of the fibers are severed from a parent cell. Each of these techniques has limitations: on the whole, however, those studies employing Nissl stain to study retrograde degeneration and those restricted to *terminal degeneration* when the silver stain is used, are the most reliable. The latter, however, may also demonstrate connections which are sparse.

Following lesions of the olfactory bulb (or, in monkey, of the tract emerging from the bulb), degenerating fibers may be traced in the rostral part of the anterior commissure to the bulb on the opposite side (32, 39, 49, 105, 124, 166). Such lesions also result in degenerating fibers reaching the olfactory tubercle and, via the medial olfactory tract, the anterior portion of the supracallosal hippocampal rudiment. In addition, degenerating fibers can be traced to the prepyriform area, and the periamygdaloid cortex (39, 105). Johnston (73) had divided this complex into corticomedial and basolateral groups on a comparative morphological basis. Only the corticomedial group receives direct fibers from the olfactory bulb.

Discrete destructions separating those parts of the amygdaloid complex which receive olfactory afferents from those receiving none have not been accomplished. However, some information regarding connections can be gained from lesions limited to periamygdaloid cortex (155), others including the entire amygdaloid complex (47), and still others involving the stria terminalis (49). Periamygdaloid cortex sends fibers to at least some portions of the frontotemporal juxtallocortex and to the basolateral amygdaloid nuclei (13), which, in turn, give rise to the major portion of the stria terminalis (the latter also includes fibers from the bed nucleus of the stria, a part of the corticomedial group). In these experiments the fibers of the stria terminalis can be traced to the septal region. Components of the anterior commissure are also found degenerated following amygdala lesions and can be traced

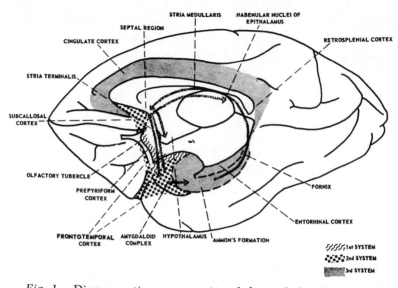

Fig. 1. Diagrammatic representation of the mediobasal surface of a monkey brain outlining the formations discussed in this review and their relationships.

to the amygdaloid complex of the opposite side (47). Finally, fibers can be traced from lesions of the amygdaloid complex (especially the basolateral group) to the ventromedial nucleus of the anterior hypothalamus (2).

We turn to the interconnections of the third system as demonstrated by the methods of experimental anatomy. Whereas lesions of the amygdaloid complex do *not* result in degenerating fibers reaching the entorhinal cortex (13), those of entorhinal (12) and cingulate cortex (1, 3) give rise to degenerating fibers which can be traced to Ammon's formation. Experimental evidence confirms the findings based on normal material that the fornix serves as the major efferent from this formation to the rest of the nervous system (11, 57, 141, 147). Simpson's (141) study divides the fornix into two divisions, a precommissural and a postcommissural. The former, and several times larger by fiber count, terminates in the septal region; the latter, in the mammillary body. Furthermore, when lesions are restricted to the anterior part of Ammon's formation, degenerating fibers can be traced only to the septal region (82, 119) although an abnormal number of *boutons terminaux* appear in the mammillary nuclei

(41); lesions involving the posterior portion of Ammon's formation result in fiber degeneration which extends to the mamillary
body (109, 141). Degenerated fibers from lesions in the septal
region have also been traced to the mammillary body (113). By
means of the Marchi method, some fibers are reported to course
back in the dorsal fornix to Ammon's formation (57). It is, however, somewhat difficult to ascertain the directionality of the degenerating fibers with this method.

From lesions of the mammillary body, Le Gros Clark (36, 38)
traced fibers to the anterior nuclei of the thalamus. These, in
turn, project to the cingulate cortex (22, 120, 130, 160, 161)
which, as we have already seen, is the origin of some of the
fibers to Ammon's formation.

Another "circuit" has recently come to light. As mentioned
above, the stria terminalis connects the amygdaloid complex and
the septal nuclei with the anterior hypothalamus. This, in turn,
sends fibers to the midline and intralaminar nuclei of the thalamus (37, 110). Silver techniques have shown these thalamic
nuclei to project to the prepyriform, subcallosal, cingulate, and
entorhinal cortices which provide afferents to Ammon's formation (114). These findings were anticipated by the results of
several studies utilizing the retrograde degeneration in the
thalamus which follows cortical resections (14, 119, 131).

Recently still another experimental technique has been applied to the olfactory system by Bodian (23). Extensive studies
had shown that the spread of poliomyelitis virus within the
nervous system conforms to known neural pathways. After
inoculation of the olfactory mucosa, poliomyelitic lesions were
found in the (a) bulbs, (b) olfactory tubercle, (c) nucleus of
the diagonal band, (d) prepyriform cortex, and (e) corticomedial group of the amygdaloid complex. In addition, some
degeneration was found in the hypothalamus, the inferior claustrum, midline thalamic and habenular nuclei, and globus pallidus. No lesions were found in Ammon's formation, mammillary
nuclei, putamen, caudate nucleus, or lateral thalamus. On the
other hand, injection of the fornix causes extensive destruction in
Ammon's formation. Thus the relatively direct connection between olfactory receptor and the first system is again validated;
the lack of such connections with the third system is again
emphasized.

Summary. (See Fig. 1.) On the basis of experimental anatomical studies, a more definitive description of the primary olfactory system may be given: from the olfactory bulb (either directly or via the anterior olfactory nuclei), olfactory afferents reach medially to the olfactory tubercle, the anterior extremity of the supracallosal hippocampal rudiment, and laterally to the prepyriform and periamygdaloid cortex. Direct connections from the bulb could *not* be traced to any other structures discussed heretofore: specifically, *no* olfactory afferents reached the septal nuclei, the basolateral group of the amygdaloid complex, the entorhinal, and cingulate cortex or Ammon's formation. Thus a clearer picture of the *second* system emerges from the experimental studies as compared with that obtained from normal material: the frontotemporal (and possibly the subcallosal) juxtallocortex, the basolateral group of the amygdaloid complex, and septal nuclei are now included. In keeping with the semicortical classification of this system, parts of it are cortical, parts form subcortical nuclei.

The impressions concerning the organization of the third system derived from normal anatomy are verified and considerably amplified by experimental studies. This system centers around Ammon's formation, which receives fibers from the entorhinal and cingulate cortex. The main efferent path of Ammon's formation, the fornix, projects to the septal nuclei and to the mammillary body of the posterior hypothalamus. The septal nuclei also send fibers to the mammillary body, and both septal and amygdaloid complexes project to the anterior hypothalamus via the stria terminalis. From anterior and posterior hypothalamus, pathways have been traced via anterior and midline thalamus to prepyriform, entorhinal, and cingulate cortex. Thus, multiple closed loops characterize the connections of the third system; these involve the structures of the second system and those of the hypothalamus as well as those of the anterior and midline dorsal thalamus.

D. Electrographic Anatomy

The histological techniques discussed so far are applied to the study of the brain *in vitro*. Since the development of electrical stimulation, amplification, and recording devices, pathways may also be traced in the living animal. Another method for checking the relationships of neural structures is thus available.

When the olfactory apparatus is exposed to stimulants (*e.g.,* guiacol, cloves, asafetida, indol, chinolin, or smoke), changes can be observed in the electrical activity in the region of the olfactory bulb and tract, olfactory tubercle, septal region, prepyriform and periamygdaloid cortex, and Ammon's formation (4, 10, 63, 100). Because of technical difficulties, stimulus control has been crude; in addition, systematic mapping of responsive and nonresponsive points has not yet been done. Thus the results are tentative, but they indicate that many of the structures included in each of the three systems may be excited by stimulation of the olfactory apparatus. Precise data are more easily obtained from experiments utilizing electrical stimulation of neural structures. As the olfactory fila are difficult to explore in most mammals, the olfactory bulb has been the choice of most investigators using this technique.

TABLE 2. SUMMARY OF ELECTROGRAPHIC RESPONSES TO OLFACTORY BULB STIMULATION

Neural Formation	Rose & Woolsey (129)	Fox, et al. (48)	Kaada (77)	Berry, et al. (19)
Olfactory tract	+	+	+	+
Olfactory tubercle	0	+	+	+
Diagonal band	0	0	−	+
Septal region	−	0	0*	+
Prepyriform cortex	+	+	+	+
Periamygdaloid cortex	+	+	+	+
Basolateral amygdaloid nuclei	−	0	+	+
Frontotemporal cortex	−	−	+	−
Anterior entorhinal area	+ (small)	−	+** (inconsistent)	+
Retrosplenial area	0	−	−	+
Cingulate cortex	−	−	0	+
Ammon's formation	0	0	0*	+
Caudate (head)	−	−	−	+
Putamen	−	+	−	+
Globus pallidus	−	+	−	+
Claustrum	−	−	−	+

* Present under chloralose anesthesia
** In posterior portion: only under chloralose anesthesia

+ = Response
0 = No Response
− = Not Reported

Electrical stimulation of the olfactory bulb results in abrupt changes in the electrical potential recorded from presumably related structures. Using the conventional techniques of recording with a large exploring electrode, all of the structures which have been classified on an experimental anatomical basis as belonging to the first system have been shown to be activated by bulb stimulation in at least two independent studies, although discrepancies exist (see Table 2). All of these structures respond with sufficiently short latency to preclude the probability of multisynaptic connection and can, therefore, be designated as "primary."

With regard to the second and third systems as defined on the basis of anatomical data, the results of electrical studies are less clear. All of the investigations using a conventional electrode have produced negative results, except for some scanty observations using chloralose anesthesia (77). However, Berry, Hagamen, and Hinsey (19), using small (50 micra) bipolar electrodes, which by virtue of their size might be expected to record potentials from only a few elements, have been able to record potentials from some of the structures which have been designated as second and third systems on histological grounds. Differences in latencies distinguish the response in different systems: structures in the first system respond within 4 msec.; in the second system, within 10 msec.; and, in the third, at widely varying intervals longer than 10 msec. For example, the prepyriform cortex yields a response 1.2–3.0 msec. after bulb stimulation, the response from the periamygdaloid cortex is obtained at 2.5–4.0 msec., whereas the responses from Ammon's formation were found after latencies of 10–32 msec. and those near the mammillothalamic tract after 25–34 msec. Responses also appeared in the frontotemporal juxtallocortex and parts of the striatum, supporting prior findings of comparative anatomists (64, 75).

Electrical stimuli have also been applied to structures included in the third system, and the resultant electrical activity in other neural structures has been investigated. Essentially, these experiments confirm the previously outlined interrelationships within this system. Thus, Renshaw, Forbes, and Morison (125) show that the hippocampus is activated by entorhinal stimulation; a both afferent and efferent relationship between Ammon's formation and the septal region via the fornix has been found (52); and the posterior cingulate cortex was activated by stimulation of the mammillary body (164).

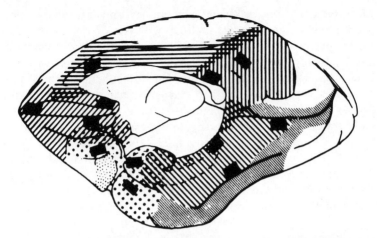

Fig. 2. Diagrammatic representation of the mediobasal surface of a monkey brain showing the distribution of neuronographically determined subdivisions. Black rectangles indicate representative sites of strychninizations: hilar sites of allo- and justallocortex, more peripheral ones of isocortex. Coarse stippling or striations indicate regional parcellations based on reciprocally related cortical points. Finer stippling or striations represent maximum additional cortex unidirectionally activated from within a region. Taken from Pribram and MacLean (122).

A further check of these relationships comes from the changes in electrical potentials induced by chemical stimulation of neural structures, usually by the local application of strychnine. Such "neuronographic" studies (Fig. 2), in addition to confirming most of the findings discussed above, substantiate the relation, proposed on the basis of anatomy, of much of the mediobasal cortex with Ammon's formation (101, 121, 122, 152). These studies support the conception that, in spite of the increased development which the juxtallocortex shares with isocortex in primates, juxtallocortical areas are better classified with the particular allocortical formations to which they are related.

Summary. In reviewing the electrographic data, therefore, one finds an independent method which supports the conceptions derived from ontogenetic, normal, and experimental anatomy. Allo- and juxtallocortical formations may be grouped into three systems. The first system consists of olfactory tubercle, area of the diagonal band, prepyriform cortex, and the corticomedial nuclei of the amygdala. This system has direct connections with

the olfactory bulb. A second system has only secondary connections with the olfactory bulb. It consists of the basolateral
nuclei of the amygdala, the septal nuclei, the frontotemporal
(and possibly the subcallosal) juxtallocortex, and probably includes basal parts of the striatum. On histogenetic grounds, the
structures grouped as first and second system (semicortex and
perisemicortex) were distinguished from Ammon's formation
and related cortex (archicortex and periarchicortex). This distinction is supported by axonography. The third allo- and juxtallocortical system composed of Ammon's formation and cingulate and entorhinal cortex has abundantly demonstrated
electrographic as well as histological intraconnections and is
only remotely related by any technique to the olfactory bulb.

Discussion

Because of recent interest in the possible role in emotional behavior of parts of the forebrain which previously had been
thought to serve olfaction, we have reviewed observations and
experiments concerning the anatomy of the "olfactory brain" or
"rhinencephalon." We have chosen to include all morphological
formations not typically isocortical; i.e., those which do not
definitely pass through a six-layered stage in ontogeny. This
choice has been determined by two considerations. Speculation
has included transitional (juxtallocortical) formations as well as
allocortical ones in the neural substrate of emotion; data can be
more simply organized when both allo- and juxtallocortical
formations are included. In mammals, and especially primates,
the increase in isocortical relative to allocortical formations is
shared by the increased development of the juxtallocortical ones.
Thus the classical distinction between neocortical and older
formations is modified in favor of the distinction between isocortex on the one hand and allo- and juxtallocortex on the other.
In addition, the classical distinction between paleo- and archicortex is broadened to include the transitional formations related
to each type of allocortex (semi- and perisemicortex on the one
hand; archi- and periarchicortex, on the other). The histogenetic
evidence upon which these distinctions are based has been reviewed.

Lorente de Nó (96) has pointed out the limitation of all
cytoarchitectonic classifications based on Nissl preparations.
Essentially, his criticism is that differences which appear be-

tween cortical areas in Nissl preparations do not appear when other staining methods are used. Such criticism implies that the cerebral cortex may be subdivided in only one way which can be specified by the application of a variety of anatomical techniques. An alternative conception would consider that different methods of subdivision are possible, each delineated by one of several techniques and each correlating with different functions. One cortical area might thus be part of two differently organized cerebral systems. In this frame of reference, different anatomical techniques might be expected to uncover different principles of cerebral organization. The relevance of *each* principle to function would have to be established separately. A static conception of "the" function of a cerebral area is replaced by a dynamic conception which considers the different functions of an area under different conditions. The conditions examined in this review are those leading to olfactory and emotional behavior; the relevance to such behavior of the morphological distinctions outlined rather than their *anatomical* generality is in question. Nevertheless, support for the acceptance of the classification based on histogenetic data has come from a review of the interrelationships between the several morphological units included under allo- and juxtallocortex. An additional distinction could be made between those structures receiving axons from the olfactory bulb and those which do not. Thus, on the basis of connections, three systems were described: the distinction between the second and third supporting a similar distinction based on histogenesis.[5] The three systems are defined as follows: the first, or primary, system receives afferents from the olfactory bulb: the second and third do not. The second system is defined in terms of direct connections with the primary; the third system has no such connections, but is connected with the second. As primary system we have included the olfactory tubercle, area of the diagonal band, prepyriform cortex, and the corticomedial nuclei of the amgydaloid complex. The main components of the second system are not all cortical; they include the subcallosal and

---

[5] Actually, the distinction between first and second system can also be made on a histogenetic basis: the first system is semicortical: the second, perisemicortical and subcortical. However, a similar distinction between archi- and periarchicortical formations was not made on the basis of axonography. (It could have been, if a more complex definition had been invoked.) Thus, whether allo- and juxtallocortical formations are grouped into three or four systems is arbitrary.

frontotemporal juxtallocortex, the basolateral nuclei of the amygdaloid complex, and the septal nuclei; in addition, there is evidence that at least portions of the striatum ("olfactory" striatum) should be included, evidence which is in congruence with the semicortical ontogeny of this system. The third system centers around Ammon's formation; it includes also the entorhinal, cingulate, and retrosplenial juxtallocortical areas.

The major interrelationships between the three systems may be described as follows: beginning at the olfactory bulb, fibers can be traced to a *primary* olfactory system consisting of olfactory tubercle, olfactory trigone, the prepyriform cortex, and the corticomedial nucleus of the amygdaloid complex. The primary system of each hemisphere is connected to that of the opposite hemisphere by the rostral fibers of the anterior commissure. This system is connected with the subcallosal and frontotemporal cortex and through the medial and lateral striae with the septal nuclei, nuclei of the diagonal band, and the basolateral part of the amygdaloid complex. These structures make up the second system interconnected through the anterior commissure and stria terminalis. As noted, some comparative studies and electrographic data suggest that parts of the striatum might profitably be included in this system. Efferents from the septal nuclei and amygdaloid complex reach the epithalamus and anterior hypothalamus; in turn, the latter connects with the midline and intralaminar nuclei of the dorsal thalamus. These nuclei apparently project to the juxtallocortex. Ammon's formation receives fibers from the cingulate, retrosplenial, and entorhinal part of this cortex, thus making up the third system. This system, in addition to the circuit involving *anterior* hypothalamus via the fornix and the septal nuclei, is also related to the *posterior* hypothalamus (mammillary bodies) via the fornix. The mammillothalamic tract, and the projections from the anterior thalamic nuclei to the cingulate juxtallocortex, and the fibers to Ammon's formation from the cingulate cortex complete the circuit.

Summary. A definition of "rhinencephalon" which includes juxtallocortical as well as allocortical formations was chosen because of recent interest in the possible functions of these portions of the brain in emotional as well as olfactory behavior. This choice has proved useful in subsuming a large body of data derived from the application of phylogenetic, ontogenetic, axonographic, and electrographic data. This definition of "rhinen-cephalon" modifies the classical distinction between neocortical and older formations in favor of a distinction between isocortex on the one hand and allo- and juxtallocortex on the other. Find-ings have been reviewed which support the classification of "rhinencephalic" structures as thus defined into three systems (see Table 3). The distinction between the first and second

TABLE 3. SUMMARY SYSTEMATIZATION OF
RHINENCEPHALIC FORMATIONS

System	Definition	Morphological Formations Included
First	Direct connections with ol-factory bulb	Olfactory tubercle: area of diagonal band; prepyri-form cortex; corticomedial nuclei of the amygdaloid complex
Second	Direct connections with first system but none with bulb	Subcallosal and frontotem-poral juxtallocortex; septal nuclei and basolateral nu-clei of the amygdaloid complex
Third	Direct connections with sec-ond system but none with bulb or first system	Ammon's formation: ento-rhinal, retrosplenial, and cingulate juxtallocortex.

systems on the one hand and the third system on the other are extensions of the phylogenetic distinction between paleo- and archicortical formations. This distinction is supported by histo-genetic, axonographic, and electrographic data. The distinction between the first and second systems is most reliably rooted in experimental histological studies. The inclusion of subcortical as well as cortical formations in the second system is derived as well from phylogenetic, ontogenetic, axonographic, or electro-graphic techniques. Each system is abundantly intraconnected. Both second and third systems are efferently related to the hypo-thalamus and afferently related to the anterior and midline thalamus. These intra- and interconnections provide the anatomi-cal base for a consideration of the functions of these systems which follows.

III. FUNCTIONS OF "RHINENCEPHALIC" SYSTEMS

A. Experimental Physiology

We now turn from investigations concerning the organization of the "olfactory brain" to investigations of function. As already noted, changes in electrical potential can be recorded in many of the formations considered in this review when the olfactory apparatus is exposed to stimulants. The initiation of such changes is not limited to "olfactory" stimulation, however. MacLean, Horwitz, and Robinson have shown that, in the prepyriform, periamygdaloid, and entorhinal cortex, in the basolateral amygdaloid nuclei, and in Ammon's formation, such changes may also be produced by placing salt on the animal's tongue or pinching its tail and extremities (100). There is some additional though scanty evidence (56, 127) that tactile, auditory, and visual stimuli affect the electrical activity of the third system (specifically Ammon's formation and the cingulate gyrus); it is thus likely that, while the several morphological formations included in this review have been shown to be influenced by olfactory stimuli, they are influenced, as well, by "nonolfactory" stimuli.

Such experiments delineating the afferent physiological control of the structures reviewed have been few. On the other hand, recent observations of the efferent control this system exerts on effectors have been many. Numerous investigators have electrically and chemically stimulated the various morphological formations under consideration (54, 86, 93, 126, 144). Some of the effects of such stimulation might have been predicted on the basis of the respiratory and vascular responses which follow inhalation of various odoriferous gases (5, 6, 20, 85). In addition, gross movements apparently not somatotopically localized have been described repeatedly and have been reviewed by Kaada (77) and Gastaut (55). Such effects have been systematically studied. Stimulation of every structure included in the first and second systems as well as the anterior portions of the third (bulb, tract, tubercle, diagonal band, septal region, prepyriform cortex, amygdaloid complex, and frontotemporal, subcallosal, and anterior cingulate regions) has resulted in respiratory, vascular, and gross motor changes (78). In addition, respiratory and vascular responses have been found on electrical stimulation of the habenula and anterior and midline thalamic nuclei, but not elsewhere in the thalamus (138). Similar effects from Ammon's formation are more readily demonstrated by chemical (sodium citrate) stimulation (7). The characteristics of these responses have recently been reviewed by Kaada (77) and Gastaut (55). In this presentation it is sufficient to point out that in view of other efferent as well as afferent relationships most allo- and juxtallocortical formations cannot be solely designated as olfactory. Recently the control of visceral function (through the autonomic nervous system) by these formations has been promulgated and other relationships neglected. In the light of the efferent control of somatic movement exerted by allocortex and juxtallocortex and, conversely, the control of the autonomic nervous system exerted by the lateral isocortex (65, 80, 118, 137, 159), it seems preferable to emphasize the massive and diffuse nature of the allo- and juxtallocortical control of both smooth and striped muscle (as contrasted with the more discrete control exerted by the lateral isocortex).

With respect to delineation of a specific function for allocortical and related systems, another electrophysiological finding is of interest: electrical stimulation of many of these formations results in a spread of altered electrical activity to the other related formations (prolonged after-discharge, activation and depression of spontaneous rhythms, and abolition of strychnine spikes and burst potentials) and, under certain conditions, to the rest of the cerebrum as well (76, 77, 89, 90, 125). These phenomena could possibly be mediated via the midline and intralaminary nuclei from which "recruiting" responses are obtained (41, 51, 69, 70, 71, 111, 115). It is more likely that interaction between midline-intralaminar and anterior thalamic nuclei, the cortex to which they project (prepyriform, subcallosal, frontotemporal, cingulate, and entorhinal), and Ammon's formation provides the basis for such generalized changes in cerebral electrical activity. Another related finding of great interest is that peripheral stimulation which "arouses" the animal and "activates" the electrical activity of the isocortex (50, 51, 52, 69, 70, 71, 91, 92, 102, 103, 112, 117, 148, 149, 150) apparently results in electrical hypersynchrony in Ammon's formation (59).

Summary. Physiological experiments support the conception that the allo- and juxtallocortical formations have different functions from typically isocortical formations. These experiments

emphasize the diffuse nature of the relationships between allo-
and juxtallocortical formations and peripheral structures, confirming Herrick's earlier findings utilizing phylogenetic material
(64). There appears to be no basis for the substitution of "visceral" for "rhinal" in designating the functions of most of these
formations: both terms suggest a particular selective function
common to all formations included in this part of the brain which
is not supported by evidence. (See discussion of MacLean by
Pribram (98).) On the other hand, the diffuseness of the relationships of these formations with peripheral structures contrasts
sharply with the discreteness of the organization of afferent and
efferent projection systems to parts of the isocortex. This difference may prove to be fundamental.

B. Experimental Psychology

There remains to be considered another type of evidence regarding the functions of the "rhinencephalon": studies of the
behavior of the animal following excision or stimulation of
neural structures. Can the three systems delineated by anatomical and physiological techniques be distinguished on the basis of
their relation to olfactory or emotional behavior? Is such a relationship, if demonstrated, a selective one? These questions cannot yet be answered fully because of the paucity of available
data. However, a beginning has been made, and these experiments are reviewed.

Extensive and clearcut experiments on olfactory discriminations were performed by Swann (153, 154). Using 130 rats
trained in a T maze in which odorous wood shavings were
placed on one side, he found that olfactory bulb excision and
section of the intermediate olfactory stria impaired discrimination. Sections of the (a) medial and (b) lateral olfactory stria,
and (c) lesions of the septal region, (d) prepyriform cortex,
(e) amygdaloid complex, and (f) Ammon's formation failed to
interfere with performance. Neither small isocortical lesions nor
extensive ones involving as much as 85 per cent of the total cortex interefered with performance. Additional experiments by
Brown and Ghiselli (30) failed to confirm Swann on the effects
of sections of the intermediate olfactory stria and, in addition,
showed that extensive lesions of many subcortical masses also
failed to interfere with such discriminations. The only structures
classified as "olfactory brain" by anatomists which were not in-

volved in these experiments were studied by Lashley and Sperry (88). In these experiments, the radiations from the anterior nuclei of the thalamus to the cingulate cortex were interrupted, and time for retrograde degeneration was allowed to elapse. Again, no alteration in discrimination performance resulted. It seems, therefore, that, with respect to the most elementary behavior determined by olfactory cues, only the olfactory bulb has been shown to be significant.

A somewhat more complicated olfactory discrimination utilizing the conditioned foreleg response of dogs was used by Allen (8, 9). He found that lesions of pyriform cortex and amygdaloid complex and the associated frontotemporal cortex resulted in the loss of a "negative" conditioned habit (though the "positive" was retained). In other words, animals which had been trained (using aversive stimulation) to raise the foreleg whenever cloves were presented and to refrain from raising the leg when asafetida was used as stimulus, after surgery, raised the foreleg to both cues. Ablation of Ammon's formation failed to alter preoperative performance. None of these lesions affected the ability of a blindfolded dog to pick out a bag containing meat from others containing sawdust. These results essentially confirm those of Swann: the loss of the "negative" conditioned response may be due either to a *selective* loss of ability to discriminate between several olfactory cues or to a more *general* change affecting either the reaction to aversive stimulation or a whole range of complex discriminations.

Because of the difficulties in separating introspectively the sensations of smell and taste, and the occurrence of "uncinate" seizures in man which sometimes include both, it has been suggested that the amygdaloid complex and Ammon's formation are concerned in gustatory as well as olfactory functions. We have already seen that gustatory stimulation will alter the electrical activity of these structures. Quantitative tests on monkeys' preference for water over a bitter quinine solution show, however, that the insular-opercular cortex rather than the amygdaloid complex or Ammon's formation are implicated in "primary" gustatory functions (14, 21). On the other hand, a change in dietary habits is observed following ablations of the amygdaloid complex and surrounding cortex (119), an effect *not* obtained from lesions elsewhere (either in the insular-opercular, Ammon's, or lateral isocortical formations). These changes in gustatory behavior following amygdala resections, may be explained, as in the case of olfaction, in one of two ways: (a) the animal may be unable to *select* between several cues whether these are olfactory or gustatory and the change is limited to these modalities, or (b) the animal may be more *generally* impaired with respect to any complex discrimination. The latter interpretation is untenable in the light of a considerable body of experimental evidence. Resections limited to the second system fail to interfere with learned visual discriminations (119) or with performance of such tasks as delayed response and delayed alternation (119). These findings take on added significance from the fact that isocortical ablations adjacent to the second allo- and juxtallocortical system markedly impair an animal's performance of these tasks (108, 109, 123).

However, disturbance is not limited to olfactory and gustatory behavior when the second system is stimulated or extirpated. Changes in temperature regulation, in quantity of food intake, and in sleep-activity cycles have been reported (119). While one is tempted to look for some phrase which subsumes all of these categories of behavior, it is probably best to wait for additional evidence before making the attempt. The advisability of waiting is emphasized by yet another series of disturbances in behavior which follow lesions of allo- and juxtallocortex; *i.e.*, disturbances of "emotional" behavior.

Following the almost simultaneous publication of the effects of resection of the entire temporal lobe of monkeys (including the amygdaloid and Ammon's formations) by Klüver and Bucy (81, 82, 83) and the theoretical inferences derived from anatomy about "emotional behavior" by Papez (116), a number of investigators have become interested in this problem. Klüver and Bucy, confirming an older report by Brown and Schäfer (31), found, amongst other effects, that temporal lobectomy resulted in marked taming of monkeys. Papez suggested that the circuit nature of Ammon's formation, fornix, mammillary body, anterior thalamic nucleus, cingulate cortex, Ammon's formation, constitutes an anatomical base for emotional behavior. Experiments by Smith (143) and Ward (162), in which the anterior cingulate gyrus was resected with effects on general behavior similar to those described by Klüver and Bucy, tended to support the Papez hypothesis.

Another series of experiments, motivated by considerations

other than those described above, have implicated the anterior rhinencephalic structures (especially of carnivores) in "emotional" behavior. Spiegel, Miller, and Oppenheimer (146), in acute preparations showed that the "rage reactions" observed previously in decorticated cats (17) and after prechiasmal incisions (53) could be obtained from lesions in the region of the olfactory tubercle and amygdaloid complex. In an extensive series of chronically observed cats, Bard and Mountcastle (16) showed that ablation of the entire isocortical mantle failed to produce such symptoms; in fact, such cats became refractory to most stimulation. If additional damage was inflicted on either the midline (cingulate) cortex or to the region of the amygdaloid complex, the animal's threshold of excitation dropped markedly and "rage reactions" were displayed. When isocortex was uninjured, such reactions resulted only from ablations of the region of the amygdaloid complex—though, in many instances, only after a delay of several weeks. Removal of Ammon's formation resulted in a more "placid" animal. More recently Schreiner, Kling, and Galambos (139) reported another series of carnivores in which extirpations of the region of the amygdaloid complex had been made. Contrary to Bard and Mountcastle, these authors found a marked diminution of "aggressive" behavior following such lesions. These latter results are in consonance with those obtained in primates; however, until adequate comparison of the precise locus of lesions is possible and until the postoperative environmental variables are controlled, no definitive statement resolving this discrepancy is possible. Nevertheless, irrespective of the direction of change, all studies agree that the dimension of change is "emotional" behavior.

Corroboration for some of the alterations observed to follow ablations of these structures comes from electrical and chemical stimulation. "Arrest," "avoidance," and "attack" may be provoked by such stimulation of the amygdaloid complex in the unanesthetized animal (55, 99). In addition, ablation experiments in the immediate past have supported the findings that the structures classified as the second system (frontotemporal juxtallocortex, amygdaloid complex, and septal region) are implicated in "emotional" behavior (25, 54, 113, 145, 163).

In some of these experiments, social (135) and other (25, 163) environmental conditions have been rigorously controlled and the anatomical effect of surgery carefully specified. One series of such experiments demonstrated that behavior based on "fear" as measured by a conditioned avoidance response is especially disturbed by lesions of the frontotemporal cortex and amygdaloid complex. This finding, taken together with previously reviewed evidence, confirms the impression obtained from studies involving olfactory and gustatory behavior as well as those involving energy relationships (food intake, sleep, activity, and temperature regulation) that the second system serves a variety of functions which, thus far at least, cannot be easily subsumed under any "primary" category.

The major portion of the hypothesis of Papez has not fared as well in gaining adequate experimental support. Although promulgated and amplified in an excellent review by MacLean (97), exploration of the effects of stimulation and resection of the supposed anatomical substrate of emotion have thus far been few and crude. The experiments of Smith and Ward concerning the effects of cingulate ablations have not been confirmed. Since neither Smith nor Ward presented anatomical verification of their lesions, or explored behavior by any systematic techniques, subsequent findings (58, 120) must be considered. In addition, as already mentioned, systematic analysis (21, 34, 35, 108, 109, 119, 135, 163) of the syndrome reported by Klüver and Bucy has thus far related the "emotional" and "social" changes in behavior following temporal lobectomy to involvement of the region of the amygdaloid complex. Studies from other laboratories (25, 156, 158) confirm these findings and extend them to include the effects of lesions of the septal nuclei (113). Thus, at present, an abundance of evidence implicates the second rather than the third system in emotional and social behavior whereas evidence with respect to the functions of the third system remains sparse. A few stimulation studies (67, 99) indicate that arrest of ongoing behavior sometimes results. These observations, however, are still fragmentary. Often seizure discharges can be recorded from Ammon's formation in the absence of any observable changes in an animal's behavior. We must face the fact that up to now there have been no reliable clues from behavioral studies as to the function of the third system.

Summary. The results of experiments utilizing behavioral techniques may be summarized as follows: Only the olfactory bulb has been implicated in simple olfactory discriminations. It is possible that resections of the primary system were not complete enough to result in olfactory discrimination deficits, since it has been found that, in vision (62, 140), somesthesis (136, 167, 168, 169), audition (42, 44, 73, 104), and gustation (14), removals of primary projection cortex must include practically the entire system before any discrimination deficit results.

Deficits in olfactory discriminations utilizing "negative" responses have, however, been reported to follow ablations in the region of the amygdaloid complex. Similar changes with respect to gustatory discriminations follows such lesions. These changes are not *generalized* to visual behavior nor do they extend to such tasks as delayed response. However, the effect of amygdala lesions is not *restricted* to olfactory-gustatory behavior. Changes in regulation of quantity of food intake, temperature regulation, and sleepactivity cycles occur. Furthermore, lesions anywhere in the second system (amygdaloid complex, septal region, and frontotemporal and subcallosal juxtallocortex) affect emotional behavior (*e.g.*, as measured by conditioned avoidance responses). It seems, therefore, premature to speculate regarding the "essential" function of the second system.

The third system has remained recalcitrant to date. Behavioral investigations have thus far been too crude and sparse to support Papez' much publicized speculations regarding the neural substrate of emotion.

Discussion

Studies of function have so far implicated only the olfactory bulb in simple olfactory discriminations. This may be due in part to difficulty in making total removals of the primary system, which is spread out along the length of the olfactory striae. A working hypothesis (based on anatomical knowledge of the connections of the primary olfactory system and the neuropsychological data obtained for the primary projection systems in vision, gustation, and somesthesis) would predict olfactory discrimination deficits to follow only when the greater portion of cortex which receives direct afferents from the olfactory bulb is removed. This hypothesis is testable with available surgical-anatomical and behavioral techniques provided a macrosmatic species is used.

A profusion of changes in an organism's behavior follows resections or stimulations of the second system. The following three formulations of these effects are possible:

(a) A simple hypothesis may be suggested to account for the variety of changes. It is possible that the second system as defined in this review must be further subdivided and that a separate function may ultimately be ascribed to each subdivision. If this is the case, the syndrome which follows lesions of the second system could be analyzed into components by selective ablations.

(b) On the other hand, the observed changes in olfactory-gustatory behavior (not simple preference threshold changes) *might* be related to changes in quantitative food intake, sleep-activity cycles, and basal temperature. These, in turn, *might* be related to the changes in "emotional" behavior as measured by the change in social reactions and in conditioned avoidance responses. At present, data are insufficient to formulate such a relationship in precise terms. Imprecisely, this hypothesis would consider one basic change in the organism's reaction to its environment to underlie the various manifestations. The changes in behavior following lesions of the second system are reminiscent of those following hypothalamic lesions; however, they are less drastic. Whereas an animal with hypothalamic damage will be either unreactive or become abruptly and vigorously hyperreactive to environmental change, the animal with lesions in the second allo- and juxtallocortical system will be hypo- or hyperactive within the limits of apparently adaptive and thus less "abnormal" behavior. It has often been stated that the key to understanding the cerebral isocortex lies in the dorsal thalamus; in a similar manner, the key to understanding the second allo- and juxtallocortical system may be found in the hypothalamus. As was pointed out, these changes in behavior cannot be ascribed solely to the relationship of hypothalamus and second system with autonomic and visceral mechanisms. There is no evidence of a *selective* afferent of efferent relationship between the autonomic nervous system and allo- and juxtallocortical formations. As is the case with stimulation of the hypothalamus, the massive autonomic discharge which follows excitation of many of the structures of the second system has obscured the equally massive mobilization of the somatic motor system which frequently occurs, especially in unanesthetized animals. The current obfuscation derives in part from the effects on emotional behavior produced by such stimulation; the acceptance of "visceral" theories of emotion, such as those of James (68) and

Lange (87); and the still older conceptualization of the basis of "feeling" which are carried in our everyday language.

(c) A third hypothesis concerning the variety of effects which follow resections and stimulations of the second system must be considered. It is possible that the second system (as well as the hypothalamus) serves several functions, not because it is composed of several subdivisions, each of which is related to some separate function, but because the second system may, in the living organism, become a part of several larger systems. For example, it is possible that the olfactory-gustatory functions of the second system depend on the relationship between it and the primary olfactory and primary gustatory projections. The metabolic functions of the system may, on the other hand, depend on the relationship of the second system to the hypothalamus. Finally, the changes in socio-emotional behavior may be the result of interference with the interrelationship between the second system and the frontal isocortex. This hypothesis is based on a principle of cerebral organization other than the classical static one derived exclusively from the organization of the peripheral nervous system. Such a principle, that of "dynamic" organization, was proposed earlier in this review in a discussion of the criticisms of histogenetic data.

It seems fruitful to pursue investigations designed to test any of the hypotheses concerning the functions of the second system. At present there seems to be no basis for choosing one hypothesis rather than another except by personal preference which depends, in part, on the investigator's relative facility with anatomical, electrophysiological, surgical, or behavioral techniques.

In spite of the wealth of anatomical knowledge concerning the third system, experiments have contributed little to our understanding of its function. The hypothesis that this portion of the brain forms the neural substrate of emotion has thus far failed to find much experimental support. This may be due, at least in part, to the lack of careful behavioral investigation of the effects of stimulation or resection of portions of this system; investigations which are long overdue. The finding that stimuli which result in an animal's "arousal" and in "activation" of the electrical activity of the isocortex produce electrical hypersynchrony in Ammon's formation provides another avenue of approach to the problem. Part of the difficulty has been the surgical inaccessibility of these structures, a difficulty which has recently been overcome. Thus, relevant data may be expected to become available in the immediate future.

Summary. We have examined the basis for the current interest in the "olfactory brain." Of two acceptable definitions of "rhinencephalon," the broader, including both allo- and juxtallocortex, has been chosen because it subsumes available data parsimoniously. On anatomical grounds, three allo- and juxtallocortical systems have been distinguished. The first (made up of olfactory tubercle, area of the diagonal band, prepyriform cortex, and the corticomedial nuclei of the amygdala) is considered a "primary" olfactory system on the basis of its direct connections with the olfactory bulb. A second system (made up of subcallosal and frontotemporal juxtallocortex and the septal and basolateral amygdaloid nuclei) is connected with the primary system but not with the olfactory bulb and is characterized by subcortical as well as cortical components. The lack of anatomical differentiation between cortex and subcortex in this system is found whether phylogenetic, histogenetic, axonographic, physiological, or behavioral data are considered. This system has been implicated in diverse functions: olfactory-gustatory, metabolic, and socio-emotional. Future investigation must determine whether some unitary function underlies the others, whether the multiplicity of functions reflects a multiplicity of subdivisions within the second system, or whether this system is, under different conditions, part of one or another larger system. Finally, a third allo- and juxtallocortical system (made up of Ammon's formation, entorhinal, and retrosplenial and cingulate cortex) can be distinguished from the others on a histogenetic, axonographic, and electrographic basis. The hypothesis that this system is the neural base of emotion has so far failed to receive conclusive experimental confirmation. This may be due in part to the lack of quantitative behavioral studies of the effects of stimulation or ablation of portions of this system and to their surgical inaccessibility. These shortcomings are being overcome and relevant data should be forthcoming.

We must end this review with the thought that the "olfactory brain," as defined, is not primarily olfactory though parts of it serve olfactory functions. Nor is the current conception of a "visceral brain" more tenable though viscero-autonomic functions are also served. It is clear that the formations in this portion of the brain, though they share several characteristics, are not, at this time, usefully thought of as *a* brain serving any *one* function. Since at least three distinct systems can be delineated, each might profitably be investigated separately before an attempt is made to define what functions they have in common. Current speculation has provided impetus to the systematic accumulation of data; however, if this accumulation is to continue, the formation of hypotheses must become more specific and remain sufficiently flexible to incorporate its product.

REFERENCES

1. Adey, W. R. An experimental study of the hippocampal connections of the cingulate cortex in the rabbit. *Brain,* 1951, **74,** 233.
2. Adey, W. R., & Meyer, M. Hippocampal and hypothalamic connections of the temporal lobe in the monkey. *Brain,* 1952, **75,** 358.
3. Adey, W. R., & Meyer, M. An experimental study of hippocampal afferent pathways from prefrontal and cingulate areas in the monkey. *J. Anat.,* 1952, **86,** 58.
4. Adrian, E. D. Olfactory reactions in the brain of the hedgehog. *J. Physiol., London,* 1942, **100,** 459.
5. Allen, W. F. Effect on respiration, blood pressure and carotic pulse of various inhaled and insufflated vapors when stimulating one cranial nerve and various cranial nerves. III. Olfactory and trigeminals stimulated. *Amer. J. Physiol.,* 1929, **88,** 117.
6. Allen, W. F. Effect of various inhaled vapors on respiration and blood pressure in anesthetized, sleeping and anosomic subjects. *Amer. J. Physiol.,* 1929, **88,** 620.
7. Allen, W. F. An experimentally produced premature systolic arythmia (pulsus bigeminus) in rabbits. IV. Effective areas in the brain. *Amer. J. Physiol.,* 1931, **98,** 344.
8. Allen, W. F. Effect of ablating the frontal lobes, hippocampi, and occipitoparieto-temporal (excepting pyriform areas) lobes on positive and negative olfactory conditioned reflexes. *Amer. J. Physiol.,* 1940, **128,** 754.
9. Allen, W. F. Effect of ablating the pyriform-amygdaloid areas and hippocampi on positive and negative olfactory conditioned reflexes and on conditioned olfactory differentiation. *Amer. J. Physiol.,* 1941, **132,** 81.
10. Allen, W. F. Distribution of cortical potentials resulting from insufflation of vapors into the nostrils and from stimulation of the olfactory bulb and pyriform lobe. *Amer. J. Physiol.,* 1943, **139,** 553.
11. Allen, W. F. Degeneration of the dog's mammillary body and Ammon's horn following transection of the fornix. *J. comp. Neurol.,* 1944, **80,** 283.

12. Allen, W. F. Fiber degeneration in Ammon's horn resulting from extirpation of the pyriform and other cortical areas and from transection of the horn at various levels. *J. comp. Neurol.*, 1948, **88**, 425.

13. Allison, A. C. The morphology of the olfactory system in the vertebrates. *Biol. Rev.*, 1953, **23**, 195.

14. Bagshaw, M. H., & Pribram, K. H. cortical organization in gustation. *J. Neurophysiol.*, 1953, **16**, 499.

15. Bailey, P., & von Bonin, G. *The isocortex of man.* Urbana, Ill.: Univer. of Illinois, 1951.

16. Bard, P., & Mountcastle, V. B. Some forebrain mechanisms involved in expression of rage with special reference to suppression of angry behavior. *Res. Publ. Ass. nerv. ment. Dis.*, 1948, **27**, 362.

17. Bard, P., & Rioch, D. A study of four cats deprived of neocortex and additional protions of the forebrain. *Johns Hopk. Hosp. Bull.*, **60**, 73.

18. Beck, E. *Morphogenie der Hirnrinde.* Berlin: J. Springer (cited from Bailey & Bonin.[15])

19. Berry, C. M., Hagamen, W. D., & Hinsey, J. C. Distribution of potentials following stimulation of olfactory bulb in cat. *J. Neurophysiol.*, 1952, **15**, 139.

20. Beyer, H. Athem Reflexe auf Olfactorinsreiz. *Arch. Anat. u. Physiol.* 1901, 261.

21. Blum, J. S., Chow, K. L., & Pribram, K. H. A behavioral analysis of the organization of the parieto-temporo-preoccipital cortex. *J. comp. Neurol.*, 1950, **93**, 53.

22. Bodian, D. Studies on the diencephalon of the Virginia opossum. III. The thalamo-cortical projection. *J. comp. Neurol.*, 1942, **77**, 525.

23. Bodian, D. The non-olfactory character of the hippocampus as shown by experiments with poliomyelitis virus. *Anat. Rec.*, 1950, **106**, 178.

24. Bonin, G. von, & Bailey, P. *The neocortex of Macaca mulatta.* Urbana, Ill.: Univer. of Illinois 1947.

25. Brady, J. V., Schreiner, L., Geller, I., & Kling, A. The effect of bilateral amygdaloidectomy upon the acquisition and retention of a conditioned avoidance response in cats. *Amer. Psychologist*, 1953, **8**, 325 (abstract).

26. Broca, P. Localisations cérébrales; récherches sur les centres olfactifs. *Rev. anthrop.*, 1879, **2**, 385.

27. Brodal, A. The hippocampus and the sense of smell. *Brain*, 1947, **70**, 179.

28. Brodal, A. The origin of the fibers of the anterior commissure in the rat: experimental studies. *J. comp. Neurol.*, 1948, **88**, 157.

29. Brodmann, K. *Vergleichende Lokalisationslehre der Grosshirnrinde in ihren Principien dargestellt auf Grund des Zellenbaues.* Leipzig: Barth, 1909.

30. Brown, C. W., & Ghiselli, E. E. Subcortical mechanisms in learning. IV. Olfactory discrimination. *J. comp. Psychol.*, 1938, **26**, 109.
31. Brown, S., & Schäfer, E. A. An investigation into the functions of the occipital and temporal lobes of the monkey's brain. *Philos. Trans.*, 1888, **179B**, 303.
32. Cajal, S. Ramon y. Origin y terminocion de las fibrias nerviosas olfactorias. *Gac. son. de Barcel.*, 1890.
33. Cajal, S. Ramon y. *Histologie du système nerveux de l'homme et des vertébrés.* (Trans. from the Spanish, L. Azouley) Paris: A. Maloine, 1911. 2 vols.
34. Chow, K. L. Effects of partial extirpation of the posterior association cortex on visually mediated behavior in monkeys. *Comp. psychol. Monogr.*, 1951, **20**, 187.
35. Chow, K. L. Further studies on selective ablation of associative cortex in relation to visually mediated behavior. *J. comp. physiol. Psychol.* 1952, **45**, 109.
36. Clark, W. E. LeGros. The structure and connections of the thalamus. *Brain*, 1932, **55**, 406.
37. Clark, W. E. LeGros. Morphological aspects of the hypothalamus, in *The Hypothalamus*. Edinburgh: Oliver and Boyd, 1938.
38. Clark, W. E. LeGros, & Boogon, R. H. On the connections of the medial cell groups of the thalamus. *Brain*, 1933, **56**, 83.
39. Clark, W. E. LeGros, & Meyer, M. The terminal connections of the olfactory tract in the rabbit's brain. *Brain*, 1947, **70**, 304.
40. Crosby, E. C., & Humphrey, T. Studies of the vertebrate telencephalon. II. The nuclear pattern of the anterior olfactory nucleus, tuberculum olfactorium and the amygdaloid complex in adult man. *J. comp. Neurol.*, 1941, **74**, 309.
41. Dempsey, E. W., & Morison, R. S. The production of rhythmically recurrent cortical potentials after localized thalamic stimulation. *Amer. J. Physio.*, **135**, 301.
42. Diamond, I., & Neff, D. Role of auditory cortex in discrimination of tonal patterns. *Fed. Proc.*, 1953, **12**, 33.
43. Economo, C. von, & Koskinas, G. H. *The cytoarchitectonics of the human cerebral cortex.* (Trans., S. Parker) London: Oxford, 1929.
44. Evarts, E. V. Effect of auditory cortex ablation on frequency discrimination in monkey. *J. Neurophysiol.*, 1952, **15**, 443.
45. Filimonoff, I. N. A rational subdivision of the cerebral cortex. *Arch. Neurol. Psychiat.*, 1947, **58**, 296.
46. Fox, C. A. Certain basal telencephalic centers in the cat. *J. comp. Neurol.*, 1940, **72**, 1.
47. Fox, C. A. Amygdalo-thalamic connections in Macaca mulatta. *Anat. Rec.*, 1949, **103**, 537.
48. Fox, C. A., McKinley, W. A., & Magoun, H. W. An oscillographic study of the olfactory system in cats. *J. Neurophysiol.*, 1944, **7**, 1.

49. Fox, C. A., & Schmitz, J. T. A Marchi study of the distribution of the anterior commissure in the cat. *J. comp. Neurol.*, 1943, **79**, 297.

50. French, J. D., Amerongen, F. K. v., & Magoun, H. W. An activating system in brain stem of monkey. *Arch. Neurol. Psychiat.*, 1952, **68**, 577.

51. French, J. D., & Magoun, H. W. Effects of chronic lesions in central cephalic brain stem of monkeys. *Arch. Neurol. Psychiat.*, 1952, **68**, 591.

52. French, J. D., Verzeano, M., & Magoun, H. W. An extralemnical sensory system in the brain. *Arch. Neurol. Psychiat.*, 1953, **69**, 505.

53. Fulton, J. F., & Ingraham, F. D. Emotional disturbances following experimental lesions of the base of the brain. *J. Physiol.*, 1929, **67**, 27.

54. Fulton, J. F., Pribram, K. H., Stevenson, J. A. F., & Wall, P. D. Interrelations between orbital gyrus, insula, temporal tip and anterior cingulate. *Trans. Amer. neurol. Ass.*, 1949, 175.

55. Gastaut, H. Correlations entre le système nerveux vegetatif et le système de la vie de relation: Dans le rhinencephale. *J. Physiol. Path. gén.*, 1952, **44**, 431.

56. Gerard, R. W., Marshall, W. H., & Saul, L. J. Electrical activity of the cat's brain. *Arch. Neurol. Psychiat.*, 1936, **36**, 675.

57. Gerebtzoff, M. A. Note anatomo-expérimentale sur le fornix, la corne d'Ammon et leurs rélations avec diverses structures encéphaliques. *J. belge Neurol. Psychiat.*, 1941-1942, **41-42**, 199.

58. Glees, P., Cole, J., Whitty, M., & Cairns, H. The effects of lesions in the cingular gyrus and adjacent areas in monkeys. *J. Neurol. Neurosurg. Psychiat.*, 1950, **13**, 178.

59. Green, J. D., & Arundi, A. Rhinencephalic responses to afferent stimulation, in *XIX int. physiol. Congr.* (Abstracts of communications) 1953, 409.

60. Gurdjian, E. S. Olfactory connections of the albino rat, with special reference to stria medullaris and anterior commissure. *J. comp. Neurol.*, 1925, **38**, 127.

61. Haeckel, E. *Anthropogenie oder Entwickelungsgeschichte des Menschen.* Leipzig: Wilhelm Engelmann, 1891. 2 vols.

62. Harlow, H. F. Recovery of pattern discrimination in monkeys following unilateral occipital lobectomy. *J. comp. Psychol.*, 1939, **27**, 467.

63. Hasama, B. Über die electrischen Beglecterscheinungen an der Reichsphäre bei der Geruchsempfindung. *Pflüg. Arch. ges. Physiol.*, 1934, **234**, 748.

64. Herrick, C. J. The functions of the olfactory parts of the cortex. *Proc. nat. Acad. Sci., U.S.*, 1933, **19**, 7.

65. Hoff, E. C., & Green, H. D. Cardiovascular reactions induced by electrical stimulation of the cerebral cortex. *Amer. J. Physiol.*, 1936, **117**, 411.

66. Humphrey, T. The telencephalon of the bat. The non-cortical

nuclear masses and certain pertinent fiber connections. *J. comp. Neurol.*, 1936, **65**, 603.

67. Hunter, J., & Jasper, H. H. Effects of thalamic stimulation in unanesthetized animals. *EEG clin. Neurophysiol.*, 1949, **1**, 305.

68. James, W. *The principles of psychology.* New York: Dover, 1918. 2 vols.

69. Jasper, H. H. Diffuse projection systems: The integrative action of the thalamic reticular system. *EEG clin. Neurophysiol.*, 1949, **1**, 405.

70. Jasper, H. H., & Ajmone-Marsan, C. Thalamocortical integrating mechanisms. *Res. Publ. Ass. nerv. ment. Dis.*, 1950, **30**, 493.

71. Jasper, H. H., Ajmone-Marsan, C., & Stoll, J. Corticofugal projections to the brain stem. *Arch. Neurol. Psychiat.*, 1952, **67**, 155.

72. Jasper, H. H., & Droogleever-Fortuyn, J. Experimental studies on the functional anatomy of petit mal epilepsy. *Res. Publ. Ass. nerv. ment. Dis.*, 1947, **26**, 272.

73. Jenson, H. J., & Neff, W. D. Effect of cortical ablation in the monkey on discrimination of auditory patterns. *Fed. Proc.*, 1953, **12**, 73.

74. Jeserich, M. W. The nuclear pattern and fiber connections of certain noncortical areas of the telencephalon of the mink (*Mustela vison*). *J. comp. Neurol.*, 1945, **83**, 173.

75. Johnston, J. B. Further contributions to the study of the evolution of the forebrain. *J. comp. Neurol.*, 1923, **35**, 337.

76. Jung, R. Der Elekrokrampf in Corticalen und Subcorticalen Hirngebieten Demonstration und Diskussion des zentralen Krampf-mechanismus. *Ber. ges. Physiol.*, 1950, **139**, 211.

77. Kaada, B. R. Somato-motor, autonomic and electrocorticographic responses to electrical stimulation of rhinencephalic and other structures in primates, cat and dog. *Acta Physiol. scand.*, 1951, **23** (suppl.), 83.

78. Kaada, B. R., Pribram, K. H., & Epstein, J. A. Respiratory and vascular responses in monkeys from temporal pole, insula, orbital surface and cingulate gyrus. *J. Neurophysiol.*, 1949, **12**, 347.

79. Kappers, C. U., Huber, G. C., & Crosby, E. C. *The comparative anatomy of the nervous system of vertebrates, including man.* New York: Macmillan, 1936.

80. Kennard, M. A. The cortical influence on the autonomic system. *Bumke u. Foerster's Handb. Neurol.*, 1937, **2**, 476.

81. Klüver, H. Brain mechanisms and behavior with special reference to the rhinencephalon. *Lancet*, 1952, **72**, 567.

82. Klüver, H., & Bucy, P. C. An analysis of certain effects of bilateral temporal lobectomy in the rhesus monkey, with special reference to "psychic blindness." *J. Psychol.*, 1938, **5**, 33.

83. Klüver, H., & Bucy, P. C. Preliminary analysis of functions of the temporal lobes in monkeys. *Arch. Neurol. Psychiat.*, Chicago, 1939, **42**, 979.

84. Kölliker, A. *Handbuch der Gewebelehre des Menschen.* Leipzig: Wilhelm Engelmann, 1870, 2 vols., 6 Aufl.
85. Kratschmer, F. *Über Reflexe der Nasenscheimbaut auf Athmung und der Tiere.* Leipzig: Wilhelm Engelmann, 1870. 2 vols.
86. Kremer, F. Autonomic and somatic reactions induced by stimulation of the cingular gyrus in dogs. *J. Neurophysiol.,* 1947, **10,** 371.
87. Lange, C. *Über Gemuthsbewegungen.* (Trans., H. Kurella) Leipzig: 1887. Cited in James (68).
88. Lashley, K. S., & Sperry, R. W. Olfactory discrimination after destruction of the anterior thalamic nuclei. *Amer. J. Physiol.,* 1943, **139,** 446.
89. Lennox, M. A., Dunsmore, R. H., Epstein, J. A., & Pribram, K. H. Electrocorticographic effects of stimulation of posterior orbital, temporal and cingulate areas of Macaca mulatta. *J. Neurophysiol.,* 1950, **13,** 383.
90. Liberson, W. T., & Akert, K. Personal communication.
91. Lindsley, D. B. Psychological phenomena and the electroencephalogram. *EEG clin. Neurophysiol.,* 1952, **4,** 443.
92. Lindsley, D. B., Schreiner, L. H., Knowles, W. B., & Magoun, H. W. Behavioral and EEG changes following chronic brain stem lesions in the cat. *EEG clin. Neurophysiol.,* 1950, **2,** 483.
93. Livingston, R. B., Fulton, J. F., Delgado, J. M. R., Sachs, E., Jr., Brendler, S. J., & Davis, G. D. Stimulation and regional ablation of orbital surface of frontal lobe. *Res. Publ. Ass. nerv. ment. Dis.,* 1948, **27,** 405.
94. Lorente de Nó, R. Studies on the structure of the cerebral cortex. I. The area entorhinalis. *J. Psychol. u. Neurol.,* 1934, **46,** 113.
95. Lorente de Nó, R. Studies on the structure of the cerebral cortex. II. Continuation of the study of the ammonic system. *J. Psychol. u. Neurol.,* 1934, **46,** 113.
96. Lorente de Nó, R. Cerebral cortex: Architecture, intracortical connections, motor projections, in Fulton, *Physiology of the nervous system.* New York: Oxford, 1949.
97. MacLean, P. D. Psychosomatic disease and the "visceral brain": Recent developments bearing on the Papez theory of emotion. *Psychosom. Med.,* 1950, **11,** 338.
98. MacLean, P. D. Some psychiatric implications of physiological studies on frontotemporal portion of limbic system (visceral brain). *EEG clin. Neurophysiol.,* 1952, **4,** 407.
99. MacLean, P. D., & Delgado, J. M. R. Electrical and chemical stimulation of frontotemporal portion of limbic system in the waking animal. *EEG clin. Neurophysiol.,* 1953, **5,** 91.
100. MacLean, P. D., Horwitz, N. H., & Robinson, F. Olfactory-like responses in pyriform area to non-olfactory stimulation. *Yale J. Biol. Med.,* 1952, **25,** 159.
101. MacLean, P. D., & Pribram, K. H. A neuronographic analysis of

the medial and basal cerebral cortex. I. Cat. *J. Neurophysiol.*, 1953, **16**, 312.

102. Magoun, H. W. Caudal and cephalic influences of the brain stem reticular formation. *Physiol. Rev.*, 1950, **30**, 459.
103. Magoun, H. W. The ascending reticular activating system. *Res. Publ. Ass. nerv. ment. Dis.*, 1950, **30**, 480.
104. Meyer, D. R., & Woolsey, C. H. Effects of localized cortical destruction on auditory discriminative conditioning in cat. *J. Neurophysiol.*, 1952, **15**, 149.
105. Meyer, M., & Allison, A. C. An experimental investigation of the connections of the olfactory tracts in the monkey. *J. Neurol. Neurosurg. Psychiat.*, 1949, **12**, 274.
106. Meynert, T. Der Bau der Grosshirnrinde und seine ortlichen Verschiedenheiten, nebst einer pathologisch-anatomischen corollarium. *Viertel Yahrschr. Psychiat.*, 1867-1868, **1**, 77-93, 125-217, 318-403; **2**, 88-113.
107. Minot, C. S. The olfactory lobes. *Brit. Ass. Advancement Sci. Rep.*, 1896.
108. Mishkin, M. Visual discrimination performance following ablations of the temporal lobe. II. Ventral surface versus hippocampus. *J. comp. physiol. Psychol.*, [1954, **47**, 187-193].
109. Mishkin, M., & Pribram, K. H. Visual discrimination performance following partial ablations of the temporal lobe. I. Ventral versus lateral. *J. comp. physiol. Psychol.*, [1954, **47**, 14-20].
110. Morin, F. An experimental study of hypothalamic connections of the guinea pig. *J. comp. Neurol.*, 1950, **92**, 193.
111. Morison, R. S., & Dempsey, E. W. A study of thalamocortical relations. *Amer. J. Physiol.*, 1942, **135**, 281.
112. Moruzzi, G., & Magoun, H. W. Brain stem reticular formation and activation of the EEG. *EEG clin. Neurophysiol.*, 1949, **1**, 455.
113. Nauta, W. J. H., & Brady, J. V. An exploratory study of the relationship between subcortical lesions and emotional behavior in the albino rat: The septal areas of the forebrain. *Amer. Psychologist*, 1952, **7**, 257.
114. Nauta, W. J. H., & Whitlock, D. J. Personal communication.
115. O'Leary, J. L. Structure of the primary olfactory cortex of the mouse. *J. comp. Neurol.*, 1937, **67**, 1.
116. Papez, J. W. A proposed mechanism of emotion. *Arch. Neurol. Psychiat.*, 1937, **38**, 725.
117. Penfield, W. Epileptic automatism and the centrencephalic integrating system. *Res. Publ. Ass. nerv. ment. Dis.*, 1952, **30**, 513.
118. Pinkston, J. O. & Rioch, D. M. The influence of the cerebral cortex on peripheral circulation. *Amer. J. Physiol.*, 1938, **121**, 49.
119. Pribram, K. H., & Bagshaw, M. H. Further analysis of the temporal lobe syndrome utilizing frontotemporal ablations in monkeys. *J. comp. Neurol.*, 1953, [**99**, 347-375].

120. Pribram, K. H., & Fulton, J. F. An experimental critique of the effects of anterior cingulate ablations in monkey. *Brain*, [1954, **77**, 34-44].

121. Pribram, K. H., Lennox, M. A., & Dunsmore, L. H. Some connections of the orbito-fronto-temporal, limbic and hippocampal areas of *Macaca mulatta*. *J. Neurophysiol.*, 1950, **12**, 127.

122. Pribram, K. H., & MacLean, P. D. A neuronographic analysis of the medial and basal cerebral cortex. II. Monkey. *J. Neurophysiol.*, 1953, **16**, 324.

123. Pribram, K. H., Mishkin, M., Rosvold, H. E., & Kaplan, S. J. Effects on delayed-response performance of lesions of dorsolateral and ventromedial frontal cortex of baboons. *J. comp. physiol. Psychol.*, 1952, **45**, 565.

124. Probst, M. Sur Kenntnis des Faserverlaufes des Temporallappens, des Bulbus Olfactorius, etc. *Arch. Anat. u. Physiol.*, 1901 Cited from Cajal (33).

125. Renshaw, B., Forbes, A., & Morison, B. R. Activity of isocortex and hippocampus: Electrical studies with microelectrodes. *J. Neurophysiol.*, 1940, **3**, 74.

126. Rioch, D. McK., & Brenner, C. Experiments on the striatum and rhinencephalon. *J. comp. Neurol.*, 1938, **68**, 491.

127. Robinson, F., & Lennox, M. A. Sensory mechanisms in hippocampus, cingulate gyrus and cerebellum of the cat. *Fed. Proc.*, 1951, **10**, 110.

128. Rose, J. E. Sur normalen und pathologischen Architektonik der Ammonsformation. *J. Psychol. u. Neurol.*, 1938, **49**, 137.

129. Rose, J. E., & Woolsey, C. N. Potential changes in the olfactory brain produced by electrical stimulation of the olfactory bulb. *Fed. Proc.*, 1943, **2**, 42.

130. Rose, J. E., & Woolsey, C. N. Structure and relations of limbic cortex and anterior thalamic nuclei in rabbit and cat. *J. comp. Neurol.*, 1948, **89**, 279.

131. Rose, J. E., & Woolsey, C. N. Organization of the mammalian thalamus and its relationships to the cerebral cortex. *EEG clin. Neurophysiol.*, 1949, **1**, 391.

132. Rose, M. Der Allocortex bei Tier und Mensch. I. Teil. *J. Psychol. u. Neurol.*, 1926, **34**, 1.

133. Rose, M. Die sog. Riechrinde beim Menschen und beim Assen II. Teil des "Allocortex bei Tier und Mensch." *J. Psychol. u. Neurol.*, 1927, **34**, 261.

134. Rose, M. Gyrus Limbicus anterior und Regio Retrosplenialis. *J. Psychol. u. Neurol.*, 1927, **35**, 65.

135. Rosvold, H. E., Mirsky, A. F., & Pribram, K. H. Influence of amygdalectomy on social behavior in monkeys. *J. comp. physiol. Psychol.*, [1954, **47**, 173-178].

136. Ruch, T. C., Fulton, J. F., & German, W. J. Sensory discrimination in monkey, chimpanzee and man after lesions of the parietal lobe. *Arch. Neurol. Psychiat.*, 1938, **39**, 919.

137. Ruch, T. C., Patton, H. D., & Amassian, V. E. Topographical

and functional determinants of cortical localization patterns. *Res. Publ. nerv. ment. Dis.*, 1952, **30**, 403.

138. Sachs, E. On the relation of the optic thalamus to respiration, circulation, temperature and spleen. *J. Exp. Med.*, 1911, **14**, 408.

139. Schreiner, L., Kling, A., & Galambos, R. Central nervous system lesions and aggressive behavior in cats. *Fed. Proc.*, 1952, **11**, 142.

140. Settlage, P. H. The effect of occipital lesions on visually guided behavior in the monkey. *J. comp. physiol. Psychol.*, 1939, **27**, 93.

141. Simpson, D. A. The efferent fibers of the hippocampus in the monkey. *J. Neurol. Neurosurg. Psychiat.*, 1952, **15**, 79.

142. Smith, G. E. Morphology of the true "limbic lobe," corpus callosum, spetum pellucidum and fornix. *J. Anat.*, 1896, **30**, 185.

143. Smith, W. K. The results of ablation of the cingular region of the cerebral cortex. *Fed. Proc.*, 1944, **3**, 42.

144. Smith, W. K. The functional significance of the rostral cingular cortex as revealed by its responses to electrical excitation. *J. Neurophysiol.*, 1945, **8**, 241.

145. Smith, W. K. Non-olfactory functions of the pyriform amygdaloid-hippocampal complex, *Fed. Proc.*, 1950, **9**, 118.

146. Spiegel, E. A., Miller, H. R., & Oppenheimer, M. J. Forebrain and rage reactions, *J. Neurophysiol.*, 1940, **3**, 538.

147. Sprague, J. M., & Meyer, M. An experimental study of the fornix in the rabbit. *J. Anat.*, 1950, **84**, 354.

148. Starzl, T. E., & Magoun, H. W. Organization of the diffuse thalamic projection system. *J. Neurophysiol.*, 1951, **14**, 133.

149. Starzl, T. E., Taylor, C. W., & Magoun, H. W. Collateral afferent excitation of reticular formation of brain stem. *J. Neurophysiol.*, 1951, **14**, 479.

150. Starzl, T. E., Taylor, C. W., & Magoun, H. W. Ascending conduction in reticular activating system, with special reference to the diencephalon. *J. Neurophysiol.*, 1951, **41**, 461.

151. Starzl, T. E., & Whitlock, D. G. Diffuse thalamic projection system in monkey. *J. Neurophysiol.*, 1952, **15**, 449.

152. Stoll, J., Ajmone-Marsan, C., & Jasper, H. H. Electro-physiological studies of subcortical connections of anterior temporal region in cat. *J. Neurophysiol.*, 1951, **14**, 305.

153. Swann, H. G. The function of the brain in olfaction. II. The results of destruction of olfactory and other nervous structures upon the discrimination of odors. *J. comp. Neurol.*, 1934, **59**, 175.

154. Swann, H. G. The function of the brain in olfaction. III. Effects of large cortical lesions on olfactory discrimination. *Amer. J. Physiol.*, 1935, **111**, 257.

155. Takahashi, K. Experiments on the periamygdaloid cortex of cat and dog. *Folia. Psychiat. Neurol. Japon*, 1951, **5**, 147.

156. Thomson, A. F., & Walker, A. E. Behavioral alterations following lesions of the medial surface of the temporal lobe. *Arch. Neurol. Psychiat.*, 1951, **65**, 251.

157. Vogt, C., & Vogt, O. Allgemeinere Ergebnisse unserer Hirn-forschung. *J. Psychol. Neurol.*, 1919, **25**, 277.

158. Walker, A. E., Thomson, A. F., & McQueen, J. D. Behavior and the temporal rhinencephalon in the monkey. *Johns Hopk. Hosp. Bull.*, 1953, **93**, 65.

159. Wall, P. D., & Pribram, K. H. Trigeminal neurotomy and blood pressure responses from stimulation of lateral cerebral cortex of Macaca mulatta. *J. Neurophysiol.*, 1950, **13**, 409.

160. Waller, W. H. Topographical relations of cortical lesions to thalamic nuclei in the albino rat. *J. comp. Neurol.*, 1934, **60**, 237.

161. Waller, W. H. Acortical lesion causing cell reaction in antero-medial thalamic nucleus. *J. comp. Neurol.*, 1937, **66**, 443.

162. Ward, A. A., Jr. The cingular gyrus: Area 24. *J. Neurophysiol.*, 1948, **11**, 13.

163. Weiskrantz, L. Behavioral changes associated with ablation of the amygdala. *Amer. Psychologist*, 1953, **8**, 452 (abstract).

164. Woolsey, C. N., Dick, F. M., & Frantz, R. H. Electrical re-sponses in gyrus cinguli evoked by electrical stimulation of ipsilateral mammillary body in cat and monkey. *Fed. Proc.*, 1946, **5**, 116.

165. Young, M. W. The nuclear pattern and fiber connections of the noncortical center of the telencephalon in the rabbit. *J. comp. Neurol.*, 1936, **65**, 295.

166. Young, M. W. Degeneration of the fiber tracts following ex-perimental transection of the olfactor bulb. *Anat. Rec.*, 1941, **79**, 65.

167. Zubek, J. P. Studies in somesthesis. I. Role of the somesthetic cortex in roughness discrimination in the rat. *J. comp. physiol. Psychol.*, 1951, **44**, 339.

168. Zubek, J. P. Studies in somesthesis. II. Role of somatic sensory areas I and II in roughness discrimination in the cat. *J. Neuro-physiol*, 1952, **15**, 401.

169. Zubek, J. P. Studies in somesthesis. III. Role of somatic areas I and II in the acquisition of roughness discrimination in the rat. *J. Psychol., Canada*, 1952, **6**, 183.

[ADDENDA FROM THE ORIGINAL PRINTING OF THIS ARTICLE: IN REFERENCE TO PRIBRAM: *Department of Neurophysiology, Institute of Living, Hart-ford, Conn.* IN REFERENCE TO KRUGER: *Department of Physiology, Yale University School of Medicine, New Haven, Conn.* ACKNOWLEDGMENTS: *The authors are deeply grateful for the extensive help given by Paul Mac-Lean, Jerzy Rose, and Hans-Lukas Teuber in the preparation of this re-view. S. Rains Wallace and Joseph Weitz made constructive criticisms of early drafts; and Mortimer Mishkin, Lawrence Weiskrantz, and William Wilson aided in the preparation of the final draft. We are especially in-debted to Mrs. Marilyn Tucker whose painstaking care and unlimited patience made the innumerable revisions possible.*]

BRAIN STEM RETICULAR FORMATION AND ACTIVATION OF THE EEG ❋ *G. Moruzzi and H. W. Magoun*

TRANSITIONS from sleep to wakefulness, or from the less extreme states of relaxation and drowsiness to alertness and attention, are all characterized by an apparent breaking up of the synchronization of discharge of elements of the cerebral cortex, an alteration marked in the EEG by the replacement of high-voltage slow waves with low-voltage fast activity. The magnitude of the electrical change parallels the degree of transition, and that most commonly observed in clinical electroencephalography is a minimal one, consisting of an alpha-wave blockage during attention to visual stimulation. Such activation of the EEG may be produced by any type of afferent stimulus that arouses the subject to alertness, or it may be centrally generated, but the basic processes underlying it, like those involved in waking from sleep, have remained obscure.

Recent experimental findings which may contribute to this subject have stemmed from the observation that EEG changes

REPRINTED FROM *Electroencephalography and Clinical Neurophysiology,* 1:455-473. COPYRIGHT © 1949 BY ELSEVIER PUBLISHING COMPANY.

seemingly identical with those in the physiological arousal reactions can be produced by direct stimulation of the reticular
formation of the brain stem. The following account describes
such features of the response and its excitable substrate as have
been determined, provides an analysis of changes in cortical
and thalamic activity associated with it, and explores the relations of this reticular activating system to the arousal reaction to
natural stimuli. Alterations produced by acute lesions in this
system are presented in a succeeding paper. The effects of
chronic lesions within it are under investigation.

METHODS

The experiments were performed in cats under chloralosane
anesthesia (35–50 mgm./K, intraperitoneally) or in the "encéphale isolé" of Bremer, prepared under ether, with exposure
margins infiltrated with procaine. Ephedrine was administered
intravenously immediately after transection of the cord at C 1.
At least an hour elapsed after ether was discontinued before
work was begun.

Concentric bipolar electrodes, oriented with the Horsley-
Clarke technique, were used for stimulation of, or pickup from,
the brain stem. Condenser discharges from a Goodwin stimulator
were employed routinely. Lesions were made surgically or
electrolytically, and their positions, together with those of electrode placements, were verified histologically.

Potentials were recorded with a Grass model III amplifier and
inkwriter. Some cortical records were taken directly from the
pial surface, but usually as much of the brain case as possible
was left intact, and most cortical pickups were between two
screw electrodes, 5–10 mm. apart, inserted through burr holes
in the calvarium until their tips rested on the dura overlying
functional areas. With bipolar leads and by grounding the
scalp, stimulus artifacts were negligible. Other technical details
are given in the legends.

RESULTS

The response to reticular stimulation consisted of cessation of
synchronized discharge in the EEG and its replacement with
low-voltage fast activity. The intensity of the alteration varied

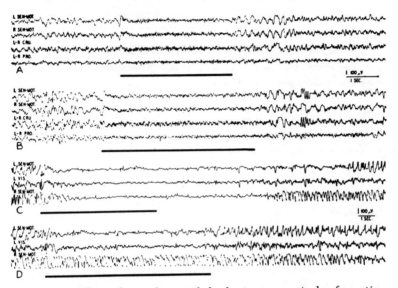

Fig. 1. Effect of stimulation of the brain stem reticular formation upon electrocortical activity of chloralosane preparations. *A* and *C.* "Encéphale isolé" with 7 mgm. chloralosane/K. Replacement of high-voltage slow waves, present in *A* and more pronounced in *B*, with low-voltage fast activity during left bulbo-reticular stimulation (1.5 V, 300/sec.). *C.* Intact cat with 50 mg. chloralosane/K. Left bulbo-reticular stimulation (3 V, 300 sec.) blocks chloralosane waves bilaterally, but more rapidly and for a longer time in the ipsilateral cortex. Note that low voltage fast activity does not appear. *D.* Like *C*, but frequency of reticular stimulation reduced to 100/sec. Effect limited to ipsilateral cortex and does not outlast stimulus. In all records, the origin of activity in different channels is given at the left: L. SEN. MOT. signifies left sensory-motor cortex; L.-R. CRU., left to right cruciate gyrus; L.-R. PRO., left to right gyrus proreus; L. VIS., left visual area; L. AUD., left auditory area; L. THAL., left thalamus. The period of bulbar stimulation is marked by a heavy line beneath the record. Calibration and time are stated.

with the degree of background synchrony present. Conspicuous effects were thus observed against the high-voltage slow waves of chloralosane anesthesia (Fig. 1C, D), while a fully activated EEG was not further affected (Fig. 2A). Responses were seen to best advantage when the unanesthetized brain exhibited some relaxation (Fig. 2B, C) or when light chloralosane anesthesia had induced synchronization without greatly impairing neural excitability (Fig. 1A, B). With deeper chloralosane, slow waves

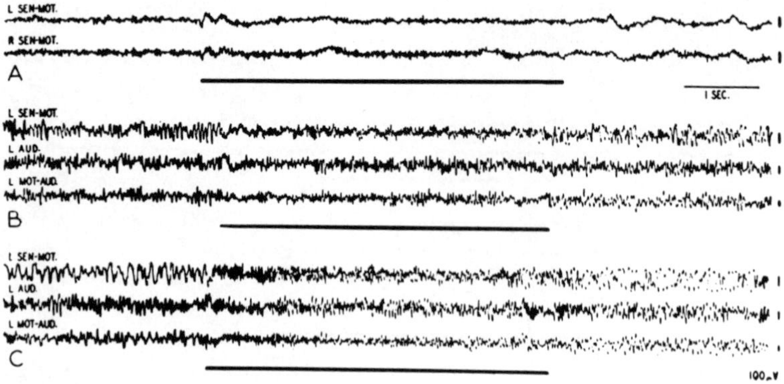

Fig. 2. Effect of reticular stimulation on electrocortical activity of the unanesthetized "encéphale isolé." *A-C.* Left bulbo-reticular stimulation (3 V, 300/sec.) is without effect upon the fully activated cortex (*A*), but evokes characteristic low-voltage fast activity when spontaneous synchrony is present (*B* and *C*).

were blocked, but low-voltage fast activity was not elicited (Fig. 1C, D).

The response was a generalized one, being observed in the sensory-motor cortex (Fig. 1), where it was often most pronounced, and in the visual (Fig. 1C) and auditory (Fig. 2B, C) cortical areas as well. With minimal reticular stimulation, alterations were best obtained in the ipsilateral hemisphere and were sometimes limited to it (Fig. 1D).

The response was readily obtained with low intensities of

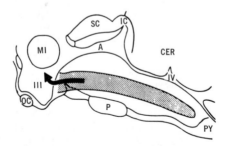

Fig. 3. Reconstruction of midsagittal plane of cat's brain stem upon which is projected, with cross-lining, the distribution of the ascending reticular activating system. Abbreviations are as follows: A, aqueduct; CER, cerebellum; IC, interior colliculus; MI, massa intermedia; OC, optic chiasma; P, pons; PY, pyramidal crossing; SC, superior colliculus; III, third ventricle; IV, fourth ventricle.

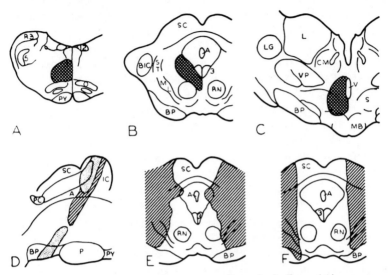

Fig. 4. A-C. Transverse sections through bulbar (*A*), mesen-cephalic (*B*), and caudal diencephalic (*C*) levels, with cross-lining indicating the area from which reticular responses were elicited with lowest voltage and without complications from exciting other ascend-ing or descending neural connections. D. Reconstruction of midsagit-tal plane of the midbrain upon which is projected, with stipple, the position of tectal and peduncular lesions which failed to block the EEG response to bulbo-reticular stimulation. Cross-lining marks the position of a tegmental lesion which abolished this response to bulbar stimulation. E-F. Transverse sections through the midbrain of two cats, showing the extent of lesions which interrupted the medial and lateral lemnisci and spinothalamic tracts, but which failed to impair the EEG response to bulbo-reticular stimulation. Abbreviations are as follows: A, aqueduct; BIC, brachium of inferior colliculus; BP, basis pedunculi; CM, centre médian; IC, inferior colliculus; L, lateral thalamic nucleus; LG, lateral geniculate body; MB, mammillary body; ML, medial lemniscus; O, inferior olive; P, pons; PY, pyramid; RB, restiform body; S, subthalamus; SC, superior colliculus; ST, spino-thalamic tract; VP, posterior part of ventral thalamic nucleus; 3, oculo-motor nucleus; 5, spinal fifth tract and nucleus; 12, hypoglossal nucleus.

reticular stimulation; voltages of 1–3 being usually employed. Brief shocks, with a falling phase of 1 msec. were used routinely and were as effective as longer lasting ones. Stimulus frequencies of 50/sec. were the lowest at which definite alterations could be elicited and the response was considerably improved by increas-ing frequencies up to 300/sec., which were regularly utilized.

Thus the EEG response to reticular excitation was best obtained with low-voltage, high-frequency stimulation.

These responses were not secondary to any peripheral effects of brain stem stimulation. By direct test they were independent of changes in respiration, blood pressure and heart rate. They occurred in the isolated brain after full atropinization and curarization. As will be seen, they were unquestionably mediated by neural connections between the reticular formation and the cerebral hemisphere.

The distribution of the excitable area is projected upon a reconstruction of the midsagittal plane in Figure 3, and includes the central core of the brain stem, extending from the bulbar reticular formation forward through the pontile and mesencephalic tegmentum into the caudal diencephalon. At the bulbar level, excitable points were distributed in the ventro-medial reticular formation and the area of their distribution coincided with that from which suppression of motor activity (Magoun & Rhines, 1946) could be elicited (Fig. 4A). Exploration of the overlying cerebellum has revealed excitable points in its fastigial nuclei, the responses possibly being mediated by connections of the roof nuclei with the brain stem reticular formation (Snider, Magoun, & McCulloch, 1949). In the midbrain, responses were obtained from the tegmentum bordering the central grey and extending in a paramedian position beneath it (Fig. 4B). In the caudal diencephalon, effective points were located near the midline in the dorsal hypothalamus and subthalamus (Fig. 4C). From this region, the excitable system is evidently distributed to the overlying thalamus, through which its effects are exerted upon the cortex, and some data bearing on its thalamic mediation will be given later.

The distribution of this ascending system within the midbrain was studied further by observing the effect of lesions here upon the EEG response to bulbo-reticular stimulation. Such responses were unimpaired following sections of the cerebral peduncles or tectum, but were blocked by injury to the mesencephalic tegmentum (Fig. 4D). Typical cortical responses to bulbo-reticular stimulation were still obtained after bilateral destruction of all laterally placed mesencephalic structures, including the medial and lateral lemnisci and the spinothalamic tracts (Fig. 4E, F), leaving intact only the paramedian region from which responses were obtained on direct stimulation (Fig. 4B).

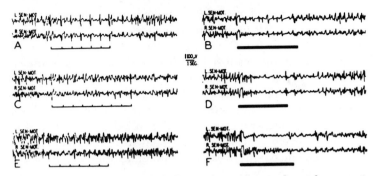

Fig. 5. Comparison of the effects of stimulating the right posterior column (*A, B*) and the left reticular activating system at bulbar (*C, D*) and midbrain (*E, F*) levels, under full chloralosane anesthesia. Stimulus frequency is 1/sec. in left records (*A, C, E*) and 300/sec. in right records (*B, D, F*); intensity is 3 V throughout. Single shock stimuli to the posterior column evoke sensory potentials in the cortex (*A*), not elicited by similar reticular stimulation (*C, E*). High-frequency stimulation of the posterior column causes some desynchronization of the EEG (*B*), but more pronounced effects are induced by reticular stimulation (*D, F*).

A series of ascending reticular relays is presumed to constitute the structural substrate of this brain stem activating system. That responses are not attributable to the antidromic excitation of corticifugal paths, or to the dromic stimulation of known afferent paths, bordering the reticular area, is indicated by a variety of data.

As regards the pyramidal tract, movements referable to its excitation never accompanied EEG responses to reticular stimulation, and the latter were still obtained from the bulbar level after section of the fibers of this tract in the basis pedunculi (Fig. 4D). Furthermore, single shock stimuli to effective reticular sites did not evoke antidromic potentials in the sensorymotor cortex (Fig. 5C, E) (Fig. 10A), nor did direct stimulation of the bulbar pyramid reproduce the EEG response to reticular stimulation.

A cortico-bulbo-reticular path from area 4-S is distributed to the excitable reticular area of the lower brain stem (Fig. 4A) (McCulloch, Graf, & Magoun, 1946), but it is similarly impossible to attribute the EEG responses to its antidromic stimulation. This path accompanies the pyramidal tract in the basis pedunculi (McCulloch, Graf, & Magoun, 1946) section of which, as noted, left reticular responses unimpaired. The absence of antidromic potentials in the sensory-motor cortex, on single shock stimuli to the bulbar reticular formation (Figs. 5C, 10A), might be explained by the small size of the suppressor areas in the cat (Garol, 1942), but a more likely possibility is that the unmyelinated terminals of·this extrapyramidal path were never excited with the low intensities of reticular stimulation employed in the present experiments. Reticular responses elicited from brain stem levels cephalad to the bulb are, moreover, impossible to explain on the basis of antidromic stimulation of this extrapyramidal pathway.

It is equivalently impossible to ascribe reticular responses to the dromic activation of known afferent pathways ascending to the cortex through the brain stem. The medial lemniscus is adjacent to the excitable reticular area through much of its course, and high-frequency stimulation of the lemniscal system, like that of the sciatic nerve (Gellhorn, 1947), exerts a desynchronizing influence upon the EEG (Fig. 5B). This influence is not as pronounced as that of the reticular formation, and higher voltages of stimulation are required to induce it than those which yield primary and secondary cortical sensory responses.

Three lines of evidence clearly show, however, that the desynchronizing influence of the reticular formation cannot be attributed to activation of the lemniscal system, either through physical spread of stimulating current, or by antidromic excitation of possible lemniscal collaterals to the brain stem reticular formation. First, single-shock stimuli to excitable reticular points at bulbar (Fig. 5C) or midbrain (Fig. 5E) levels never evoked potentials in the sensory-motor cortex, as was invariably the case when such shocks were applied to the lemniscal system (Fig. 5A), and this simple control was routinely applied throughout the work. Second, the distribution of the excitable reticular area was distinct from that of the course of the medial lemniscus through the brain stem (Fig. 4A-C). Third and finally, EEG responses to bulbar stimulation were unaffected by mesencephalic lesions which bilaterally interrupted the medial and lateral lemnisci and the spino-thalamic tracts (Fig. 4E, F).

Elimination of these possibilities and the distribution of excitable points through the brain stem both indicate that this response is mediated by a paramedian system of ascending reticular connections. Single-shock stimuli to effective bulbar sites do not evoke potentials at effective midbrain or diencephalic sites, however, suggesting that a number of relays are present and that the synapses involved are iterative in nature.

Having now described the desynchronization of the EEG induced by brain stem stimulation and presented evidence that this alteration results from exciting a system of reticular relays ascending to the diencephalon, attention may next be directed to the effect of reticular stimulation upon types of evoked activity in the cortex.

Effect upon evoked sensory potentials. In the chloralosane cat, a single afferent volley, initiated either by natural stimuli or by shocks to the sciatic nerve or posterior column, evokes primary and secondary[1] cortical potentials and sensory "after-discharge" succeeding them. The secondary response and after-discharge occur generally in the cortex and are readily observed in the EEG. During stimulation of the brain stem reticular formation, such secondary responses continued to be evoked by afferent volleys, usually without alteration (Fig. 6A), but sometimes with reduction of amplitude and simplification of potential form, particularly in cortical areas outside the sensory-motor region (Fig. 8B). Following conclusion of reticular stimulation, transient enhancement of the secondary response was occasionally observed (Fig. 6B).

The succeeding high-voltage slow waves, called sensory after-discharge, were invariably abolished during reticular stimulation (Fig. 6A-C). In full anesthesia, the cortical record then became flat between secondary responses (Fig. 6A, B), while, if anesthesia was light, low-voltage fast activity was present in these intervals (Fig. 6C). The abolition of sensory after-discharge might thus be simply another manifestation of the desynchronization of the EEG induced by brain stem stimulation. Such sensory after-discharge was not impaired, however, during cortical desynchronization induced by high-frequency stimulation of the sciatic nerve (Fig. 8D).

Effect upon evoked pyramidal discharge. In the chloralosane cat, afferent volleys arriving at the cortex there evoke pyramidal

[1] These "secondary potentials" resemble those of Forbes and Morison (1939) recorded, in deep barbiturate anesthesia, in and also outside the somatic receiving area and disappearing when the frequency of afferent stimuli rose above 5/sec. Since under chloralosane anesthesia, they are associated with pyramidal discharge they correspond to the "efferent waves" of Adrian (1941).

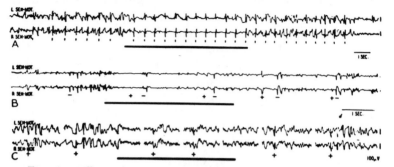

Fig. 6. Effect of reticular stimulation upon cortical sensory responses. *A.* Tapping skin of ankle. *B.* Make and break shocks to the sciatic nerve, under full chloralosane anesthesia as in *A. C.* Single shocks to the upper end of the posterior column, in "encéphale isolé" with 7 mgm. chloralosane/K. In each instance the evoked sensory spike is unaffected, while consequent after-discharge is abolished. Note low-voltage fast activity during reticular stimulation in *C*, with minimal anesthesia, and its absence in *A* and *B*, with full anasthesia.

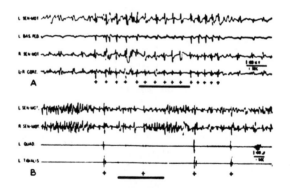

Fig. 7. Effect of reticular stimulation on pyramidal discharges and chloralosane jerks. *A.* Break shocks to sciatic nerve cause sensory cortical responses and corresponding pyramidal discharge, recording from the basis pedunculi (channel 2). The latter and sensory after-discharge are almost abolished by bulbo-reticular stimulation (3 V, 300/sec.), which leaves cortical sensory spikes unaffected. *B.* Break shocks to sciatic nerve cause chloralosane jerks, recorded in myograms of the quadriceps and tibialis (channels 3 and 4). Movement was abolished during stimulation of the midbrain tegmentum (3 V, 300/sec.), although cortical sensory potentials were still elicited. Such midbrain stimulation had no effect on spinal reflexes.

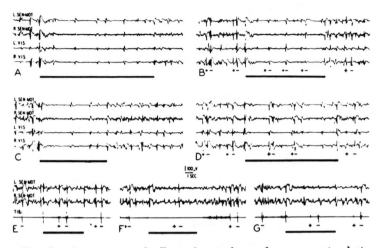

Fig. 8. Comparison of effect of reticular and sensory stimulation upon spontaneous and evoked electrocortical activity. A, C. Abolition of chloralosane waves during (A) bulbo-reticular stimulation (2 V, 300/sec.) and (C) sciatic nerve stimulation (3 V, 300/sec.). B, D. Sensory cortical potentials evoked by make and break shocks to sciatic nerve are reduced by bulbo-reticular stimulation at 2 V, 300/sec. (B), but not by stimulation of the contralateral sciatic nerve at 3 V, 300/sec (D). E, F. Chloralosane jerks evoked by break shocks to the sciatic nerve, and recorded in myograms of the tibialis anticus were augmented (E) by contralateral sciatic nerve stimulation (3 V, 300/sec.) and abolished (F) by stimulation of the midbrain tegmentum (3 V, 300/sec.). Such midbrain stimulation did not influence tibialis contraction in the ipsilateral flexor reflex (G).

discharges which are responsible for the jerky movements characteristic of this anesthesia (Adrian & Moruzzi, 1939). Although afferent volleys continued to reach the cortex during stimulation of the brain stem reticular formation, such pyramidal discharge, recorded from the basis pedunculi, was reduced or abolished (Fig. 7A) and contraction of leg muscles, induced by it, disappeared (Figs. 7B, 8F). This disappearance of movement was not attributable to spinal inhibition, for reflexly induced contraction of the same muscles was not affected by such midbrain stimulation (Fig. 8G). The movements induced by this pyramidal discharge were not reduced during desynchronization of cortical electrical activity by high-frequency sciatic stimulation (Fig. 8E), and the facilitation observed might have been due to spinal alterations. Whether the more pronounced cortical desynchro-

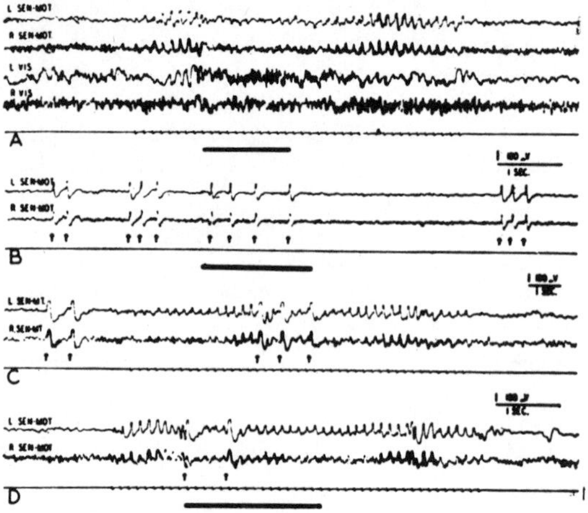

Fig. 9. Effect of reticular stimulation upon recruiting response and cortical strychnine spikes. *A.* Recruiting response to left thalamic stimulation (5 V, 7.5/sec.) in "encéphale isolé," abolished by left bulbo-reticular stimulation (2 V, 300/sec.). *B.* Strychnine spikes in both sensory-motor areas, induced by local application of strychnine to left motor cortex, were not decreased by left bulbo-reticular stimulation (2 V, 300/sec.). *C.* Decrease of recruiting response (evoked as in *A*), following interspersed strychnine spikes. *D.* Recruiting response (evoked as in *A*) markedly decreased by left bulbo-reticular stimulation (2 V, 300/sec.) which did not affect strychnine spikes.

nization resulting from reticular stimulation (Fig. 5B, D, F) opposed simultaneous discharge of a sufficient number of interneurons connecting the sensory with the motor cortex to prevent threshold activation of the cells of origin of the pyramidal tract, or whether these cells were somehow rendered incapable of being excited by afferent cortical volleys, during brain stem stimulation, remains unsettled.

Effect upon cortical strychnine spikes. The recurring spikes produced by local strychninization of the sensory-motor cortex were not prevented by exciting the brain stem reticular formation, nor was conduction of this discharge to the opposite cortex interfered with (Fig. 9B). Synchronized convulsive waves in a cortical fit, induced by supramaximal stimulation of the motor cortex, were similarly unaffected by bulbo-reticular stimulation.

Effect upon recruiting response. The cortical response to low-frequency stimulation of the diffuse thalamic projection system consists of a series of high-voltage slow waves, one for each

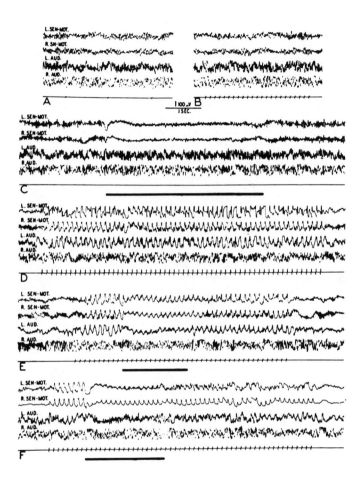

Fig. 10. Effect of reticular stimulation upon recruiting response. Left bulbo-reticular stimulation at 3 V in "encéphale isolé." *A.* Single shocks to bulb do not evoke cortical potentials. *B.* Bulbar stimulation at 7.5 sec. does not evoke recruiting response. *C.* Bulbar stimulation at 300/sec. activates EEG. *D.* Recruiting response evoked by left thalamic stimulation (5 V, 7.5 sec.). *E.* Recruiting response to left thalamic stimulation reduced or abolished by left bulbar stimulation (3 V, 300/sec.). *F.* Recruiting response to right thalamic stimulation reduced or abolished by left bulbar stimulation (3 V, 300/sec.).

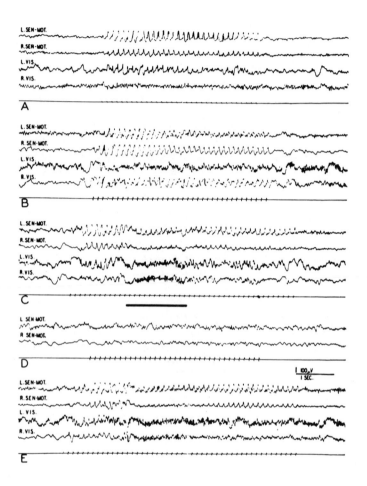

Fig. 11. Reproduction of reticular response by high-frequency stimulation of diffuse thalamic projection system. *A, B.* Recruiting responses induced by left (*A*) and right (*B*) thalamic stimulation (5 V, 7.5/sec.) in "encéphale isolé." *C.* Recruiting response to left thalamic stimulation reduced or abolished by stimulating the same right thalamic site as in *B*, but with 5 V, 300/sec. *D.* Right electrode lowered into subthalamus, the stimulation of which with 5 V, 7.5/sec., fails to induce a recruiting response. *E.* Subthalamic stimulation, with 5 V, 300/sec., reduces or abolishes the recruiting response to left thalamic stimulation.

shock, which recruit to a maximum during the initial period of stimulation (Figs. 10, 11, 12, 13) (Morison & Dempsey, 1942; Dempsey & Morison, 1942; Jasper & Droogleever-Fortuyn, 1946; Jasper, 1949). These waves may be confined to the ipsilateral hemisphere, but are usually present, though smaller, contralaterally as well. Depending upon the site of thalamic stimulation, they may be distributed anteriorly, posteriorly, or generally in the cortex.

In the unanesthetized "encéphale isolé," such a recruiting response, in both sensory-motor cortices and the ipsilateral auditory area (Fig. 10D), was either abolished or greatly reduced in all regions during intercurrent bulbo-reticular stimulation and recruited again upon its cessation (Fig. 10E, F). Exciting the rostral end of the reticular system in the subthalamus had a similar effect (Fig. 11E). Another instance is shown in Figure 9A, in which case strychnine was then applied locally to the cortex. The recruiting response was transiently abolished following strychnine spikes interspersed in its course, suggesting that identical cortical neurons were involved in these two activities (Fig. 9C). Subsequent repetition of reticular stimulation again opposed the recruiting response without, as noted above, altering the spikes induced by strychnine (Fig. 9D). It should be noted that low-frequency stimulation of the ascending reticular system, even in the subthalamus, did not itself induce a recruiting response (Figs. 10B, 11D).

Of the different types of evoked cortical activity upon which the effect of reticular stimulation was tested, certain ones, then, secondary sensory responses and strychnine spikes, exhibited little or no alteration, while others, sensory after-discharge and recruiting responses, were abolished. Of the two types of transcortical conduction observed, that from the sensory to the motor cortex, underlying the pyramidal discharge to afferent volleys under chloralosane anesthesia, was blocked, while the other, from a strychninized area of the cortex to the opposite cortex, was unaffected. It is not at present possible to decide whether any common factors underlie these similarities and differences.

Thalamic mediation of response. The generalized distribution of the alteration in the EEG induced by reticular stimulation has implications for the manner of its mediation by the thalamus. It seems likely that the reticular formation could exert its influence upon all parts of the cortex either by acting generally upon the thalamus or by influencing its diffuse projection system alone. At present, each possibility appears relevant, for there is indication both that the diffuse projection system is involved and that the reticular influence may not operate exclusively through it.

Evidence for the mediation of the reticular effect by the diffuse thalamic projection system is presented in Figure 12. The low-frequency stimulation of a portion of this system, on one side of the midline, induced recruiting responses not only in both cortices but in a corresponding region of the opposite thalamus as well (Fig. 12A). This evoked intrathalamic activity was then abolished during intercurrent bulbo-reticular stimulation and returned again upon its cessation (Fig. 12B, C), thus demonstrating a reticular influence upon the diffuse projection system at the thalamic level. It is uncertain whether the corresponding cortical changes were secondary to those in the thalamus in these instances, however, for though cortical recruiting responses were greatly reduced, small cortical waves were still present during reticular stimulation at a time when all synchronized activity was absent from the record of this thalamic sample (Fig. 12B, D: compare left cortical and thalamic channels). This same preparation was next lightly anesthetized with chloralosane, with the development of characteristic high-voltage slow waves both in the cortex and subcortically, within and between components of the diffuse thalamic projection system. Bulbo-reticular stimulation then desynchronized this activity as effectively in the electrothalamogram as in the EEG (Fig. 12D, E).

Further indication that the reticular influence may be mediated by the diffuse thalamic projection system is provided by comparing its effect upon the EEG with that of direct, intrathalamic stimulation of this system. Recruiting responses were obtained by successively stimulating portions of the diffuse system in the left (Fig. 11A) and right (Fig. 11B) sides of the thalamus. The recruiting response to left thalamic stimulation was then repeated and intercurrent stimulation of the same right thalamic site at 300/sec. abolished it as effectively (Fig. 11C) as did subsequent stimulation of the rostral end of the reticular system in the subthalamus (Fig. 11E). As regards the diffuse thalamic projection system, then, reticular stimulation has the same effect upon the electrogram of its thalamic components that it does upon the EEG, and this influence upon the EEG

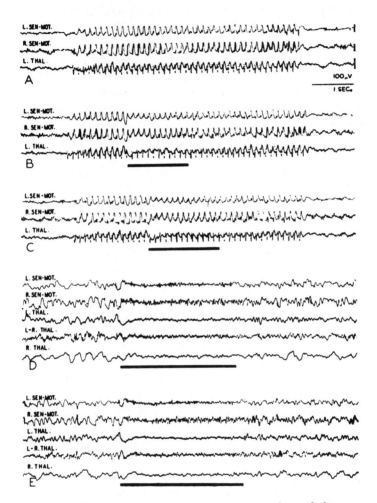

Fig. 12. Effect of reticular stimulation upon electrothalamogram of diffuse projection system. *A-C.* Unanesthetized "encéphale isolé." *A.* Recruiting response to right thalamic stimulation (8 V, 7.5/sec.) is recorded both from cortex and from and between thalamic sites yielding recruiting responses or response on stimulation. *B, C.* Recruiting response in cortex and left thalamus, evoked by right thalamic stimulation as in *A*, is reduced or abolished during left bulbo-reticular stimulation (3 V, 300/sec.). *D, E.* Same preparation with 7 mgm. chloralosane/K. Chloralosane waves recorded from cortex and from left thalamic site (channel 3), which itself yielded a recruiting stimulation, are abolished in all areas and replaced by low-voltage fast activity during left bulbo-reticular stimulation (2 V, 300/sec.).

can be reproduced by the direct high-frequency stimulation of this system within the thalamus.

Similar desynchronization, both of spontaneous activity and of the recruiting response has been observed, however, to result from high-frequency stimulation of the discretely projecting, posterior part of the ventral thalamic nucleus, and the effect was generalized in the cortex. It remains for further study to determine whether such responses were mediated by direct cortical projections or, as seems more likely, through other subcortical systems.

After ipsilateral destruction of the intralaminar thalamic region, bulbo-reticular stimulation still desynchronized the EEG bilaterally and as markedly as in initial controls. After extending the lesion until the massa intermedia and intralaminar regions of the thalamus were destroyed bilaterally, bulbar stimulation still seemed to have some effect upon the EEG, but cortical activity was then so reduced that it was difficult to draw conclusions concerning the signficance of the results. These findings only serve to introduce the problem of thalamic mediation of the lower brain stem influence upon the EEG, and much added study will be necessary to clarify this subject.

The reticular effect and arousal reactions. In the acute study of arousal reactions, anesthesia cannot be employed, for its major action is to block them, nor is the unanesthetized "encéphale isolé" suitable, for its EEG is typically activated and only rarely exhibits spontaneous synchrony. In the latter preparation, however, recruiting responses sometimes provide a background of cortical activity upon which the arousal effect of natural stimuli can be tested. Figure 13 shows a series of such instances, in which the high-voltage slow waves of the recruiting response were abolished and replaced by low-voltage fast activity, during loud whistling (A), rubbing the nose (B), and blowing air on the head (C) and eyes (D). Indistinguishable from these changes to natural stimuli, except for somewhat faster low-voltage activity, were those produced by electrical stimulation of the posterior column (E) and bulbar reticular formation (F).

Such abolition of recruiting responses by natural or bulbar stimulation was observed only when the frequency and intensity of thalamic stimulation yielding the recruiting response was just above threshold, and in some cases reticular stimulation could still abolish the recruiting response at a time when natural

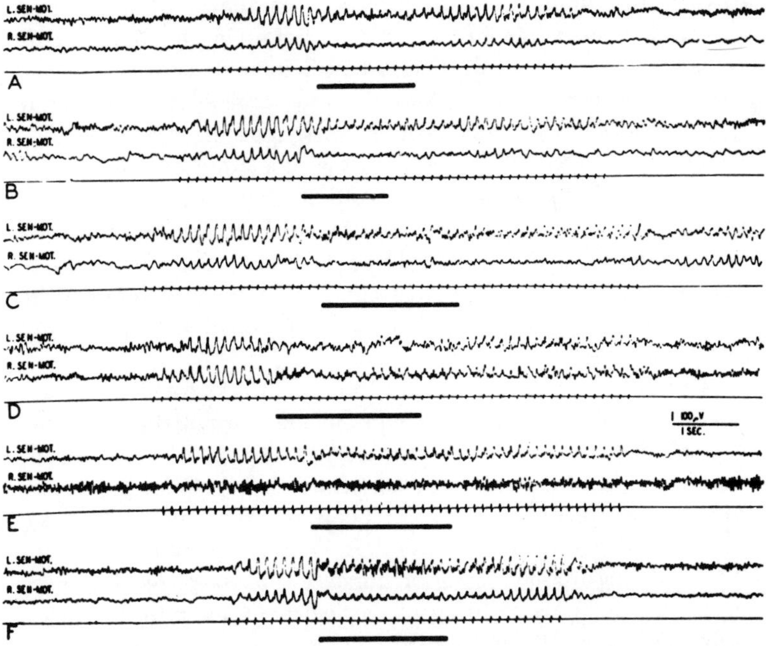

Fig. 13. Abolition of recruiting responses by sensory and reticular stimulation. Recruiting responses, evoked by left thalamic stimulation (5 V, 300/sec.) in an "encéphale isolé," identically reduced or abolished by loud whistling (*A*), blowing air on head (*B*), rubbing nose (*C*), blowing air on eyes (*D*), stimulating the right posterior column at 2 V, 300/sec. (*E*), and stimulating the left bulbar reticular formation at 2 V, 300/sec. (*F*).

stimuli were ineffective. Because of these and other difficulties in securing stable testing conditions, attempted repetition of arousing natural stimuli after differential interruption of ascending sensory and reticular paths in the anterior brain stem was abandoned in favor of chronic preparations.

DISCUSSION

The evidence given above points to the presence in the brain stem of a system of ascending reticular relays, whose direct stimulation activates or desynchronizes the EEG, replacing high-voltage slow waves with low-voltage fast activity. This effect is exerted generally upon the cortex and is mediated, in part, at least, by the diffuse thalamic projection system. Portions of this activating system, chiefly its representation in the basal diencephalon, have previously been identified.

In the pioneer studies of Morison and his associates, in which the foundation for so much current work upon the EEG was laid, hypothalamic, subthalamic and medial thalamic excitation was found, in 1943, to suppress intermittent Dial bursts without affecting other types of cortical activity, such as responses to sensory stimulation (Morison, Finley & Lothrop, 1943: Dempsey & Morison, 1943). The effect was considered to be inhibitory in nature and was attributed to the excitation of afferent pathways simply passing through this region.

Two years later, Murphy and Gellhorn (1945) found this suppression of Dial bursts on hypothalamic stimulation, to be accompanied by dispersal of strychnine spikes and by prolonged increase in the frequency and amplitude of low-voltage, background, electrocortical activity. They pointed out that these latter alterations were excitatory or facilitatory in nature, and attributed the disappearance of bursts to an associated lessened degree of synchrony of firing of cortical neurons, rather than to inhibition. Connections from the hypothalamus to the dorsomedial and intralaminar thalamic region, and thence to cortex, were suggested to provide the channels by way of which these effects were produced and, though the study was undertaken principally to elucidate hypothalamic facilitation of the motor cortex, the generalized distribution of the EEG changes was emphasized.

More recently still, Jasper and his associates (1948) observed a generalized acceleration of spontaneous electrocortical activity, simulating an arousal or waking reaction, from stimulation of the periaqueductal portion of the midbrain, the posterior hypothalamus, and the massa intermedia of the thalamus; and Ward (1949) obtained a prolonged generalized increase in both voltage and frequency of the EEG following stimulation of the bulbar reticular formation.

While interpretation of these findings has been varied, their basic similarity can leave little doubt that each of these investigators has dealt with manifestations of the same system as that described above. The present work thus confirms, extends, and interrelates these earlier contributions and, from the mass of observations brought to bear upon it, the existence of this brain stem activating system now seems firmly established.

In discussing the general significance of these findings for electroencephalography, attention should certainly be focussed upon the arousal reaction. The breaking-up of synchronous cortical discharge by afferent stimulation, first observed by Berger (1930) as alpha blockade on opening the lids, and since found to be a common response to any type of afferent stimulation, is currently attributed to the desynchronizing action of afferent volleys arriving directly at the receiving areas of the cerebral cortex (Adrian & Matthews, 1931; Adrian, 1947; Bremer, 1938, 1944; Walter & Walter, 1949). A number of relevant observations are difficult to explain on this basis, however.

More than a decade ago, Ectors (1936) and Rheinberger and Jasper (1932) observed that serially repeated stimulation soon failed to induce activation, though afferent volleys presumably continued to reach the cortex, and it was noted that, in order to be effective in this regard such stimuli must arouse the subject to alertness or attention. In addition, when an activation pattern was so induced, it was by no means confined to the receiving area of the afferent system stimulated (see also Bremer, 1943), nor did it appear first in this area and radiate from it. Whether somatic, auditory or, to a lesser extent, visual stimulation was employed, when an arousal reaction was evoked, it appeared simultaneously in all parts of the cortex and often continued for considerable periods in it after afferent stimulation had ceased.

More recently, Monnier's (1949) analysis of the sequence of EEG events induced by visual stimulation in man has shown that alpha blockade is not initiated for a considerable period after the electrocortical changes evoked by the afferent volley are completed, and its prolonged latency might more easily be explained by invoking a subsidiary mechanism than by accounting for it through direct cortical action. Furthermore, the generalized arousal reaction to vestibular stimulation has been shown by Gerebtzoff (1940) to be still elicitable after ablation of the cortical receiving area for this afferent system.

In the present experiments, typical EEG arousal reactions have been reproduced by stimulating the brain stem reticular formation, without exciting classical sensory paths. Crucial evidence that the reticular formation is involved in the arousal reaction to natural stimuli may not yet be obtained but, in addition to being suggested by the data at hand, such a possibility might offer an explanation for the failure of afferent stimuli to evoke arousal from somnolence, lethargy, or coma, resulting from injury to the upper brain stem, which left the major sensory paths to the cortex intact (Ingram, Barris, & Ranson, 1936; Ranson, 1939; Magoun, 1948). A conception of the arousal reaction in which collaterals from sensory paths first activated the brain stem reticular formation and exerted their influence upon cortical electrical activity indirectly through it, seems a logical postulate from all these observations, and was, in fact, proposed as long ago as 1940 by Gerebtzoff to account for his observations to which reference was made above.

The proposed participation of the brain stem activating system in the arousal reaction, if established, might represent an aspect of its function concerned with alerting the cortex to abrupt and more or less pronounced alterations in the external environment. It may next be proposed that the presence of a steady background of less intense activity within this cephalically directed brain stem system, contributed to either by liminal inflows from peripheral receptors or preserved intrinsically, may be an important factor contributing to the maintenance of the waking state, and that absence of such activity in it may predispose to sleep.

Bremer's fundamental discovery (1935, 1938) that the EEG of the unanesthetized cerebrum, isolated from the rest of the nervous system by mesencephalic transection, resembled that of an intact brain in natural sleep or under barbiturate anesthesia, led him to the conclusion that sleep is the result of deafferentation of the cerebral cortex. Afferent impulses from olfactory and visual receptors are still accessible to such a "cerveau isolé," and more recent work has indicated that sleep changes in the EEG are best produced by basal diencephalic injury (Lindsley, Bowden, & Magoun, 1949). But putting these qualifications aside, it should be pointed out that at the time Bremer's discovery was made, classical sensory paths were the only known connections ascending through the midbrain, to the interruption of which the ensuing sleep changes in the "cerveau isolé" could be attributed. The present identification of a second, parallel system of ascending reticular relays, whose direct stimulation induces EEG changes characteristic of wakefulness, now raises a possible alternative interpretation of Bremer's observations, for the obvious question arises: Is the production of sleep in the cerebrum, following mesencephalic transection, to be attributed to deafferentation in the strict sense, or to the elimination of the waking influence of the ascending reticular activating system? Two lines of evidence favor this latter possibility.

As regards barbiturate sleep, Forbes, Battista, & Chatfield (1949) have recently pointed out that the ready conduction of afferent impulses to the cortex under deep barbiturate anesthesia is inconsistent with the view that the sleep-inducing properties of these drugs depend upon functional deafferentiation.[2] Conversely, it has been found in the present study that under barbiturate anesthesia, bulbo-reticular stimulation is much less effective in activating the EEG than in a chloralosane or unanesthetized preparation. The fact that hypothalamic stimulation is effective under such anesthesia (Morison, Finley, & Lothrop, 1943; Murphy & Gellhorn, 1945; Jasper, Hunter, & Knighton, 1948) suggests that the blocking of reticular relays within the brain stem may be involved in the production of sleep by barbiturates.

As regards sleep induced by rostral brain stem injury, prolonged somnolence has followed chronic lesions in the basal diencephalon and anterior midbrain which did not involve afferent pathways to the cortex, but which were placed medial and ventral to them in the region of distribution of the ascending reticular activating system (Ingram, Barris & Ranson, 1936; Ranson, 1939), and similar results have followed injury to this region from tumors (Fulton & Bailey, 1929) or encephalitis (von Economo, 1918; Richter & Traut, 1940) in man.

Though somnolence was incontestable, EEG studies were not undertaken in the animals or patients to which reference is made, but more recently Ingram, Knott, & Wheatley (1949) have studied alterations in the EEG following chronic, experimental hypothalamic lesions, and the results of acute basal diencephalic and lower brain stem destruction are reported in the succeeding paper (Lindsley, Bowden, & Magoun, 1949). In the latter investigation, sleep changes in the EEG, identical with those of bar-

[2] This argument would appear to apply only to the conduction of a single afferent volley. W. H. Marshall (*J. Neurophysiol.*, 1941, 4, 25-43) has observed impairment of conduction of repeated afferent volleys to the cortex under nembutal anesthesia, due to great prolongation of thalamic recovery time.

biturate anesthesia, resulted from basal diencephalic and anterior midbrain lesions which spared sensory pathways to the cortex, but interrupted the rostral distribution of the ascending reticular activating system. Conversely, extensive deafferentiation of the cortex, by section of ascending pathways in the lateral portion of each side of the midbrain, together with bilateral interruption of the optic and olfactory tracts, failed to induce such alterations.

The conception of sleep as a functional deafferentation of the cerebrum is not opposed by this evidence if the term "deafferentation" is broadened to include interruption of the ascending influence of the brain stem reticular activating system, the contribution of which to wakefulness now seems more important than that conducted to the cortex over classical sensory paths.

SUMMARY

1. Stimulation of the reticular formation of the brain stem evokes changes in the EEG, consisting of abolition of synchronized discharge and introduction of low-voltage fast activity in its place, which are not mediated by any of the known ascending or descending paths that traverse the brain stem. The alteration is a generalized one but is most pronounced in the ipsilateral hemisphere and, sometimes, in its anterior part.

2. This response can be elicited by stimulating the medial bulbar reticular formation, pontile and midbrain tegmentum, and dorsal hypothalamus and subthalamus. The bulbar effect is due to ascending impulses relayed through these more cephalic structures. The excitable substrate possesses a low threshold and responds best to high frequencies of stimulation.

3. Some background synchrony of electrocortical activity is requisite for manifestation of the response. In the "encéphale isolé," reticular stimulation has no additional effect upon the fully activated EEG. With synchrony, in spontaneous drowsiness or light chloralosane anesthesia, the effect of reticular stimulation is strikingly like Berger's alpha wave blockade, or any arousal reaction. In full chloralosane anesthesia, high-voltage slow waves are blocked but no increase in lower amplitude, fast activity occurs. With barbiturate anesthesia, the reticular response is difficult to elicit or is abolished.

4. In the chloralosane preparation, the secondary cortical response evoked by a sensory volley is generally unaffected by

reticular stimulation. Consequent sensory after-discharge is abolished, however, as is pyramidal tract discharge and jerky movements referable to it. Outside the sensory receiving area, secondary responses themselves may be reduced or prevented.

5. The convulsive spikes produced by local strychnine and those of a fit following supramaximal cortical excitation, are not decreased by stimulating the reticular formation.

6. The cortical recruiting response induced by low frequency stimulation of the diffuse thalamic projection system is reduced or abolished by reticular stimulation.

7. There is some indication that the cortical effect of reticular stimulation may be mediated by this diffuse thalamic projection system, for synchronized activity within it is similarly prevented by reticular excitation, and direct high-frequency stimulation of this system, within the thalamus, reproduces the reticular response. It is possible, however, that other mechanisms may be involved in its mediation.

8. The reticular response and the arousal reaction to natural stimuli have been compared in the "encéphale isolé," in which EEG synchrony was present during spontaneous relaxation or was produced by recruiting mechanisms, and the two appear identical.

9. The possibility that the cortical arousal reaction to natural stimuli is mediated by collaterals of afferent pathways to the brain stem reticular formation, and thence through the ascending reticular activating system, rather than by intracortical spread following the arrival of afferent impulses at the sensory receiving areas of the cortex, is under investigation.

10. The possibility is considered that a background of maintained activity within this ascending brain stem activating system may account for wakefulness, while reduction of its activity either naturally, by barbiturates, or by experimental injury and disease, may respectively precipitate normal sleep, contribute to anesthesia, or produce pathological somnolence.

CONCLUSIONS

Experiments on cats have identified a cephalically directed brain stem system, the stimulation of which desynchronizes and activates the EEG, replacing high-voltage slow waves with low-voltage fast activity.

This system is distributed through the central core of the brain stem and appears to comprise a series of reticular relays ascending to the basal diencephalon. Its effects are exerted generally upon the cortex and are mediated, in part, at least, by the diffuse thalamic projection system.

Possible implication of this system in the arousal reaction to afferent stimulation and in the maintenance of wakefulness is discussed.

REFERENCES

Adrian, E. D. Afferent discharges to the cerebral cortex from peripheral sense organs. *J. Physiol.*, 1941, **100**, 159-191.

Adrian, E. D. *The physical background of perception.* Oxford: Clarendon, 1947.

Adrian, E. D., & Matthews, B. H. C. The interpretation of potential waves in the cortex. *J. Physiol.*, 1934, **81**, 440-471.

Adrian, E. D., & Matthews, B. H. C. The Berger rhythm: potential changes from the occipital lobes in man. *Brain*, 1934, **57**, 355-385.

Adrian, E. D., & Moruzzi, G. Impulses in the pyramidal tract. *J. Physiol.*, 1939, **97**, 153-199.

Berger, H. Über das Elektrenkephalogramm des Menschen. II. *J. Physiol. Neurol.*, 1930, **40**, 160-179.

Bremer, F. Cerveau isolé et physiologie du sommeil. *C. R. Soc. Biol., Paris*, 1935, **118**, 1235-1242.

Bremer, F. L'activité cérébrale et le problème physiologique du sommeil. *Boll. Soc. It. Biol. Sp.*, 1938, **13**, 271-290.

Bremer, F. *L'activité électrique de l'écorce cérébrale.* Paris: Hermann, 1938.

Bremer, F. Etude oscillographique des réponses sensorielles de l'aire acoustique corticale chez le chat. *Arch. Int. Physiol.*, 1943, **53**, 53-103.

Bremer, F. Aspect théorique de l'électro-encéphalographie. *Arch. Néerl. Physiol.*, 1944-47, **28**, 481-482.

Dempsey, E. W., & Morison, R. S. The production of rhythmically recurrent cortical potentials after localized thalamic stimulation. *Amer. J. Physiol.*, 1942, **135**, 293-300.

Dempsey, E. W., & Morison, R. S. The electrical activity of a thalamocortical relay system. *Amer. J. Physiol.*, 1943, **138**, 283-298.

Economo, C. von. *Die Encephalitis lethargica.* Vienna: Deuticke, 1918.

Ectors, L. Étude de L'activité électrique du cortex cérébrale chez le lapin non narcotisé ni curarisé. *Arch. Int. Physiol.*, 1936, **43**, 267-298.

Forbes, A., Battista, A. F., Chatfield, P. O., & Garcia, I. P. Refractory phase in cerebral mechanisms. *EEG clin. Neurophysiol.*, 1949, **1**, 141-193.

Forbes, A., & Morison, B. R. Cortical responses to sensory stimulation under deep barbiturate narcosis. *J. Neurophysiol.*, 1939, **2**, 112-128.

Fulton, J. F., & Bailey, P. Tumors in the region of the third ventricle: Their diagnosis and relation to pathological sleep. *J. nerv. ment. Dis.*, 1929, **69**, 1-25, 145-164, 261-272.

Garol, H. W. The functional organization of the sensory cortex of the cat. *J. Neuropathol. exp. Neurol.*, 1942, **1**, 320-329.

Gellhorn, E. Effect of afferent impulses on cortical suppressor areas. *J. Neurophysiol.*, 1947, **10**, 125-132.

Gerebtzoff, M. A. Récherches sur la projection corticale du labyrinthique sur l'activite electrique de l'ecorce cerebrale. *Arch. int. Physiol.*, 1940, **50**, 59-99.

Hunter, J., & Jasper, H. Reactions of unanesthetized animals to thalamic stimulation. *Trans. Amer. neurol. Ass.*, 1948, **73**, 171-172.

Ingram, W. R., Barris, R. W., & Ranson, S. W. Catalepsy, an experimental study. *Arch. Neurol. Psychiat., Chicago*, 1936, **35**, 1175-1197.

Ingram, W. R., Knott, J. R., & Wheatley, M. D. Electroencephalograms of cats with hypothalamic lesions. III. *Meeting Amer. EEG Soc.*, 1949.

Japer, H. H., & Droogleever-Fortuyn, J. Experimental studies on the functional anatomy of petit mal epilepsy. *Res. Publ. Ass. nerv. ment. Dis.*, 1947, **26**, 272-298.

Jasper, H., Hunter, J., & Knighton, R. Experimental studies of thalamocortical systems. *Trans. Amer. neurol. Ass.*, 1948, **73**, 120-212.

Lindsley, D. B., Bowden, J., & Magoun, H. W. Effect upon the EEG of acute injury to the brain stem activating system. *EEG clin. Neurophysiol.*, 1949, **1**, 475-486.

Magoun, H. W. Coma following midbrain lesions in the monkey. *Anat. Rec.*, 1948, **100**, 120.

Magoun, H. W., & Rhines, R. An inhibitory mechanism in the bulbar reticular formation. *J. Neurophysiol.*, 1946, **9**, 165-171.

McCulloch, W. S., Graf, C., & Magoun, H. W. A cortico-bulbo-reticular pathway from area 4-S. *J. Neurophysiol.*, 1946, **9**, 127-132.

Monnier, M. Retinal time, retino-cortical time and motor reaction time in man. III. *Meeting Amer. EEG Soc.*, 1949.

Morison, R. S., & Dempsey, E. W. A study of thalamocortical relations. *Amer. J. Physiol.*, 1942, **135**, 281-292.

Morison, R. S., Finley, K. H., & Lothrop, G. N. Influence of basal forebrain areas on the electrocorticogram. *Amer. J. Physiol.*, 1943, **139**, 410-416.

Murphy, J. P., & Gellhorn, E. The influence of hypothalamic stimulation on cortically induced movements and on action potentials of the cortex. *J. Neurophysiol.*, 1945, **8**, 339-364.

Ranson, S. W. Somnolence caused by hypothalamic lesions in the monkey. *Arch. Neurol. Psychiat., Chicago*, 1939, **41**, 1-23.

Rheinberger, M. B., & Jasper, H. H. Electrical activity of the cerebral cortex in the unanesthetized cat. *Amer. J. Physiol.*, 1937, **119**, 186-196.

Richter, R. B., & Traut, E. F. Chronic encephalitis. Pathological report of a case with protracted somnolence. *Arch. Neurol. Psychiat., Chicago*, 1940, **44**, 848-866.

Snider, R. S., Magoun, H. W., & McCulloch, W. S. A suppressor cerebello-bulbo-reticular pathway from anterior lobe and paramedian lobules. *Fed. Proc.*, 1947, **6**, 207.

Walter, W. G., & Walter, V. J. The electrical activity of the brain. *Ann. Rev. Physiol.*, 1949, **11**, 199-230.

Ward, A. A. The relationship between the bulbar-reticular suppressor region and the EEG. *EEG clin. Neurophysiol.*, 1949, **1**, 120.

[ADDENDA FROM THE ORIGINAL PRINTING OF THIS ARTICLE: IN REFERENCE TO THE AUTHORS: *Department of Anatomy, Northwestern University Medical School. Aided by a grant from the National Institute of Mental Health, U. S. Public Health Service.* IN REFERENCE TO MORUZZI: *University of Pisa, Italy. Visiting Professor of Neurology, supported by the Rockefeller Foundation.*]

HYPOTHALAMIC LESIONS AND ADIPOSITY IN THE RAT ❧

A. W. Hetherington and S. W. Ranson

THE ASSOCIATION of lesions at the base of the diencephalon with abnormal obesity in both man and animals has been observed many times. As a result of these observations it is quite generally believed that some structure, either neural or glandular, situated in this region is involved in the metabolism of fats. There is, however, the most emphatic disagreement concerning the nature of the regulatory mechanism.

Little advantage would accrue at this time from an extensive review of the controversy between those who have championed an hypophysial origin of pathological adiposity as opposed to others who have maintained the primacy of hypothalamic factors. It may be worth while, however, to mention briefly those principal contributions which have suggested the importance of the hypothalamus.

Shortly after Fröhlich (1901) published his well-known description of a still-living patient, Erdheim (1904) announced that study of the pathology at the base of the brain of a number of cases whose history was known indicated that injury to the hypothalamus and not to the hypophysis must have been re-

REPRINTED FROM *The Anatomical Record*, 78:149-172. COPYRIGHT © 1942 BY THE WISTAR INSTITUTE OF ANATOMY AND BIOLOGY.

sponsible for the symptoms. From the experimental side Aschner (1912) soon added evidence that at least in adult dogs something more than hypophysectomy seemed to be necessary to produce marked obesity. Other workers, including Bailey and Bremer (1921), Camus and Roussy (1922), Grafe and Grünthal (1929), and Biggart and Alexander (1939) have insisted that obesity can be produced in dogs by hypothalamic lesions in the presence of an intact anterior lobe. Smith (1927) has made the same observation for the rat.

The considerable confusion still persisting regarding the relative importance of the hypothalamic and the hypophysial factors in pathological obesity of this type has made a reexamination of the whole question seem desirable. There appears, moreover, to be no clear-cut notion, even on the part of those who have supported its primary role, as to exactly what structures in the hypothalamus must be destroyed to obtain this derangement of fat metabolism. In an effort to bring these problems a step nearer solution the following experiments were begun. Two preliminary reports covering a portion of this work have already appeared (Hetherington and Ranson, 1939; Hetherington, 1940a).

METHODS

Two different groups of animals have been used. One group consisted of young albino rats weighing from 90 to 110 grams at the time of operation. The other group was made up of rats definitely past the age when sex maturity appears: the females weighed about 175 grams and the males over 250 grams when operated. All animals of the series were operated under Evipal (0.1 gram per kilogram of body weight) anesthesia. Lesions were placed in the hypothalamus by the Horsley-Clarke technic, employing Clark's (1939) modification of the stereotaxic instrument which enables one to use the apparatus on rats. No chart series of the rat hypothalamus has as yet been made; and since a separate chart series would be necessary for each new variation in weight-range it has been found more practical to determine any desired set of Horsley-Clarke coordinates by operating a couple of animals of a given size and examining the lesions macroscopically at once. Following this practice we have in all rats selected coordinates which would result in the orienting of a lesion on each side at the base of the diencephalon, at a rostro-caudal level about opposite the attachment of the stalk to the hypothalamus, and at a point about midway between the mid-line and the optic tracts. From animal to animal a certain amount of variation in the precise location of the lesion is to be expected, but this is seldom so great as to be an inconvenience. The damage done has always consisted of two electrolytic lesions on each side, one a millimeter ahead of the other—four lesions in all —and at each point of insertion a current of 2 milliamperes applied for 20 seconds has been used. The pair of lesions on either side invariably fuses into one large area of damage.

Animals so operated recover promptly from the anesthesia, but display as a rule a very stormy convalescent period. Often they will not eat or drink for a number of days and must be fed forcibly, and kept from being dehydrated by subcutaneous injections of physiological salt solution. Temperature regulatory mechanisms appear usually to be disturbed as well, and the animals must be kept in a rather warm room. After a week or so, however, those animals which survive (and more than three-quarters do) commonly begin to eat and get along very well in comfortably warm quarters without much further attention.

All the animals and their littermate controls have been fed the stock diet used in the laboratory, namely, bread and milk and cracked corn, with frequent additions of meat, carrots, and some leafy vegetables. Food is present in the individual cages most of the time, and water is supplied freely.

The nose-anus and tail lengths of each animal were determined under anesthesia at the times of operation and of sacrifice, and the animals were weighed at weekly intervals during the experimental period. This period was never less than 3 months, and a number of the rats have been allowed to survive much longer. The animals were killed by decapitation. The brains were then removed and placed in formalin, the hypophyses in Champy's fixative, and the thyroids, adrenals, and gonads in Zenker-formol (Helly's) fixative. On occasion various other tissues have been removed for special study. Some of the brains were embedded in paraffin, sectioned at 15μ, and every fifth section stained for cells with cresyl violet. For some of these animals a parallel series of sections stained for myelin sheaths by Weil's method was prepared. Others of the brains were embedded in nitro-

TABLE 1. SHOWING THE DATA ON THE OBESE RATS

Rat No.	Sex	Op. or Con.	TIME OF OPERATION			Max. Wt.
			Age	Wt.	Length	
Rb- 1	M	O	47	95	164	447
Rb- 2	M	C	47	85	163	319
Rb- 3	F	O	47	106	170	398
Rb- 4	F	C	47	82	155	177
Rb- 5	M	O	45	92	158	576
Rb- 6	M	O	45	93	164	484
Rb- 7	M	O	45	90	162	447
Rb- 8	M	C	45	88	162	407
Rb- 9	M	O	52	112	170	475
Rb-10	M	C	52	92	161	365
Rb-11	F	O	52	97	166	339
Rb-12	F	O	52	92	160	387
Rb-13	F	C	52	86	156	203
Rb-14	M	O	67	109	173	460
Rb-15	M	O	67	105	168	447
Rb-16	M	O	67	98	166	521
Rb-17	M	O	67	96	168	372
Rb-18	M	C	67	92	165	404
Rb-25	M	O	141	242	225	508
Rb-26	M	O	141	250	224	454
Rb-27	M	O	141	256	224	451
Rb-28	M	C	141	245	220	310
Rb-29	M	O	117	261	227	377
Rb-31	M	C	117	270	229	407
Rb-32	M	O	96	259	226	587
Rb-33	M	C	96	290	231	431
Rb-34	F	O	125	171	200	437
Rb-35	F	C	125	170	205	220
Rb-36	F	O	105	185	200	444
Rb-37	F	O	105	177	198	430
Rb-38	F	O	105	182	199	413
Rb-39	F	C	105	176	203	242

TIME OF AUTOPSY Days Post-Op.	Wt.	Length	INHIBITION OF GROWTH	DEGREE OF ADIPOSITY	Rat No.
83	447	219	Slight	Marked	Rb- 1
84	319	235	—	—	Rb- 2
85	371	213	None	Marked	Rb- 3
85	177	201	—	—	Rb- 4
198	576	—	—	Marked	Rb- 5
274	370	228	Slight	Moderate	Rb- 6
151	423	198	Marked	Moderate	Rb- 7
276	386	257	—	—	Rb- 8
185	375	—	—	Marked	Rb- 9
185	365	—	—	—	Rb-10
140	328	201	None	Marked	Rb-11
104	299	196	None	Marked	Rb-12
140	203	200	—	—	Rb-13
189	452	—	—	Marked	Rb-14
251	395	227	Slight	Moderate	Rb-15
192	521	—	—	Marked	Rb-16
167	370	—	Marked	Marked	Rb-17
251	404	240	—	—	Rb-18
246	480	240	Slight	Marked	Rb-25
139	315	226	Slight	Marked	Rb-26
206	451	236	Slight	Moderate	Rb-27
246	310	246	—	—	Rb-28
168	307	229	Slight	Moderate	Rb-29
168	407	251	—	—	Rb-31
209	576	238	Slight	Marked	Rb-32
209	429	250	—	—	Rb-33
193	388	213	None	Marked	Rb-34
193	220	214	—	—	Rb-35
85	405	213	None	Marked	Rb-36
179	395	—	—	Marked	Rb-37
188	321	215	None	Marked	Rb-38
188	241	216	—	—	Rb-39

cellulose, and sectioned at 40μ; these too were stained with cresyl violet and by Weil's method. The hypophyses and other glands are being saved for subsequent study.

RESULTS

Of a total of twenty-two animals operated so far twenty-one have displayed various grades of adiposity from moderate to marked. Twelve were of the group operated at about the beginning of sex maturity; these without exception became very fat. Ten underwent operation as adults, and it is in this group that the single nonobese rat falls. This exceptional animal was only recently sacrificed, and in consequence the lesion has not been studied in mircroscopic preparation. From the appearance of the base of the brain, however, the lesion was asymmetrical and too caudally placed.

Physical characteristics. The body weights and body lengths (nose-anus) of the twenty-one fat animals and their controls at the time of operation and at the time of autopsy are summarized in Table 1. The maximum weight of all of the individuals during that interval is also recorded. Length figures for some of the animals are lacking because the rats died during the summer vacation and could not be properly examined.

As a rule the younger rats showed 2 or 3 weeks postoperatively the onset of a rapidly progressing obesity. Several, such as Rb-7 and Rb-15, took a couple of months to build up a visibly excessive amount of body fat, and in these animals the level of adiposity attained never became as impressive as in the others, even though a longer interval elapsed before death. The major portion of the adiposity in these fat rats appeared during the first 3 or 4 months of the postoperative period. After that time there was a gradual levelling-off of the animals' weight curve, until weight increases over a given interval were of the same order as, or even smaller than, those of the controls. The increases in body weight and length for four of the obese rats and their controls have been shown graphically in Figures 1 to 4. Rats Rb-1, Rb-3, and Rb-11 were operated at an age of about 7 weeks; Rb-32 at about 14 weeks. The parallel straight lines above the weight curves show the nose-anus length of the specimens at operation and at death. The upper, shorter pair represents, of course, the lengths at the earlier date.

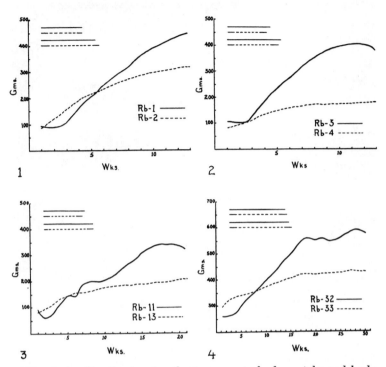

Figs. 1–4. Graphs showing the increases in body weight and body length of four obese rats (in solid lines) and their controls (in broken lines). Body length is represented by the pairs of lines above each pair of weight curves, and is given at the times of operation (the upper pair) and of autopsy (the lower pair) only.

Among the adults adiposity was somewhat slower in becoming definite. One or two of the animals were noticeably large of girth at the end of the first month after operation, but several months were necessary for the remainder of the group to grow unmistakably obese. It may not be said, however, that the final level of adiposity was any less in the animals operated as adults than it was in those operated at the time of puberty. On the contrary, several of the older rats (Rb-32 and Rb-36) outweighed even the fattest of the younger series. Figure 5 is a picture of obese rat Rb-25, one of the older series, and its control.

Furthermore, when the obesity of any animal had been very rapidly established and had reached a very high level there seemed to develop at the same time a strikingly lowered vitality.

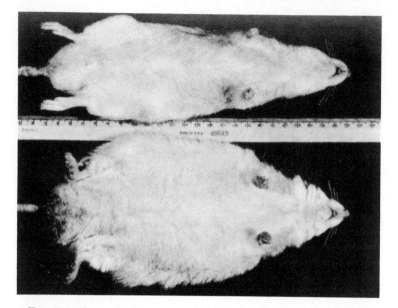

Fig. 5. Obese rat Rb-25, photographed at autopsy, 8 months after operation, and Rb-28, its control. Hypothalamic lesions were made at the age of 4½ months.

Sometimes without any other particularly obvious symptoms of disease such an animal would begin suddenly to lose weight, until after a couple of weeks perhaps 25% of the total would have been lost. Occasionally these cases have recovered spontaneously from their apparent illness and regained all of their weight and more, but the more usual outcome has been progressively greater morbidity and death. Often autopsy reveals nothing more serious than a slight cold to explain the rapid failure in health.

At first the only physical characteristics which distinguished the operated rats from their littermate controls were the appearance of paunchiness, and, often, the failure of the hair to grow back rapidly over the clipped area on the head. Later on, however, the hair all over the body became sparse, discolored, and rough. The skin showing through was somewhat scaly and irritated looking. Occasionally small breaks and scabs which then healed up and went away would appear at numerous points over the body, particularly upon the back. Figure 6 is a picture of obese rat Rb-11, which shows this condition well, and its control. In most cases thick moist calluses developed on the heels

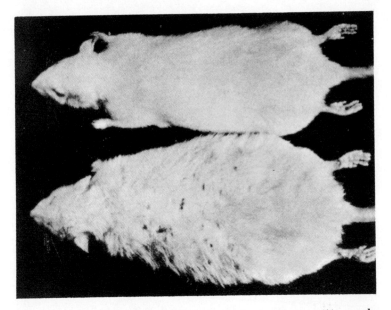

Fig. 6. Obese rat Rb-11, photographed at autopsy, 4½ months after operation, and Rb-13, the control. Hypothalamic lesions were made at the age of 7 weeks. Note the sparse hair and scabbed, scaly skin of the fat rat.

of the hind feet, probably from the pressure upon those points caused by the animals' great weight and their tendency to sit in one spot without moving for long periods. Sometimes these areas would bruise and bleed, but medication would relieve the condition.

A short time after operation the males usually developed rather shrunken scrota, and in a few weeks the testes of most of the animals lay up in the inguinal canal, or were not palpable at all. A noticeable feature of the female perineum was the large subcutaneous accumulations of fat around and caudal to the vaginal opening, sometimes to the point of similarity to the males' shrunken scrotal sacs.

The effect of the lesions upon growth (body length) was not in most instances very evident during life, two exceptions being Rb-7 and Rb-17, which were appreciably stunted. Length measurements made at the time of sacrifice, however, generally revealed the fat males to be from one to several centimeters shorter in body length than their controls. The females, on the other hand, do not show at first glance the same tendency, and they are so indicated in Table 1. Thus Rb-11, for instance, was found at autopsy to be just as long as its normal littermate, and the others seem to be about the same way. This appearance may be misleading, however, as it will be noted that by coincidence the young obese females were somewhat longer than their controls at the time of operation; whereas among the males, also by coincidence, the measurements were for the most part more nearly equal. For that reason approximate equality in autopsy lengths in the females and their controls may in reality represent some lag in growth on the part of the former; nevertheless, this tendency may not be so great as in the males.

Autopsy findings. Invariably the fat animals have shown enormous accumulations of adipose tissue in the abdomen. In the mesenteries, around the kidneys, and along the aorta the collection of fat is so great that it is sometimes difficult to find and dissect out the ovaries and adrenals. There are also usually large pads of fat in the perineal region and over the neck and upper chest. Subcutaneous fat depots are, as a matter of fact, quite generally increased in both the males and the females.

The livers of these animals have in almost every case been either a mottled mixture of red and yellow or a practically pure yellow in color; frozen sections of the organ stained with Sudan III have confirmed the diagnosis of marked fatty infiltration. The thyroid and adrenals are as a rule grossly normal in appearance, but the gonads fall in a different category.

The testes of the males were in the majority of instances somewhat less than the normal size, some being just as small as in an hypophysectomized animal, and they were commonly to be found either in the inguinal canal or actually up in the abdominal cavity. The accessory reproductive glands showed a parallel degree of atrophy. Because of the fact that the taking of vaginal smears had a distinctly adverse effect upon the body weight and well-being of the obese females this line of inquiry was not pressed. For this reason no information was available as to the stage of the estrous cycle in which the animals were killed; consequently it was a little difficult to gauge with certainty the condition of the ovaries or uteri at autopsy from gross inspection.

A more thoroughgoing description of the histological condition obtaining in the thyroids, adrenals, and gonads is planned in a later publication; and insofar as the first two glands are concerned this promise must suffice, since only the gonads have to date been examined in histological preparations. Some sort of a sex dystrophy has been produced by the operation, but its nature is not clear. The ovaries of all females examined so far have contained large numbers of follicles in all stages of development, but have lacked corpora lutea. The testes of the males have shown a less constant condition. Some have shown a complete disappearance of spermatogenesis and a very marked diminution of tubule diameter as well as of total size of the organ. A few are not easily distinguishable from those of normal animals. The majority fall somewhere in between these two extremes.

At the base of the brain conditions appeared to be always about the same. The hypophyses could usually be shelled out of their dural capsules with ease, and most of them showed grossly a normal appearance and no scarification. This would indicate that they could not for the most part have been directly involved by the lesion in the hypothalamus. Further support for this opinion has been added by examination in serial sections of an hypophysis which was left attached to the base of the brain. Owing to the fact that the animal (Rb-37) had been dead for some time when it was found the brain and pituitary were judged too soft for careful separation. The hypophysis of this rat seemed to be wholly isolated from the scarification at the base of the hypothalamus by its dural sheath, and to be present in its entirety. The nature of the microscopic preparation naturally precluded any study of the condition of the individual cells. The remainder of the glands have not as yet been prepared for careful histological study.

The dura was always firmly attached to the areas of lesion on each side of the tuber cinereum, and generally a large part of the hypothalamus behind the optic chiasma was flattened and slightly brownish. The optic chiasma and optic tracts displayed only twice in the entire series any macroscopically detectable injury.

Chemical analyses. Work which Hetherington and Weil ('40) have reported elsewhere in more detail was done to ascertain quantitatively how much greater was the storage of fat in the bodies of the obese animals than in their normal litter mates. The fatty constituents of the animals' skinned carcasses were extracted first with acetone and then with hot absolute alcohol; the figures in Table 2 represent the combined results of the two extractions, and are calculated as percentages of the wet skinned carcass weight.

TABLE 2. SHOWING THE PERCENTAGE OF LIPOIDS IN THE BODIES OF THE FAT RATS AND THEIR CONTROLS

Rat No.	Sex	Type	Per Cent of Carcass Weight
Rb- 1	M	Obese	46.9
Rb- 2	M	Control	19.7
Rb- 3	F	Obese	48.3
Rb- 4	F	Control	17.8
Rb-11	F	Obese	42.8
Rb-13	F	Control	16.7

As mentioned before, the weight curves of these six rats from the time of operation until sacrifice are shown in Figures 1, 2, and 3.

Hypothalamic lesions. When the lesions of the obese rats were examined microscopically they turned out to be somewhat larger than had been anticipated from inspection of the freshly made lesions in other specimens. In general they were found to begin at some point not far behind the caudal edge of the optic chiasma and to proceed caudally all the way to the mammillary body, frequently including most of that structure also. Lying at the base, the lesions commonly extended laterally practically out to the optic tracts in the rostral region of the tuber cinereum and into the lateral hypothalamic area in the caudal portion, and medially almost to the ventricle. As a matter of fact the thin wall between the cyst made by electrolysis and the ventricle was often broken through; so that one continuous cavity was formed (Fig. 28). The dorsal extent of the destruction was subject to considerable variation, being materially added to on occasion by areas of hemorrhagic softening lying near the needle tracks down through the medial portion of the thalamus (Fig. 20). Usually, however, the dorsal edge of the lesion stopped short of, or at the ventral boundary of, the thalamus, although the lesions on the two sides sometimes fused with each other across the midline dorsal to the ventricle (Figs. 13, 16).

In terms of nuclear and fiber areas such a large region of destruction has naturally often been difficult to interpret. The task has been complicated even further by the fact that in the larger number of instances there has seemed to be an appreciable decrease in the concentration of nerve cells in areas not apparently directly involved in the lesion. This phenomenon has been most frequently observed in such sites as the arcuate nuclei (Figs. 12, 8), or perhaps the medial zones of the ventromedial and dorsomedial hypothalamic nuclei, in cases where a band of tissue between the lesion and the ventricular wall was spared from direct damage (Figs. 11, 15). Sometimes the supraoptic nuclei have shown similar neuron loss, and in this case injury to the median eminence or to the anterior region of the tuber cinereum near the midline causing at least partial interruption of the supraoptico-hypophysial tract was seemingly the cause. The filiform nucleus also occasionally displayed a paucity of cells.

In spite of the fact that the lesions in all the rats were very extensive, there was enough variation in the precise localization of the destruction that a good deal of the damage lying on the outskirts of the lesion could be disregarded as not significant; and the important portions of the injured regions could be narrowed down somewhat to the central overlapping area destroyed in all. Briefly, this central core of eliminated tissue may be said to include the ventromedial and dorsomedial hypothalamic nuclei, the arcuate nucleus, the medial portion of the lateral hypothalamic area which lies ventral to the fornix (between the rostral and caudal poles of the first two of the cell groups just mentioned), the fornix, and possibly also the ventral premammillary nucleus. Figures 23–26 (Rb-17) and Figures 27–30 (Rb-38) illustrate fairly well this type of lesion.

An attempt to diminish still further the limits of the damage which has produced obesity in our rats would, perhaps, be unjustified, inasmuch as mere size of lesion might conceivably be of itself a factor in the causation of the syndrome. On the whole, however, the complete destruction of the parts nearer the base has seemed to be more important to the production of a marked level of adiposity than injury to the more dorsally disposed portions. Rats Rb-1 (Figs. 7–10), Rb-3 (Figs. 11–14), Rb-12, and Rb-16, for instance, could be classified as markedly obese, yet each had remaining on either one side or the other a large portion of the dorsomedial hypothalamic nucleus. Rats Rb-6, Rb-7, and Rb-15 (Figs. 19–22), on the other hand, which could only be called moderately fat, were revealed on examination to possess a fair share of the ventromedial and arcuate nuclei on one side intact. This latter group of animal suggests, furthermore, the likelihood that symmetrical damage at the base is necessary for maximum adiposity.

The importance of the invariable elimination of that most medial portion of the lateral hypothalamic area which underlies the fornix, and of the fornix itself, is a little difficult to assess. The evidence from these experiments would seem to dictate the crediting of these structures as well as the medial nuclear masses with a share of the responsibility for the obesity; and so far as the portion of this zone which lies at the base is concerned the chance of its being significant to the result appears considerable. In three rats showing varying amounts of fat deposition reported by Hetherington (1940 b), however, the fornix was not involved.

Finally, it is apparent from the investigation of the mammillary body that the nuclei present in that area, though they have often been included in the general destruction, bear no constant relationship to the resultant adiposity. A number of the most obese rats displayed almost complete destruction of the mammillary body. But Rb-16 had only the ventral premammillary nuclei and the ventral portion of the medial mammillary nucleus on one side damaged, and Rb-17 (Figs. 23–26) only the former nuclei alone; nevertheless, both were very fat. Rb-29, moderately obese, showed almost no injury even to the ventral premammillary nucleus.

Figures 7 to 30 consist of a series of diagrammatic drawings of transverse sections through the hypothalami of six of the obese rats. The areas of destruction are indicated by the blacked out areas in the drawings. The left side of the hypothalamus is always to the reader's right. Each of these six animals was selected as the representative of a group of animals having essentially similar lesions. The detailed description of the damage in each rat which follows is intended to supplement the drawings by making more explicit the exact amount of injury done to the various hypothalamic nuclei.

Rat Rb-1. This was a markedly obese animal (Fig. 1 and Figs. 7–10). The lesions begin a short distance behind the chiasma, about opposite the filiform nucleus, and promptly extend to the base. On the left side all but the rostral medial portion of the filiform nucleus is destroyed, and at more caudal levels the dorsomedial and ventro-medial hypothalamic nuclei, the arcuate nucleus, the medial half of the lateral hypothalamic area, the fornix, and the ventral portion of the posterior hypothalamic area are likewise eliminated. On the

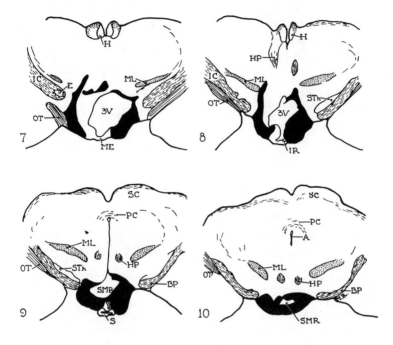

Figs. 7–10. Diagrams of sections through the hypothalamus of rat Rb-1: 7, through the rostral part of the ventromedial hypothalamic nucleus; 8, through the caudal end of the same nucleus; 9, through the posterior hypothalamus, just ahead of the mammillary body; 10, through the mammillary body.

Abbreviations

A, cerebral aqueduct
AH, anterior hypothalamus
BP, basis pedunculi
E, entopeduncular nucleus
F, fornix
H, medial habenular nucleus
HP, habenulopeduncular tract
IC, internal capsule
IR, infundibular recess
LH, lateral hypothalamic area
MB, mammillary body
ME, median eminence

ML, medial leminscus
MT, mammillothalamic tract
OT, optic tract
PC, posterior commissure
S, hypophysial stalk
SC, superior colliculus
SM, stria medullaris
SMR, submammillary recess
STh, subthalamic nucleus
ZI, zona incerta
3V, third ventricle

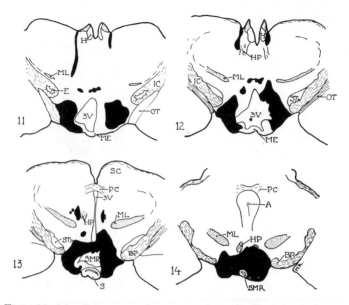

Figs. 11–14. Diagrams of sections through the hypothalamus of rat Rb-3: 11, through the rostral part of the ventromedial hypothalamic nucleus; 12, through the caudal end of the same nucleus; 13, through the posterior hypothalamus, at the rostral edge of the mammillary body; 14, through the caudal part of the mammillary body.

right side the filiform nucleus is spared (though it shows loss of cells) as is the main medial portion of the dorsomedial hypothalamic nucleus also. The ventromedial hypothalamic nucleus, all but the most medial part of the arcuate nucleus, the medial two-thirds of the lateral hypothalamic area, and the fornix are destroyed. Caudally the area of destruction includes all of the mammillary body, and of course the mammillothalamic tracts are completely degenerated on both sides.

Rat Rb-3. This was an extremely fat female (Fig. 2 and Figs. 11–14). The lesions begin in the caudal edge of the anterior hypothalamic area and reach to the base and into the medial part of the lateral hypothalamic area. On the left side the lesion spreads toward the ventricle and dorsally, destroying all but the medial rostral end of the ventromedial hypothalamic nucleus, all but the medial part of the arcuate nucleus and all of the dorsomedial hypothalamic nucleus. More caudally most of the posterior and lateral hypothalamic areas are involved also. On the right side the lesion takes out the ventromedial hypothalamic nucleus, the ventral half of the dorsomedial hypothalamic nucleus, most of the arcuate nucleus, the medial two-thirds of the lateral hypothalamic area, and

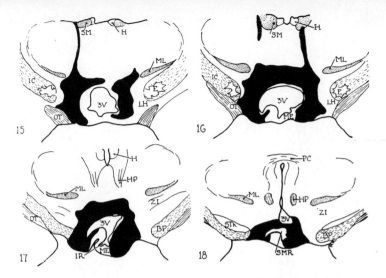

Figs. 15–18. Diagrams of sections through the hypothalamus of rat Rb-11: 15, through the rostral end of the ventromedial hypothalamic nucleus; 16, through the caudal half of the same nucleus; 17, through the caudal end of the dorsomedial hypothalamic nucelus; 18, through the rostral edge of the mammillary body.

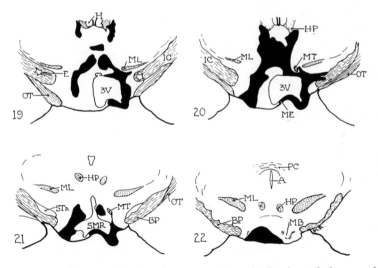

Figs. 19–22. Diagrams of sections through the hypothalamus of rat Rb-15: 19, through the rostral part of the ventromedial hypothalamic nucleus; 20, through the middle of the same nucleus; 21, through the posterior hypothalamus rostral to the mammillary body; 22, through the rostral part of the mammillary body.

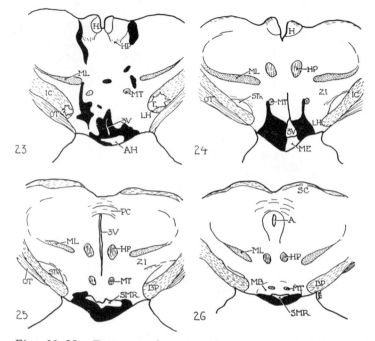

Figs. 23–26. Diagrams of sections through the hypothalamus of rat Rb-17: 23, through the rostral end of the ventromedial hypothalamic nucleus; 24, through the caudal part of the same nucleus; 25, through the rostral edge of the mammillary body; 26, through the mammillary body.

the ventral portion of the posterior hypothalamic area. The lesions on the two sides then unite dorsal to the submammillary recess of the third ventricle and destroy the entire mammillary body, extending even back into the interpeduncular nucleus of the midbrain, and interrupting part of the habenulopeduncular tract on the left side. The fornices and mammillothalamic tracts are degenerated on both sides.

Rat Rb-11. This animal was a very obese female (Figs. 3 and 6 and Figs. 15–18). The lesions begin at the level of the caudal end of the filiform nucleus on both sides. On the left the lesion destroys the caudal portion of the anterior hypothalamic area, the arcuate nucleus, and the ventromedial and dorsomedial hypothalamic nuclei. Laterally the fornix and the medial one-third of the lateral hypothalamic area are included. On the right side the rostral part of the lesion extends from the base to the thalamus through the zone between the anterior and lateral hypothalamic areas, taking out the adjacent parts of both. More caudally the lesion occupies most of

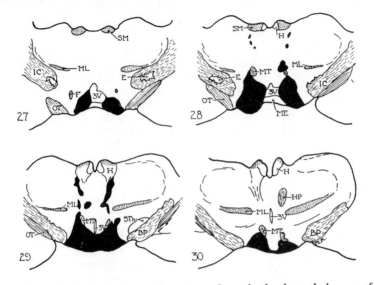

Figs. 27–30. Diagrams of sections through the hypothalamus of rat Rb-38: 27, through the caudal part of the anterior hypothalamic area; 28, through the middle of the ventromedial hypothalamic nucleus; 29, through the posterior hypothalamus rostral to the mammillary body; 30, through the rostral part of the mammillary body.

the right half of the hypothalamus, missing only the arcuate nucleus and the most medial rostral cells of the dorsomedial and ventromedial hypothalamic nuclei. The lesions join each other dorsal to the ventricle, extend into the ventral edge of the thalamus, and destroy the posterior hypothalamic area on each side, as well as the mammillary body.

Rat Rb-15. This was an only moderately fat male (Figs. 19–22). The lesion on the left begins at the level of the caudal end of the filiform nucleus. It destroys the caudal end of the anterior hypothalamic area, the dorsomedial and ventromedial hypothalamic nuclei, the arcuate nucleus, the fornix, and the medial one-third of the lateral and most of the posterior hypothalamic areas. It then subsides quickly to the base sparing most of the dorsal and ventral premammillary nuclei, but taking out the most rostral medial portion of the medial mammillary nucleus. On the right the lesion begins at a level opposite the rostral end of the median eminence. It lies at first in the zone between the medial and lateral hypothalamic areas, and extends from the base to the thalamus. More caudally it destroys the fornix, the dorsomedial hypothalamic nucleus, and the medial half of the lateral and the medial portion of the posterior hypothalamic areas. All but the most medial and lateral cells of the right half of the mammillary body are destroyed.

A large amount of hemorrhagic softening is present in the thalamus along the needle tracks.

Rat Rb-17. This was a very obese, somewhat dwarfed male (Figs. 23–26). The lesions begin on both sides at the base just caudal to the optic chiasma, and lie just ventral to the fornix. They quickly spread dorsally and toward the ventricle, destroying on both sides the ventromedial and dorsomedial hypothalamic nuclei, the arcuate nuclei, the fornices, and those portions of the lateral hypothalamic areas immediately ventral to them. Caudally only the ventral premammillary nuclei and the ventral edge of the mammillary body are involved.

Rat Rb-38. This was a very obese female (Figs. 27–30). The lesions begin on both sides at the base in the ventral edge of the anterior hypothalamic areas just caudal to the optic chiasma. They spread rapidly in all directions and engulf on both sides the caudal end of the anterior hypothalamic areas, the ventromedial and all but the most dorsal caudal cells of the dorsomedial hypothalamic nuclei, the arcuate nuclei, the fornices, and the medial halves of the lateral hypothalamic areas. Caudally the lesions destroy the ventral premammillary and the ventrolateral portions of the dorsal premammillary nuclei, as well as limited areas in the rostral ends of the medial mammillary nuclei.

DISCUSSION

The results seem to indicate unequivocally that at least one form of pathological obesity is directly traceable to a primary lesion in the hypothalamus. This conclusion is in complete agreement with the long-held ideas of many workers in both the experimental and the clinical fields. The principal objection which has stood in the way of its complete acceptance has been the inability of any investigator to produce adiposity with regularity in any animal by a controllable, easily reproducible technic. This drawback has apparently now been overcome. As a matter of fact, the ease with which the results can be duplicated should make such rats a useful variety of standard test animal for physiological experimentation.

A further fact which has distracted attention from the ability of a lesion in the tuber cinereum to cause obesity is to be found in the usual presence of damage in both that structure and the hypophysis. When the intimate relation of the reactive areas in the floor of the diencephalon to the stalk and dorsal side of the pituitary is considered, however, the frequent association of this "hypothalamic adiposity" with hypophysial or suprasellar neoplasms becomes a matter for no surprise. This is not to say, of course, that there may be no type of excessive fat deposition which is peculiar to and bound up with specifically hypophysial mechanisms. These experiments do not exclude that possibility.

With respect to the actual characteristics of the hypothalamic lesion which causes obesity, the question should, perhaps, be considered more open than the uniform nature of our results would suggest. Practically 100% of our series of rats became obese, and when the hypothalami were studied certain structures were found invariably to be more or less affected. The latter observation is accounted for, however, by the fact that a deliberate effort was made to place the hypothalamic lesions in as nearly the same location as possible in each animal. No guarantee can be made that another series of rats with equally large lesions placed in a different locality—say, farther forward, or more laterally—would not show just as large a percentage of successful results. In other words, since little or no exploration of other parts of the hypothalamus has been carried out, it is as yet impossible to conclude that the region studied is the only reactive area. The size of the lesion might be of just as much if not more significance than its disposition. Thus, a very large portion of the hypothalamus might constitute a "reactive area," and destruction of a certain minimum amount of this "reactive area" would be the stimulus necessary to produce the adiposity.

This possibility should not be lost sight of, particularly in view of the somewhat divergent results reported by other workers. Bailey and Bremer (1921) reported two cases of obesity in adult male dogs which had stab lesions in the posterior hypothalamus, between the stalk and the mammillary bodies; no nuclear damage was detailed. Grafe and Grünthal (1929) were of the opinion also that they had damaged the posterior hypothalamus in the neighborhood of the mammillary bodies, but since they could find no lesion in their histological preparations this must remain a matter for speculation.

The anterior hypothalamus has been favored by some other investigators. Camus and Roussy (1922), though they did not commit themselves to any definite region, found in histological preparations of the hypothalami of several fat dogs lesions in the pre-infundibular area mostly fairly medially disposed. These lesions were said to involve the "nuclei proprii of the tuber" and the paraventricular nuclei. Likewise, Biggart and Alexander (1939), whose observations were rather carefully recorded, believed their evidence indicated the importance of the anterior hypothalamus. Several of their obese dogs had damage to the ventral and caudal portions of the supraoptic nuclei; some had damage to the ventromedial hypothalamic nuclei; while still others had destruction anterior to the median eminence, presumably in the anterior hypothalamic areas. These authors made note of the fact that in their series of animals the lesions were so placed as to interrupt any fibers from the paraventricular nuclei to the hypophysis, and recalled Greving's (1928) idea that these nuclei control fat metabolism. Moreover, it is of some interest that Dott (1938), basing his opinion on a considerable surgical experience, has ventured to predict that the appropriate lesion will be found to concern the anterior tuberal wall.

Crooke and Gilmour (1938) produced a small group of fat rats in the process of hypophysectomy. These animals when killed were found to have lesions immediately in front of, or at the side of, the infundibulum. These lesions were described as traumatic cavities communicating with the third ventricle, but no nuclear analysis was attempted. Smith (1927) reported no details of any kind concerning the location of the hypothalamic lesions he made.

It is not necessary, of course, to accept a purely quantitative view in order to account for the variation in results obtained by the aforementioned workers. An alternative explanation might be, as Biggart and Alexander hinted, that all lesions causing obesity must lie in the path of some group of fibers. The divergent findings of various investigators would be more easily reconciled, however, if the fibers in question were considered to run a longitudinal course from the rostral to the caudal region, rather than a probably more or less vertical course from the paraventricular nucleus to the hypophysis. In the light of our results such a pathway might be fairly diffuse, and would in all likelihood be rather ventrally placed. These ideas have led us to begin experiments involving not only the placing of large lesions in other parts of the hypothalamus, but also the making of smaller, more discrete lesions within the reactive area we have discovered.

SUMMARY

A condition of marked adiposity characterized by as much as a doubling of body weight and a tremendous increase of extractable body lipoids has been produced in rats by the placing of electrolytic lesions in the hypothalamus. Examination of these lesions has shown them to be very large, but they all have in common extensive bilateral damage to the region occupied by the dorsomedial and ventromedial hypothalamic nuclei, the arcuate nucleus, the fornix, and that portion of the lateral hypothalamic area ventral to it, and probably also the ventral premammillary nucleus. Symmetrical destruction of the ventral portion of this area, including the nuclei and possibly other structures near the base, seems to be more important than injury to the more dorsal structures for the production of maximum adiposity.

REFERENCES

Aschner, Bernhard. Über die Funktion der Hypophyse. *Pflüg. Arch. ges. Physiol.*, 1912, **146**, 1.

Bailey, P., & Bremer, F. Experimental diabetes insipidus. *Arch. int. Med.*, 1921, **28**, 773.

Biggart, J. H., & Alexander, G. L. Experimental diabetes insipidus. *J. Pathol. Bacteriol.*, 1939, **48**, 405.

Camus, J., & Roussy, G. Les syndromes hypophysaires: Anatomie et physiologie pathologiques. *Rev. Neurol.*, 1922, **38**, 622.

Clark, G. The use of the Horsley-Clarke instrument on the rat. *Science*, 1939, **90**, 92.

Crooke, A. C., & Gilmour, J. R. A description of the effect of hypophysectomy on the growing rat, with the resulting histological changes in the adrenal and thyroid glands and the testicles. *J. Pathol. Bacteriol.*, 1938, **47**, 525.

Dott, N. M. Surgical aspects of the hypothalamus. In W. E. LeG. Clark, J. Beattie, G. Riddoch, & N. M. Dott, *The Hypothalamus*. Edinburgh: Oliver and Boyd, 1938.

Erdheim, J. Über Hypophysenganggeschwülste und Hirncholesteatome. *Sitzungsb. d. k. Akad. d. Wiss. Math.-naturwiss. Kl. Wein*, 1904, **113**, 537.

Frölich, A. Ein Fall von Tumor der Hypophysis cerebri ohne Akromegalie. *Wien. klin. Rundschau*, 1901, **15**, 883, 906.

Grafe, E., & Grünthal, E. Über isolierte Beeinflussung des Gesamtstoffwechsels vom Zwischenhirn aus. *Klin. Wchnschr.*, 1929, **8**, 1013.

Greving, R. Das Zwischenhirn-Hypophysensystem: Seine Morpho-
logie, Phylogenese und klinische Bedeutung. *Klin. Wchnschr.*,
1928, **7**, 734.

Hetherington, A. W. Hypothalamic lesions and adiposity in the rat.
Anat. Rec., 1940, **76** (suppl. 2), 30. (a)

Hetherington, A. W. Obesity in the rat following the injection of
chromic acid into the hypophysis. *Endocrinol.*, 1940, **26**,
264. (b)

Hetherington, A. W., & Ranson, S. W. Experimental hypothalamico-
hypophyseal obesity in the rat. *Proc. Soc. exper. Biol. Med.*,
1939, **41**, 465.

Hetherington, A. W., & Weil, A. The lipoid, calcium, phosphorus
and iron content of rats with hypothalamic and hypophyseal
damage. *Endocrinol.*, 1940, **26**, 723.

Smith, P. E. The disabilities caused by hypophysectomy and their
repair. *J. Amer. med. Ass.*, 1927, **88**, 158.

[ADDENDA FROM THE ORIGINAL PRINTING OF THIS ARTICLE: IN REFERENCE TO
THE AUTHORS: *Institute of Neurology, Northwestern University Medical
School, Chicago, Illinois.* IN REFERENCE TO ARTICLE ILLUSTRATIONS: *Thirty
Figures. Aided by a grant from the Committee on Research in Endocrin-
ology of the National Research Council.* IN REFERENCE TO THE EVIPAL MEN-
TIONED IN THE ARTICLE: *Generously supplied by Dr. J. J. Kuhn of the
Winthrop Chemical Co.*]

THE PHYSIOLOGY OF
MOTIVATION ※ *Eliot Stellar*

IN THE LAST TWENTY YEARS motivation has become a central concept in psychology. Indeed, it is fair to say that today it is one of the basic ingredients of most modern theories of learning, personality, and social behavior. There is one stumbling-block in this noteworthy development, however, for the particular conception of motivation which most psychologists employ is based upon the outmoded model implied by Cannon in his classical statement of the local theories of hunger and thirst (23). Cannon's theories were good in their day, but the new facts available on the physiological basis of motivation demand that we abandon the older conceptualizations and follow new theories, not only in the study of motivation itself, but also in the application of motivational concepts to other areas of psychology.

This argument for a new theory of motivation has been made before by Lashley (42) and Morgan (47). But it is more impelling than ever today because so much of the recent evidence is beginning to fit into the general theoretical framework which these men suggested. Both Lashley and Morgan pointed out that the local factors proposed by Cannon (e.g., stomach contractions or dryness of the throat) are not necessary conditions for the

REPRINTED FROM *Psychological Review*, 61:5-22. COPYRIGHT © 1954 BY THE AMERICAN PSYCHOLOGICAL ASSOCIATION.

arousal of motivated behavior. Instead, they offered the more inclusive view that a number of sensory, chemical, and neural factors cooperate in a complicated physiological mechanism that regulates motivation. The crux of their theory was described most recently by Morgan as a *central motive state* (*c.m.s.*) built up in the organism by the combined influences of the sensory, humoral, and neural factors. Presumably, the amount of motivated behavior is determined by the level of the *c.m.s.*

Beach (8, 11), in his extensive work on the specific case of sexual motivation, has amply supported the views of Lashley and Morgan. But the important question still remains: Do other kinds of motivated behavior fit the same general theory? As you will see shortly, a review of the literature makes it clear that they do. As a matter of fact, there is enough evidence today to confirm and extend the views of Lashley, Morgan, and Beach and to propose, in some detail, a more complete physiological theory of motivation.

There are a number of ways to present a theoretical physiological mechanism like the one offered here. Perhaps the best approach is to start with an overview and summarize, in a schematic way, the major factors at work in the mechanism. Then we can fill in the details by reviewing the literature relevant to the operation of each factor. Some advantage is lost by not taking up the literature according to behavioral topics, that is, different kinds of motivation. But the procedure adopted here lets us focus attention directly on the theory itself and permits us to make some very useful comparisons among the various kinds of motivation. Once the theoretical mechanism and the evidence bearing on it are presented, the final step will be to evaluate the theory and show what experiments must be done to check it and extend it.

THEORETICAL SCHEME

A schematic diagram of the physiological mechanism believed to be in control of motivated behavior is shown in Figure 1. The basic assumption in this scheme is that *the amount of motivated behavior is a direct function of the amount of activity in certain excitatory centers of the hypothalamus*. The activity of these excitatory centers, in turn, is determined by a large number of factors which can be grouped in four general classes: (*a*)

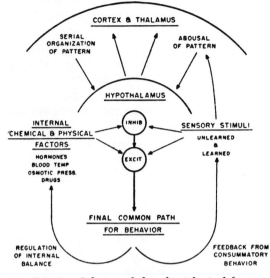

Fig. 1. Scheme of the physiological factors contributing to the control of motivated behavior. (See text.)

inhibitory hypothalamic centers which serve only to depress the activity of the excitatory centers, (*b*) *sensory stimuli* which control hypothalamic activity through the afferent impulses they can set up, (*c*) *the internal environment* which can influence the hypothalamus through its rich vascular supply and the cerebrospinal fluid, and (*d*) *cortical and thalamic centers* which can exert excitatory and inhibitory influences on the hypothalamus.

As can be seen, the present theory holds that the hypothalamus is the seat of Morgan's *c.m.s.* and is the "central nervous mechanism" Lashley claimed was responsible for "drive." Identifying the hypothalamus as the main integrating mechanism in motivation makes the experimental problem we face more specific and more concrete than ever before. But it also makes it more complicated, for the physiological control of the hypothalamus is exceedingly complex. The influence of the internal environment on the hypothalamus is changing continuously according to natural physiological cycles, and of course it may often be changed directly by the chemical and physical consequences of consummatory behavior (see Fig. 1). Sensory stimuli may also have varied effects on the hypothalamic mechanism, depending upon their particular pattern, previous stimulation, previous learning, sensory feedback from the consummatory behavior itself, and the influence the internal environment has already exerted on the hypothalamus. Similarly, the influence of the cortex and thalamus will add to the hypothalamic activity already produced by sensory stimuli and the internal environment. Presumably, these cortical and thalamic influences may result directly or indirectly from sensory stimulation, but they may also be controlled partly by the "upward drive" of the hypothalamus itself (43). Then, to complicate the picture even more, there are the inhibitory centers of the hypothalamus which are also controlled by the various internal changes, sensory stimuli, and cortical and thalamic influences. These centers, presumably, depress the activity of the excitatory centers and, therefore, attenuate their output.

Fortunately, this mechanism is not as formidable against experimental attack as it might appear. The basic experimental approach is to isolate the controlling factors in any type of motivation and determine their relative contributions to hypothalamic activity. As you will see, a number of experimental techniques like sensory deprivation, hormone and drug administration, cortical ablation, and the production of subcortical lesions may be used fruitfully to isolate these factors. But that is only half the problem. Obviously, the factors controlling hypothalamic activity and motivation do not operate in isolation. In fact, it is quite clear that their influences interact. Therefore, it becomes an equally important problem to determine the relative contribution of each factor while the others are operating over a wide range of variation.

EXPERIMENTAL EVIDENCE

Before going into the literature bearing on the operation of each of these factors in control of motivated behavior, it will help to raise a few questions that ought to be kept in mind while considering the experimental evidence. Are there different hypothalamic centers controlling each kind of motivation? Does the hypothalamus exert its influence through direct control of the final effector pathways or does it simply have a "priming" effect on effector paths controlled by other parts of the nervous system? Do all these factors operate in the control of each type of motivation or are there cases where sensory stimuli, for example, may not be important or where changes in the internal environment do not contribute? Can the same mechanism describe the control of motivation measured by simple consummatory behavior, preference, and learning? Are the same mechanisms involved in the control of simple, biological motives and complex, learned motives?

Hypothalamic centers. Review of the literature on the role of the hypothalamus in motivation brings out three general conclusions. (*a*) Damage to restricted regions of the hypothalamus leads to striking changes in certain kinds of motivated behavior. (*b*) Different parts of the hypothalamus are critical in different kinds of motivation. (*c*) There are both excitatory and inhibitory centers controlling motivation in the hypothalamus; that is, damage to the hypothalamus can sometimes lead to an increase in motivation and sometimes a marked decrease.

The evidence bearing on these three points can be summarized briefly. Many experiments have shown that restricted bilateral lesions of the hypothalamus will make tremendous changes in basic biological motivations like hunger (16, 22), sleep (49, 50, 53), and sex (6, 18, 20). Less complete evidence strongly suggests that the same kinds of hypothalamic integration is also true in the cases of thirst (61), activity (35), and emotions (5, 62). We have only suggestive evidence in the case of specific hungers (59).

It is clear that there is some kind of localization of function within the hypothalamus although it is not always possible to specify precisely the anatomical nuclei subserving these functions. The centers for hunger are in the region of the ventromedial nucleus which lies in the middle third of the ventral hypothalamus, in the tuberal region (16). (See Fig. 2.) Sleep is controlled by centers in the extreme posterior (mammillary bodies) and extreme anterior parts of the hypothalamus (49, 50). The critical region for sexual behavior is in the anterior hypothalamus, between the optic chiasm and the stalk of the pituitary gland (18, 20). The center for activity is not clearly established, but seems to be adjacent with or overlapping the centers for hunger (35). Finally, the centers for emotion are also in the vicinity of the ventromedial nucleus, perhaps somewhat posterior to the hunger centers and overlapping the posterior sleep center (50, 62).

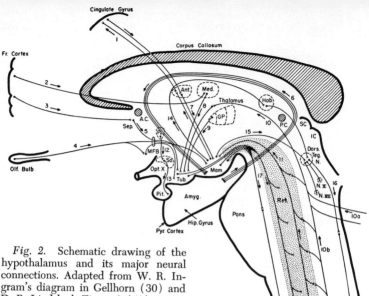

Fig. 2. Schematic drawing of the hypothalamus and its major neural connections. Adapted from W. R. Ingram's diagram in Gellhorn (30) and D. B. Lindsley's Figure 9 (43).

Abbreviations and Description of Pathways

A.C.	Anterior Commissure	MFB	Medial forebrain bundle
Amyg.	Amygdala	N.V	Motor nucleus, Vth nerve
Ant.	Anterior thalamic nuclei		
Cingulate Gyrus	Cortex of cingulate gyrus	N.VII	Motor nucleus, VIIth nerve
Dors. Teg. N.	Dorsal tegmental nucleus	Olf. Bulb	Olfactory bulb
Fr. Cortex	Cortex of frontal lobe	Opt. X	Optic chiasm
GP	Globus pallidus	P.C.	Posterior commissure
Hab.	Habenular nucleus of thalamus	Pit.	Pituitary gland
		Pv.	Paraventricular nucleus
Hip. Gyrus	Hippocampal gyrus	Pyr. Cortex	Pyriform cortex
IC	Inferior colliculus	Ret.	Reticular formation
Mam.	Mammillary nuclei	SC	Superior colliculus
Med.	Dorsal medial thalamic nucleus	Sep.	Septal nuclei
		So.	Supraoptic nucleus
		Tub.	Tuber cinereum

Afferents to Hypothalamus

1. Corticothalamic fibers
2. Frontothalamic fibers
3. Frontoseptal fibers
4. Olfacto-hypothalamic tract
5. Septo-hypothalamic fibers
6. Fornix
7. Mammillothalamic tract
8. Thalamo-hypothalamic fibers
9. Pallido-hypothalamic fibers
10. Sensory systems ascending to thalamus
    10a. cranial afferents
    10b. somatic and visceral afferents
11. Sensory collaterals to hypothalamus
12. Paraventriculo-supraoptic fibers

Efferents from Hypothalamus

13. Supraoptic hypophyseal tract
14. Mammillohabenular tract
15. Mammillotegmental tract
16. Dorsal longitudinal fasciculus
17. Descending efferents relaying in brain stem and medulla

In at least two cases it is clear that there must be both excitatory and inhibitory centers controlling motivated behavior. In the case of hunger, bilateral lesions in the ventromedial nucleus near the midline produce a tremendous amount of overeating (3, 16). Such a center is presumably an inhibitory one since removing it leads directly to an increase in eating behavior. On the other hand, lesions 1½ to 2 millimeters off the midline at the level of the ventromedial nucleus completely eliminate hunger behavior (3, 4). After such lesions animals never eat again, so we can call such centers excitatory centers. Supporting this interpretation is the fact, recently reported, that stimulating these lateral centers in the waking cat through implanted electrodes results in vast overeating (27). The same sort of mechanism turns up in the case of sleep. In the posterior hypothalamus, in the region of the mammillary bodies, there are excitatory centers or "waking" centers which operate to keep the organism awake (49, 50). When they are removed, the animal becomes somnolent and cannot stay awake. In the anterior hypothalamus, around the preoptic nucleus, there is an inhibitory center (49). When that is removed, the animal is constantly wakeful.

So far, only an excitatory center has been found in the case of sexual behavior. Bilateral lesions anterior to the pituitary stalk eliminate all mating behavior (18, 20), but no lesion of the hypothalamus has ever been reported that resulted in an exaggeration of sexual motivation. What little we know about the center for activity near the ventromedial nucleus suggests that it is also an excitatory center since lesions there produce only inactivity and not hyperactivity (35). In the case of emotions, the picture is not yet clear. Lesions near the ventromedial nucleus make cats highly emotional (62), and therefore this center must be inhibitory. But the lateral regions of the posterior hypothalamus seem to be excitatory, for lesions there make animals placid (50). Furthermore, direct stimulation of these posterior regions produces many of the signs of rage reactions (52).

There is some evidence that sheds light on how the excitatory and inhibitory hypothalamic centers may cooperate in the regulation of motivation. In the clear-cut cases of sleep and hunger it appears that the inhibitory centers operate mainly through their effects on the excitatory centers. At least we know that when both centers are removed simultaneously the effect is undistinguishable from what happens when only the excitatory centers are removed (3, 49). So it is convenient for present theoretical purposes to think of the inhibitory center as one of the factors which influences the level of activity of the excitatory center. In fact, to speculate one step further, it is worth suggesting that the inhibitory centers may constitute the primary neural mechanism regulating the satiation of motivation.

Sensory stimuli. What effects do sensory stimuli have upon the hypothalamus and how important are such stimuli in the control of motivation? Some answer to the first part of this question is given by the schematic outline of hypothalamic connections shown in Figure 2. Clearly the hypothalamus has a rich supply of afferents coming directly or indirectly from all the various sense organs. In fact the diagram is really an understatement of hypothalamic connections because it is an oversimplified and conservative representation. Physiological evidence shows, for example, that there must be connections from the taste receptors via the solitary nucleus of the medulla (36). Also there is evidence of rich connections from the visual system via the lateral geniculate of the thalamus (36). There is no doubt about the fact that the hypothalamus is under very extensive sensory control.

As to the sensory control of motivation, there is excellent reason to believe that the stimuli which can set up impulses in these pathways to the hypothalamus are of particular importance. Perhaps the best example comes from the study of sexual behavior (11). The consensus of a group of studies on different mammals is as follows. Sexual behavior is not dependent upon any single sensory system. Extirpation of any one peripheral sense organ has no appreciable influence on the arousal and execution of sexual behavior. If two sensory avenues are destroyed, however, sexual behavior may be eliminated, especially in the case of the naïve animal. With experienced animals, interestingly enough, it may take destruction of three sensory systems. But in neither case does it matter what combination of sensory systems is eliminated. We can conclude, therefore, that it is the sum total of relevant sensory impulses arriving at the central nervous system (hypothalamus) that is important in setting off sexual behavior.

Kleitman's analysis of sleep and wakefulness shows that the same kind of sensory control operates in this case (38). Wakefulness seems to be dependent upon the sum total of sensory impulses arriving at the waking center in the posterior hypothalamus, regardless of the particular sensory systems involved. Direct support of this kind of view is offered by Bremer's (14) physiological data which showed that maintenance of the waking rhythm of the brain is less a matter of any particular sensory input and more a matter of the amount of sensory input.

What we know about hunger and thirst suggests that the amount of motivated behavior in these cases should be a joint function of sensory impulses arising from gastric contractions or dryness of the throat and taste, tactile, and temperature receptors in the mouth. Unfortunately we have no sensory deprivation experiments that are a good test of this point. But all the evidence on the acceptability of foods and fluids of different temperatures, consistencies, and flavoring suggests the joint operation of many stimuli in the control of these types of motivation.

So far, we have mentioned only stimuli which arouse motivation. What stimulus changes could reduce motivation and perhaps lead to satiation? There are three general possibilities: (*a*) a reduction in excitatory stimuli, (*b*) interfering or distracting stimuli that elicit competing behavior, and (*c*) "inhibitory" stimuli. It is easy to find examples of the first two types of stimulus changes and to guess their mechanisms of operation in terms of the present theory. In the case of "inhibitory" stimuli, however, all we have is suggestive evidence. For example, the fact that dogs with esophageal fistulas eat (37) and drink (1, 13) amounts proportional to the severity of deprivation suggests that the stimuli which feed back from consummatory behavior might have a net inhibitory effect on motivation (see Fig. 1). Furthermore, some of the experiments on artificially loading the stomach suggest that a full gut may result in stimuli which inhibit further eating (37) or drinking (2, 13) over and above the possibility that there might be no room left in the stomach or that gastric contractions are reduced.

In summary, we can state the following working hypotheses about the sensory factors which operate in the control of motivation. (*a*) No one sensory avenue is indispensable in the arousal of motivated behavior. Instead, sensory stimuli have an additive effect on the excitability of the hypothalamus so that it is the sum total of relevant impulses arriving at the excitatory centers of the hypothalamus that determine the amount of motivated behavior. (*b*) Judging from the resistance of experienced animals to the effects of sensory deprivation in the case of sexual motivation, it seems clear that excitatory influences in the hypothalamus may be exerted by learned as well as unlearned stimuli. (*c*) There are afferent impulses to the hypothalamus which have a net inhibitory effect on the excitatory centers and thus serve to reduce motivation or produce satiation. The best guess at present is that these "inhibitory" stimuli operate by exerting an excitatory influence on the inhibitory centers of the hypothalamus. Presumably, impulses to inhibitory centers have the same kind of additive properties as impulses to the excitatory centers.

Internal environment. That the internal environment plays an important role in certain kinds of motivated behavior is a well-established fact. Two basic questions must be asked, however, before we can understand much about how the internal environment does its work. What kinds of changes that can occur in the internal environment are the important ones in motivation? How do changes in the internal environment influence the nervous system and, therefore, motivated behavior?

In terms of the present theory, we would expect the internal environment to operate in motivation by changing the excitability of hypothalamic centers. This is a reasonable expectation, for the hypothalamus is the most richly vascularized region of the central nervous system (24). Not only that, but the hypothalamus is also in direct contact with the cerebrospinal fluid in the third ventricle.

The case of sexual behavior again makes an excellent example. Experiments on the spayed female cat (6, 17) and spayed female guinea pig (28) have shown that hypothalamic regions must be intact and functioning if injected sex hormones are to arouse estrous behavior. If a section is made through the spinal cord, only rudimentary fragments of sexual behavior can be elicited by appropriate stimulation, and injected sex hormones make no contribution to the response. Essentially the same thing is true if the section is made high in the hind brain but excludes the hypothalamus. When the decerebration is just above the hypothalamus, full estrous reactions can be aroused by appropriate stimulation, but only if sex hormones have been administered. It is clear, then, that not only is the hypothalamus the main integrating center for sexual reactions, but it is also most likely the main site of action of the sex hormones. This point is further supported by studies of female guinea pigs with pinpoint lesions of the anterior hypothalamus. These animals fail to show sexual behavior even under the influence of massive doses of sex hormones (19).

A very similar mechanism seems to be involved in the case of motivated behavior dependent upon the organism's defenses against temperature extremes (activity, nesting, hoarding, selection of high-calorie diets). We know, for example, that reactions regulating body temperature in the face of heat and cold are integrated in two separate centers in the hypothalamus (15, 51). Lesions in the anterior hypothalamus destroy the ability to lose heat and, therefore, to survive in high temperatures. Posterior hypothalamic lesions, conversely, result in a loss of heat production mechanisms so that the animal succumbs to cold. Furthermore, artificially raising the temperature of the anterior hypothalamus will quickly induce heat loss, suggesting that normally the temperature of the blood may be important in activating the hypothalamic mechanisms (15, 44). Unfortunately our information stops here. There are no direct physiological studies on the role of these temperature-regulating mechanisms in the control of motivated behavior like activity, hoarding, nesting, or food selection. But it seems clear that the temperature of the blood may be one of the kinds of changes in the internal environment that can affect the hypothalamus, and it may be important in motivated behavior.

Ample evidence demonstrates that there are important changes in the internal environment involved in other kinds of motivated behavior. In hunger it has been shown that chemicals like insulin (32, 33, 48) and d-amphetamine (57) influence the rate of eating. It is clear that these chemicals do not operate primarily through their effects on gastric contractions, but it is only by a process of elimination that we can guess that their sites of action are in the hypothalamus. Supporting this possibility is the evidence that there are chemoreceptors in the hypothalamus which are sensitive to variations in blood sugar and important in the regulation of hunger (45). In the case of specific hungers, much evidence shows that food preference and diet selection depend upon changes in the internal environment produced by such things as pregnancy, dietary deficiencies, or disturbances of endocrine glands (54). Furthermore there are some preliminary experimental data, in the case of salt and sugar appetites, to suggest that there are separate regulatory centers in the hypothalamus which are responsive to changes in salt and sugar balance (59). Finally, in the case of thirst we know that a change in osmotic pressure, resulting from cellular dehydration, is the important internal change leading to drinking behavior (31). We know further that in the hypothalamus there are nerve cells, called "osmoreceptors," which are extremely sensitive to minute changes in osmotic pressure (61). But the direct experiment has not been done to check whether or not it is these nerve cells which are mainly responsible for the control of thirst.[1]

Obviously the experimental evidence on hunger, specific hunger, and thirst is incomplete. But enough of it fits into the scheme of the theoretical mechanism proposed here to suggest the real possibility that the internal changes important in these cases operate largely through their effects on the hypothalamus.

One question still remains. What role does the internal environment play in the mechanism of satiation? About all we have to go on at present is the very striking fact from the case of specific hungers that vastly different amounts of consummatory behavior are needed to bring about satiation for different food substances. In vitamin deficiencies only a few milligrams of substance need be consumed to produce satiation, whereas in caloric deficiencies many grams of carbohydrate, fat, or protein must be ingested. Presumably, it is not the sensory feedback from consummatory behavior that is important in these cases, but rather some inhibitory effects produced by what is consumed (Fig. 1). Within the present theoretical framework, such inhibitory effects could be produced either by depression of excitatory centers of the hypothalamus or by arousal of activity in inhibitory centers. The problem is an important one and it is wide open for study.

It is clear from the foregoing that many types of motivated behavior are dependent upon changes in the internal environment. Several points are worth emphasizing. (a) A variety of kinds of changes in the internal environment can play a role in the regulation of motivation: variation in the concentration

[1] In a recent publication, Anderson of Stockholm has shown that injection of small quantities of hypertonic NaCl directly into restricted regions along the midline of the hypothalamus produces immediate and extensive drinking in water-satiated goats. (Anderson, B. The effect of injections of hypertonic NaCl-solutions into different parts of the hypothalamus of goats. *Acta Physiol. scand.,* 1953, **28**, 188–201.)

of certain chemicals, especially hormones, changes in osmotic pressure, and changes in blood temperature. (*b*) The best hypothesis at present is that these internal changes operate by contributing to the activity of excitatory hypothalamic centers controlling motivation. (*c*) An equally important but less well-supported hypothesis is that internal changes, normally produced by consummatory behavior, operate in the production of satiation by depressing excitatory centers or arousing inhibitory centers of the hypothalamus.

Cortical and thalamic centers.   Despite the heavy emphasis laid upon the hypothalamus in this discussion, it is obvious that it is not the only neural center operating in the control of motivated behavior. In the first place, some of the sensory, motor, and associative functions of the cortex and thalamus are directly important in motivation quite apart from any influence they have on the hypothalamus. Secondly, even though the hypothalamus may be the main integrating center in motivation, it does not operate in isolation. There is much evidence that the hypothalamus is under the direct control of a number of different cortical and thalamic centers (Fig. 2).

The case of emotions offers the best example of how the cortex may operate in motivation. According to the early work of Bard and his co-workers on the production of "sham rage" by decortication, it looked as though the entire cortex might normally play an inhibitory role in emotions (5). More recent work, however, shows that cortical control of emotion is more complicated than this. Bard and Mountcastle (7), for example, have found that removal of certain parts of the old cortex (particularly amygdala and transitional cortex of the midline) produced a tremendous increase in rage reactions in cats. On the other hand, removing only new cortex resulted in extremely placid cats. Results of work with monkeys (40) and some very recent experiments with cats disagree somewhat with these findings in showing that similar old cortex removals lead to placidity rather than ferocity. The disagreement is yet to be resolved, but at least it is clear that different parts of the cortex may play different roles in the control of emotion, certain parts being inhibitory and others excitatory.

In the case of sleep, it appears so far that the cortex and thalamus play excitatory roles, perhaps having the effect of maintaining the activity of the waking center in the posterior hypothalamus. Decortication in dogs, for example, results in an inability to postpone sleep and remain awake for very long, or, as Kleitman puts it, a return to polyphasic sleep and waking rhythms (38, 39). Studies of humans, moreover, show that even restricted lesions of the cortex or thalamus alone can result in an inability to stay awake normally (25, 26). But no inhibitory effects of the cortex in sleep have yet been uncovered.

In sexual behavior it has been found that lesions of the new cortex may interfere directly with the arousal of sexual behavior (9, 11). Large lesions are much more effective than small lesions, as you might expect. Furthermore, cortical damage is much more serious in male animals than in females and is much more important in the sexual behavior of primates than it is in the case of lower mammals. On the other hand, in connection with studies of the cortex in emotions, it has been found that lesions of the amygdala and transitional cortex of the midline can lead to heightened sexuality in cats and monkeys (7, 40). So it looks as though the cortex may exert both excitatory and inhibitory influences in sexual motivation.

Evidence from other types of motivated behavior is only fragmentary, but it fits into the same general picture. In the case of hunger, it has been reported that certain lesions of the frontal lobes will lead to exaggerated eating behavior (41, 55). Hyperactivity may follow similar frontal lobe lesions and is particularly marked after damage to the orbital surface of the frontal lobe (56). The frontal areas may also be involved in what might be called pain avoidance. Clinical studies of man show that lobotomies may be used for the relief of intractable pain (29). The curious thing about these cases is that they still report the same amount of pain after operation but they say that it no longer bothers them. Presumably the frontal cortex normally plays an excitatory role in the motivation to avoid pain.

In all the cases cited so far, the anatomical and physiological evidence available suggests strongly that the main influence of the cortex and thalamus in motivation is mediated by the hypothalamus. But we do not yet have direct proof of this point and need experiments to check it.

Interaction of factors.   Up to now, we have treated the various factors that can operate in the control of motivated behavior singly. However, one of the main points of the theory proposed here is that the various factors operate together in the control of motivation. Presumably this interaction of factors occurs in the hypothalamus and takes the form of the "addition" of all excitatory influences and the "subtraction" of all inhibitory influences. Some experimental evidence bears directly on this point.

In the case of sexual behavior, for example, it is clear that excitatory influences of the cortex and hormones are additive. After sexual motivation is eliminated by cortical damage it may be restored by the administration of large doses of sex hormones (10). Since the hypothalamus is the site of action of the sex hormones, it seems likely that it is also the site of interaction of the influences of the hormones and cortex.

In a similar way, it looks as though the contributions of sensory stimulation and sex hormones add in the hypothalamus. Neither hormones nor stimulation alone is sufficient to elicit sexual reactions in most mammals, but the right combination of the two will. Still another example of the addition of excitatory influences is seen in the study of the sexual behavior of the male rabbit. In this case neither destruction of the olfactory bulbs nor decortication will eliminate mating behavior, but a combination of the two operations will (21).

It is very important to know whether excitatory, and perhaps also inhibitory, influences in other kinds of motivation have the same sort of additive properties as in sexual behavior. Indirect evidence suggests they do, but direct experiments of the sort described here are needed to check the possibility.

Most encouraging in this connection is that students of instinctive behavior in inframammalian vertebrates and invertebrates have presented considerable evidence showing that sensory, chemical, and neural influences contribute jointly to the arousal of many kinds of motivated behavior (60). For example, in a number of cases it has been shown that the threshold for arousing behavior by various stimuli is lowered considerably by appropriate changes in the internal environment. In fact, in the extreme case, when internal changes are maximal, the behavior may occur in the absence of any obvious stimulation. Presumably in these cases, as in the examples of mammalian motivation, chemical and neural influences contribute to the arousal of some central response mechanism in an additive way.

The role of learning. It is obvious to every student of mammalian motivation that learning and experience may play extremely important roles in the regulation of motivated behavior.

What does this mean in terms of the present physiological theory? Unfortunately, we cannot specify the mechanisms through which learning enters into the control of motivation because we are ignorant of the basic physiology of learning. But we can make some helpful inferences.

The basic hypothesis in the present theoretical framework is that learning contributes to hypothalamic activity along with influences from unlearned afferent impulses, internal changes, and cortical activity. In the case of sexual behavior we know that many animals learn to be aroused sexually by stimuli which were not previously adequate. Further, we know that in such experienced animals it is difficult to reduce sexual motivation by eliminating avenues of sensory stimulation, presumably because the extra excitatory effects produced by learned stimuli contribute to hypothalamic activity along with the impulses from unlearned stimuli. Along the same lines, it is known that sex hormones are relatively unimportant in man and in certain of the subhuman primates that have learned to be aroused by a wide variety of stimuli (12). Again, this may mean that the excitatory effects from the learned stimuli have added enough to the effects of unlearned stimuli to make it possible to dispense with the contribution of the sex hormones in arousing hypothalamic activity.

The evidence available on learning in other types of motivation fits in with this general theoretical picture, but direct physiological experiments have not yet carried us beyond the stage of inference. We know, for example, that vitamin-deficient rats can learn to show motivated behavior in response to certain flavors that have been associated with the vitamin in the past (34, 58). In fact, for a short while they will even pass up food containing the vitamin to eat vitamin-deficient food containing the flavor. Again, it looks as though flavor has become empowered by a process of learning to contribute to the excitability of the neural centers controlling motivation.

LIMITATIONS OF THE THEORY

Like any theoretical approach, the physiological mechanism proposed here has many limitations. Fortunately none of them need be too serious as long as it is recognized that the theory is set up as a general guide for experiments and a framework for further theorizing. Obviously the theory is going to have to be changed and improved many times before it is free of limitations. In this spirit it might be said that the limitations of the theory are not much more than those aspects of motivation which need research the most. But whether we label them limitations or urgent areas of research, they deserve explicit attention.

The concept of "center." Throughout this discussion the terms "neural center" and "hypothalamic center" have been used. "Center" is a useful and convenient term, but it is also a dangerous one, for it may carry with it the implication of strict localization of function within isolated anatomical entities. Actually this implication is not intended, for it is recognized that localization is a relative matter and that no neural mechanism operates in isolation. Furthermore, it is also possible that there may be no discoverable localization of the neural mechanisms governing some types of motivated behavior. The theory simply states at the moment that the best general hypothesis is that some degree of localization of the mechanisms controlling motivation can be found in the hypothalamus.

Execution of motivated behavior. No attempt has been made in this discussion to describe the details of the efferent pathways or effector mechanisms responsible for the execution of motivated behavior. Discussion of the pathways has been omitted because we know very little about them. About all we can do at present is to guess, from anatomical and physiological studies of hypothalamic function, that the hypothalamus exerts some kind of "priming" effect on effector pathways controlled by other parts of the nervous system. Perhaps after the relationship of the hypothalamus to motivated behavior has been more firmly established we can profitably turn to the question of how the hypothalamus does its work.

A second aspect of the execution of motivated behavior has been omitted for the sake of brevity. We all recognize that an animal with certain kinds of cortical lesions, or deprived of certain sensory capacities, may be handicapped in executing motivated behavior quite aside from any effects these operations may have on the arousal of motivation. Fortunately most investigators have been aware of this problem and have taken pains to distinguish these two effects, focusing their attention mainly on the arousal of motivation. Some day, however, this theory should address the question of what neural mechanisms govern the execution of motivated behavior.

General nature of the mechanism.   For theoretical purposes it has been assumed that essentially the same mechanism controls all types of motivated behavior. Obviously this is not likely to be the case, nor is it an essential assumption. In some types of motivation only parts of this mechanism may be involved, or factors not included in the present scheme may operate. For example, in some cases the hypothalamus may not be involved at all, or it may turn out that there are no inhibitory centers at work, or that internal chemical factors do not contribute significantly. There is no reason why we should not be prepared for these eventualities. But until specific experimental evidence to the contrary is forthcoming, the general mechanism proposed here still remains as the best working hypothesis for any particular type of biological motivation.

Inadequacy of behavioral measures.   To a large degree the present discussion is based upon measures of consummatory behavior. We all know that the various measures of motivation are not always in good agreement, so there is good possibility that what we say about consummatory behavior may not apply to motivation measured by other methods. In fact, Miller, Bailey, and Stevenson (46) have recently shown that whereas rats with hypothalamic lesions overeat in the free-feeding situation, they do not show a high degree of motivation when required to overcome some barrier to obtain food.

Confining the present discussion mainly to consummatory behavior is clearly a weakness. But the logic behind this limited approach is to work out the physiological mechanisms in the simplest case first, and then to see how they must be revised to fit the more complicated cases.

Complex motivation.   It can also be argued, of course, that the present theory is confined to the simple, biological motives. Again, it seems eminently advisable to keep the theory relatively narrow in scope until it is developed well enough to permit attack on the more complicated, learned motives.

Comparative approach.   No attempt has been made here to make it explicit how the proposed theory applies to organisms representative of different phylogenetic levels. There are many obvious advantages to the comparative approach, but unfortunately, except for the case of sexual motivation, the information we have on different species is too scattered to be useful. Judging from what we have learned from the comparative study of sexual motivation, however, we can expect the various factors governing other types of motivation to contribute somewhat differently in animals at different phylogenetic levels. Certainly learning should be more important in primates than in subprimates, and the contributions of the cortex and thalamus should be greater. Much will be gained if future research in motivation follows the excellent example set in the study of sexual behavior and provides the much needed comparative data.

ADVANTAGES OF THE THEORY

On the assumption that none of these limitations of the theory is critical, it is appropriate to ask: What is gained by proposing an explicit theory of the physiological mechanisms underlying motivated behavior? There are many positive answers to this question, and we can list some of them briefly.

Simplification of the problem. One of the main advantages of the theoretical mechanism proposed here is that it brings together, into one general framework, a number of different kinds of motivation that have been studied separately in the past. Certainly the theory encompasses the basic facts available on sex, hunger, specific hunger, thirst, sleep, and emotion. And it may also be able to handle the facts of pain avoidance, hoarding, nesting, maternal behavior, and other types of so-called instinctive behavior. As you have seen, one of the benefits deriving from this kind of simplification of the problem of motivation is the possibility of speeding up progress by applying what has been learned about physiological mechanisms from the study of one kind of motivation to the study of other kinds of motivation. Not only that, but the assumption that the hypothalamus is central in the control of all types of motivation may make it easier to explain the various types of interaction among motivations that have shown up in many studies of behavior.

Multifactor approach. Another advantage of the present theory is that it gives strong emphasis to the view that motivation is under multifactor control. Single-factor theories, so prevalent since the days of Cannon, can only lead to useless controversies over which factor is the "right" one and must always be guilty of omission in trying to account for the control of motivation. Of course, it must be stressed that the aim of the multifactor approach is not simply to list the many possible factors operating in motivation, but rather to get down to the concrete experimental task of determining the relevant factors which control motivation and the relative contribution of each.

Satiation of motivation.   Unlike most previous theories of motivation, the mechanism proposed here attempts to account for the satiation of motivation as well as its arousal. In terms of the present theory satiation is determined by the reduction of activity in the main excitatory centers of the hypothalamus. More specifically, it looks as though the inhibitory centers of the hypothalamus may constitute a separate "satiation mechanism" which is the most important influence in the reduction of the activity of the excitatory centers. The possibility is an intriguing one, and it can be directly explored by experiment.

Peripheral and central control.   In the past the study of motivation has been hampered by the controversy over whether behavior is centrally or peripherally controlled. The controversy is nonsense. The only meaningful experimental problem is to determine how the central and peripheral, or sensory, factors operate together in the control of behavior. It is this problem which the present theory addresses directly, and this is one of its greatest strengths.

Learned and innate control.   The present theory avoids another knotty controversy by directly addressing experimental problems. Much time has been lost in psychology, and particularly in the study of motivation, in arguments over whether behavior is primarily innate or instinctive or whether it is primarily learned or acquired. The answer is obviously that it is both, and again the only meaningful experimental problem is to determine the relative contribution of each type of control. As far as the mechanism proposed here is concerned, both innate and learned factors make their contributions to the control of the same hypothalamic centers. There is still much work needed to determine the details of the mechanisms of operation, particularly of the learned factors, but some headway has been made and the problem is clearly set.

Explicit nature of the theory.   Finally, a number of advantages derive simply from having an explicit statement of an up-to-date, physiological theory of motivation. In the first place, an explicit theory can serve as a convenient framework within which to organize the physiological facts we already have at our disposal. Second, the systematic organization of the facts sharply points up many of the gaps in our knowledge and suggests direct experiments that should be done in the investigation of motivated behavior. Third, an up-to-date, systematic theory provides a useful and reasonably clear conceptualization of motivation for psychologists working in other areas of research.

SUMMARY AND CONCLUSIONS

A physiological theory of motivated behavior is presented. The basic assumption in this theory is that the amount of motivated behavior is a function of the amount of activity in certain excitatory centers of the hypothalamus. The level of activity of the critical hypothalamic centers, in turn, is governed by the operation of four factors.

1. Inhibitory centers in the hypothalamus directly depress the activity of the excitatory centers and may be responsible for the production of satiation.
2. Sensory stimuli set up afferent impulses which naturally contribute to the excitability of the hypothalamus or come to do so through a process of learning.
3. Changes in the internal environment exert both excitatory and inhibitory effects on the hypothalamus.
4. Cortical and thalamic influences increase and decrease the excitability of hypothalamic centers.

Detailed experimental evidence is brought forward to show how these various factors operate in the management of different kinds of motivated behavior. The over-all scheme is shown diagrammatically in Figure 1.

Out of consideration of this evidence a number of hypotheses are generated to fill in the gaps in experimental knowledge. All these hypotheses are experimentally testable. The ones of major importance can be given here as a summary of what the theory states and a partial list of the experiments it suggests.

1. There are different centers in the hypothalamus responsible for the control of different kinds of basic motivation.
2. In each case of motivation, there is one main excitatory center and one inhibitory center which operates to depress the activity of the excitatory center.

There is already much experimental evidence supporting these two general hypotheses, but it is not certain that they apply fully to all types of basic biological motivation. The hypotheses should be checked further by determining whether changes in all types of motivation can be produced by local hypothalamic lesions and whether both increases and decreases in motivation can always be produced.

3. The activity of hypothalamic centers is, in part, controlled by the excitatory effects of afferent impulses generated by internal and external stimuli.
4. Different stimuli contribute different relative amounts to hypothalamic activity but no one avenue of sensory stimulation is indispensable.
5. It is the sum total of afferent impulses arriving at the hypothalamus that determines the level of excitability and, therefore, the amount of motivation.

The neuroanatomical and neurophysiological evidence shows that the hypothalamus is richly supplied with afferents coming directly and indirectly from all the sense organs (Fig. 2). The behavioral evidence, furthermore, strongly suggests that motivation is never controlled, in mammals at least, by one sensory system, but rather is the combination of contributions of several sensory systems. Sensory control and sensory deprivation experiments are needed to check this point in the case of most kinds of biological motivation, particularly hunger, thirst, and specific hungers.

6. A variety of kinds of physical and chemical changes in the internal environment influence the excitability of hypothalamic centers and, therefore, contribute to the control of motivation.

The evidence shows that the hypothalamus is the most richly vascularized region of the central nervous system and is most directly under the influence of the cerebrospinal fluid. Furthermore, it is clear that changes in the internal environment produced by temperature of the blood, osmotic pressure, hormones, and a variety of other chemicals are important in motivation and most likely operate through their influence on the hypothalamus. Direct studies are still needed in many cases, however, to show that the particular change that is important in motivation actually does operate through the hypothalamus and vice versa.

7. The cerebral cortex and thalamus are directly important in the temporal and spatial organization of motivated behavior.
8. Different parts of the cortex and thalamus also operate selectively in the control of motivation by exerting excitatory or inhibitory influences on the hypothalamus.

Tests of these hypotheses can be carried out by total decortication, partial cortical ablations, and local thalamic lesions. It should be especially instructive to see what effects cortical and thalamic lesions have after significant changes in motivation have been produced by hypothalamic lesions.

9. Learning contributes along with other factors to the control of motivation, probably through direct influence on the hypothalamus.
10. The relative contribution of learning should increase in animals higher and higher on the phylogenetic scale.

A whole series of experiments is needed here. Particularly, there should be comparisons of naïve and experienced animals to determine the relative effects of sensory deprivation, cortical and thalamic damage, and hypothalamic lesions. Presumably animals that have learned to be aroused to motivated behavior by previously inadequate stimuli should require more sensory deprivation but less cortical and thalamic damage than naïve animals before motivation is significantly impaired.

11. The various factors controlling motivation combine their influences at the hypothalamus by the addition of all excitatory influences and the subtraction of all inhibitory influences.

Some experiments have already been done in the study of sexual motivation to show that motivation reduced by the elimination of one factor (cortical lesions) can be restored by increasing the contribution of other factors (hormone therapy). Many combinations of this kind of experiment should be carried out with different kinds of motivated behavior.

A number of the limitations and some of the advantages of the present theoretical approach to the physiology of motivation are discussed.

REFERENCES

1. Adolph, E. F. The internal environment and behavior. Part III. Water content. *Amer. J. Psychiat.*, 1941, **97,** 1365-1373.
2. Adolph, E. F. Thirst and its inhibition in the stomach. *Amer. J. Physiol.*, 1950, **161,** 374-386.
3. Anand, B. K., & Brobeck, J. R. Hypothalamic control of food intake in rats and cats. *Yale J. Biol. Med.*, 1951, **24,** 123-140.
4. Anand, B. K., & Brobeck, J. R. Localization of a "feeding center" in the hypothalamus of the rat. *Proc. Soc. exp. Biol. Med.*, 1951, **77,** 323-324.
5. Bard, P. Central nervous mechanisms for emotional behavior patterns in animals. *Res. Publ. Ass. nerv. ment. Dis.*, 1939, **19,** 190-218.
6. Bard, P. The hypothalamus and sexual behavior. *Res. Publ. Ass. nerv. ment. Dis.*, 1940, **20,** 551-579.
7. Bard, P., & Mountcastle, V. B. Some forebrain mechanisms involved in the expression of rage with special reference to the suppression of angry behavior. *Res. Publ. Ass. nerv. ment. Dis.*, 1947, **27,** 362-404.
8. Beach, F. A. Analysis of factors involved in the arousal, maintenance and manifestation of sexual excitement in male animals. *Psychosom. Med.*, 1942, **4,** 173-198.
9. Beach, F. A. Central nervous mechanisms involved in the reproductive behavior of vertebrates. *Psychol. Bull.*, 1942, **39,** 200-206.
10. Beach, F. A. Relative effect of androgen upon the mating behavior of male rats subjected to forebrain injury or castration. *J. exp. Zool.*, 1944, **97,** 249-295.
11. Beach, F. A. A review of physiological and psychological studies of sexual behavior in mammals. *Physiol. Rev.*, 1947, **27,** 240-307.
12. Beach, F. A. Evolutionary changes in the physiological control of mating behavior in mammals. *Psycol. Rev.*, 1947, **54,** 297-315.
13. Bellows, R. T. Time factors in water drinking in dogs. *Amer. J. Physiol.*, 1939, **125,** 87-97.
14. Bremer, F. Étude oscillographique des activités sensorielles du cortex cérébral. *C. R. Soc. Biol.*, 1937, **124,** 842-846.
15. Brobeck, J. R. Regulation of energy exchange. In J. F. Fulton (Ed.), *A textbook of physiology.* Philadelphia: Saunders, 1950.
16. Brobeck, J. R., Tepperman, J., & Long, C. N. H. Experimental hypothalamic hyperphagia in the albino rat. *Yale J. Biol. Med.*, 1943, **15,** 831-853.
17. Bromiley, R. B., & Bard, P. A study of the effect of estrin on the responses to genital stimulation shown by decapitate and decerebrate female cats. *Amer. J. Physiol.*, 1940, **129,** 318-319.
18. Brookhart, J. M., & Dey, F. L. Reduction of sexual behavior in male guinea pigs by hypothalamic lesions. *Amer. J. Physiol.*, 1941, **133,** 551-554.
19. Brookhart, J. M., Dey, F. L., & Ranson, S. W. Failure of ovarian

hormones to cause mating reactions in spayed guinea pigs with hypothalamic lesions. *Proc. Soc. exp. Biol. Med.*, 1940, **44**, 61-64.

20. Brookhart, J. M., Dey, F. L., & Ranson, S. W. The abolition of mating behavior by hypothalamic lesions in guinea pigs. *Endocrinol.*, 1941, **28**, 561-565.

21. Brooks, C. M. The role of the cerebral cortex and of various sense organs in the excitation and execution of mating activity in the rabbit. *Amer. J. Physiol.*, 1937, **120**, 544-553.

22. Brooks, C. M. Appetite and obesity. *N. Z. med. J.*, 1947, **46**, 243-254.

23. Cannon, W. B. Hunger and thirst. In C. Murchison (Ed.), *A handbook of general experimental psychology.* Worcester, Mass.: Clark Univer. Press, 1934.

24. Craigie, E. H. Measurements of vascularity in some hypothalamic nuclei of the albino rat. *Res. Publ. Ass. nerv. ment. Dis.*, 1940, **20**, 310-319.

25. Davison, C., & Demuth, E. L. Disturbances in sleep mechanism: A clinico-pathologic study. I. Lesions at the cortical level. *Arch. Neurol. Psychiat., Chicago*, 1945, **53**, 399-406.

26. Davison, C., & Demuth, E. L. Disturbances in sleep mechanism: A clinico-pathologic study. II. Lesions at the corticodiencephalic level. *Arch. Neurol. Psychiat., Chicago*, 1945, **54**, 241-255.

27. Delgado, J. M. R., & Anand, B. K. Increase of food intake induced by electrical stimulation of the lateral hypothalamus. *Amer. J. Physiol.*, 1953, **172**, 162-168.

28. Dempsey, E. W., & Rioch, D. McK. The localization in the brain stem of the oestrous responses of the female guinea pig. *J. Neurophysiol.*, 1939, **2**, 9-18.

29. Freeman, W., & Watts, J. W. *Psychosurgery.* (2nd Ed.) Springfield, Ill.: Charles C Thomas, 1950.

30. Gellhorn, E. *Autonomic regulations.* New York: Interscience, 1943.

31. Gilman, A. The relation between blood osmotic pressure, fluid distribution and voluntary water intake. *Amer. J. Physiol.*, 1937, **120**, 323-328.

32. Grossman, M. I., Cummins, G. M., & Ivy, A. C. The effect of insulin on food intake after vagotomy and sympathectomy. *Amer. J. Physiol.*, 1947, **149**, 100-102.

33. Grossman, M. I., & Stein, I. F. Vagotomy and the hunger producing action of insulin in man. *J. appl. Physiol.*, 1948, **1**, 263-269.

34. Harris, L. J., Clay, J., Hargreaves, F. J., & Ward, A. Appetite and choice of diet: The ability of the Vitamin B deficient rat to discriminate between diets containing and lacking the vitamin. *Proc. roy. Soc.*, 1933, **113**, 161-190.

35. Hetherington, A. W., & Ranson, S. W. The spontaneous activity and food intake of rats with hypothalamic lesions. *Amer. J. Physiol.*, 1942, **136**, 609-617.

36. Ingram, W. R. Nuclear organization and chief connections of the primate hypothalmus. *Res. Publ. Ass. nerv. ment. Dis.*, 1940, **20**, 195-244.

37. Janowitz, H. D., & Grossman, M. I. Some factors affecting the food intake of normal dogs and dogs with esophagostomy and gastric fistula. *Amer. J. Physiol.*, 1949, **159**, 143-148.

38. Kleitman, N. *Sleep and wakefulness.* Chicago: Univer. of Chicago, 1939.

39. Kleitman, N., & Camille, N. Studies on the physiology of sleep. VI. Behavior of decorticated dogs. *Amer. J. Physiol.*, 1932, **100**, 474-480.

40. Klüver, H., & Bucy, P. C. Preliminary analysis of functions of the temporal lobes in monkeys. *Arch. Neurol. Psychiat.*, *Chicago*, 1939, **42**, 979-1000.

41. Langworthy, O. R., & Richter, C. P. Increased spontaneous activity produced by frontal lobe lesions in cats. *Amer. J. Physiol.*, 1939, **126**, 158-161.

42. Lashley, K. S. Experimental analysis of instinctive behavior. *Psychol. Rev.*, 1938, **45**, 445-471.

43. Lindsley, D. B. Emotion. In S. S. Stevens (Ed.), *Handbook of experimental psychology.* New York: Wiley, 1951.

44. Magoun, H. W., Harrison, F., Brobeck, J. R., & Ranson, S. W. Activation of heat loss mechanisms by local heating of the brain. *J. Neurophysiol.*, 1938, **1**, 101-114.

45. Mayer, J., Vitale, J. J., & Bates, M. W. Mechanism of the regulation of food intake. *Nature*, 1951, **167**, 562-563.

46. Miller, N. E., Bailey, C. J., & Stevenson, J. A. F. Decreased "hunger" but increased food intake resulting from hypothalamic lesions. *Science*, 1950, **112**, 256-259.

47. Morgan, C. T. *Physiological psychology.* (1st Ed.) New York: McGraw-Hill, 1943.

48. Morgan, C. T., & Morgan, J. D. Studies in hunger. I. The effects of insulin upon the rat's rate of eating. *J. genet. Psychol.*, 1940, **56**, 137-147.

49. Nauta, W. J. H. Hypothalamic regulation of sleep in rats: An experimental study. *J. Neurophysiol.*, 1946, **9**, 285-316.

50. Ranson, S. W. Somnolence caused by hypothalamic lesions in the monkey. *Arch. Neurol. Psychiat.*, 1939, **41**, 1-23.

51. Ranson, S. W. Regulation of body temperature. *Res. Publ. Ass. nerv. ment. Dis.*, 1940, **20**, 342-399.

52. Ranson, S. W., Kabat, H., & Magounc H. W. Autonomic responses to electrical stimulation of hypothalamus, pre-optic region and septum. *Arch. Neurol. Psychiat.*, *Chicago*, 1935, **33**, 467-477.

53. Ranström, S. *The hypothalamus and sleep regulation.* Uppsala: Almquist and Wiksells, 1947.

54. Richter, C. P. Total self regulatory functions in animals and human beings. *Harvey Lect.*, 1942-43, **38**, 63-103.

55. Richter, C. P., & Hawkes, C. D. Increased spontaneous activity and food intake produced in rats by removal of the frontal poles of the brain. *J. Neurol. Psychiat.*, 1939, **2**, 231-242.

56. Ruch, T. C., & Shenkin, H. A. The relation of area 13 of the

orbital surface of the frontal lobe to hyperactivity and hyper-phagia in monkeys. *J. Neurophysiol.*, 1943, **6**, 349-360.

57. Sangster, W., Grossman, M. I., & Ivy, A. C. Effect of d-amphetamine on gastric hunger contractions and food intake in the dog. *Amer. J. Physiol.*, 1948, **153**, 259-263.

58. Scott, E. M., & Verney, E. L. Self selection of diet. VI. The nature of appetites for B vitamins. *J. Nutrit.*, 1947, **34**, 471-480.

59. Soulairac, A. La physiologie d'un comportement: L'appétit glucidique et sa régulation neuro-endocrinienne chez les rongeurs. *Bull. Biol.*, 1947, **81**, 1-160.

60. Tinbergen, N. *The study of instinct.* London: Oxford, 1951.

61. Verney, E. B. The antidiuretic hormone and the factors which determine its release. *Proc. roy. Soc., London*, 1947, **135**, 24-106.

62. Wheatley, M. D. The hypothalamus and affective behavior in cats. *Arch. Neurol. Psychiat.*, 1944, **52**, 296-316.

[ADDENDA FROM THE ORIGINAL PRINTING OF THIS ARTICLE: IN REFERENCE TO THE AUTHOR: *The Johns Hopkins University. Received February 26, 1953.*]

POSITIVE REINFORCEMENT PRODUCED BY ELECTRICAL STIMULATION OF SEPTAL AREA AND OTHER REGIONS OF RAT BRAIN ※ *James Olds and Peter Milner*

STIMULI have eliciting and reinforcing functions. In studying the former, one concentrates on the responses which come after the stimulus. In studying the latter, one looks mainly at the responses which precede it. In its reinforcing capacity, a stimulus increases, decreases, or leaves unchanged the frequency of preceding responses, and accordingly it is called a reward, a punishment, or a neutral stimulus (cf. 16).

Previous studies using chronic implantation of electrodes have tended to focus on the eliciting functions of electrical stimuli delivered to the brain (2, 3, 4, 5, 7, 10, 12, 14). The present study, on the other hand, has been concerned with the reinforcing function of the electrical stimulation.

REPRINTED FROM THE *Journal of Comparative and Physiological Psychology,* 47:419-427. COPYRIGHT © 1954 BY THE AMERICAN PSYCHOLOGICAL ASSOCIATION.

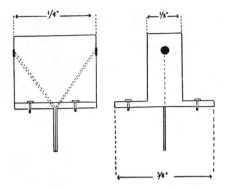

Fig. 1. Electrode design (see text
for detailed description).

METHOD

General

Stimulation was carried out by means of chonically implanted
electrodes which did not interfere with the health or free behavior
of Ss to any appreciable extent. The Ss were 15 male hooded rats,
weighing approximately 250 gm. at the start of the experiment.
Each S was tested in a Skinner box which delivered alternating
current to the brain so long as a lever was depressed. The current
was delivered over a loose lead, suspended from the ceiling, which
connected the stimulator to the rat's electrode. The Ss were given
a total of 6 to 12 hr. of acquisition testing, and 1 to 2 hr. of
extinction testing. During acquisition, the stimulator was turned on
so that a response produced electrical stimulation; during extinction,
the stimulator was turned off so that a response produced no electrical stimulation. Each S was given a percentage score denoting the
proportion of his total acquisition time given to responding. This
score could be compared with the animal's extinction score to determine whether the stimulation had a positive, negative, or neutral
reinforcing effect. After testing, the animal was sacrificed. Its brain
was frozen, sectioned, stained, and examined microscopically to
determine which structure of the brain had been stimulated. This
permitted correlation of acquisition scores with anatomical structures.

Electrode Implantation

Electrodes are constructed by cementing a pair of enameled silver
wires of 0.010-in. diameter into a Lucite block, as shown in Figure 1.
The parts of the wires which penetrate the brain are cemented together to form a needle, and this is cut to the correct length to
reach the desired structure in the brain. This length is determined
from Krieg's rat brain atlas (11) with slight modifications as found

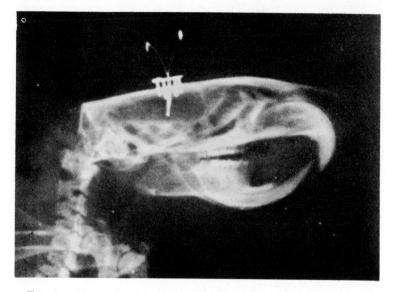

Fig. 2. X ray showing electrode in place in intact animal. There are two wires insulated completely from each other, stimulating the brain with their tips.

necessary by experience. The exposed cross section of the wire is the only part of the needle not insulated from the brain by enamel; stimulation therefore occurs only at the tip. Contact with the lead from the stimulator is made through two blobs of solder on the upper ends of the electrode wires; these blobs make contact with the jaws of an alligator clip which has been modified to insuate the two jaws from one another. A light, flexible hearing-aid lead connects the clip to the voltage source.

The operation of implantation is performed with the rat under Nembutal anesthesia (0.88 cc/Kg) and held in a Johnson-Krieg stereotaxic instrument (11). A mid-line incision is made in the scalp and the skin held out of the way by muscle retractors. A small hole is drilled in the skull with a dental burr at the point indicated by the stereotaxic instrument for the structure it is desired to stimulate. The electrode, which is clamped into the needle carrier of the instrument, is lowered until the flange of the Lucite block rests firmly on the skull. Four screw holes are then drilled in the skull through four fixing holes in the flange, and the electrode, still clamped firmly in the instrument, is fastened to the skull with jeweler's screws which exceed the diameter of the screw holes in the skull by 0.006 in. The electrode is then released from the clamp and the scalp wound closed with silk sutures. The skin is pulled tightly around the base of the Lucite block and kept well away from the contact plates. A recovery period of three days is allowed after the operation before testing. Figure 2 is an X-ray picture of an electrode in place.

Testing

The testing apparatus consisted of a large-levered Skinner box 11 in. long, 5 in. wide, and 12 in. high. The top was open to allow passage for the stimulating lead. The lever actuated a microswitch in the stimulating circuit so that when it was depressed, the rat received electrical stimulation. The current was obtained from the 60-cycle power line, through a step-down transformer, and was adjustable between 0 and 10 v. r.m.s. by means of a variable potentiometer. In the experiments described here the stimulation continued as long as the lever was pressed, though for some tests a time-delay switch was incorporated which cut the current off after a predetermined interval if the rat continued to hold the lever down. Responses were recorded automatically on paper strip.

On the fourth day after the operation rats were given a pretesting session of about an hour in the boxes. Each rat was placed in the box and on the lever by E with the stimulus set at 0.5 v. During the hour, stimulation voltage was varied to determine the threshold of a "just noticeable" effect on the rat's behavior. If the animal did not respond regularly from the start, it was placed on the lever periodically (at about 5-min. intervals). Data collected on the first day were not used in later calculations. On subsequent days, Ss were placed in the box for about 3½ hr. a day; these were 3 hr. of acquisition and ½ hr. of extinction. During the former, the rats were allowed to stimulate themselves with a voltage which was just high enough to produce some noticeable response in the resting animal. As this threshold voltage fluctuated with the passage of time, E would make a determination of it every half hour, unless S was responding regularly. At the beginning of each acquisition period, and after each voltage test, the animal was placed on the lever once by E. During extinction periods, conditions were precisely the same except that a bar press produced no electrical stimulation. At the beginning of each extinction period, animals which were not responding regularly were placed on the lever once by E. At first, rats were tested in this way for four days, but as there appeared to be little difference between the results on different days, this period was reduced to three and then to two days for subsequent animals. Thus, the first rats had about 12 hr. of acquisition after pretesting whereas later rats had about 6 hr. However, in computing the scores in our table, we have used only the first 6 hr. of acquisition for all animals, so the scores are strictly comparable. In behavioral curves, we have shown the full 12 hr. of acquisition on the earlier animals so as to illustrate the stability of the behavior over time.

At no time during the experiment were the rats deprived of food or water, and no reinforcement was used except the electrical stimulus.

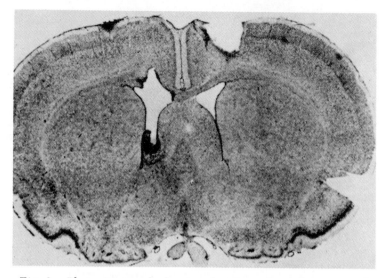

Fig. 3. Photomicrograph showing the electrode track in a cresyl-violet-stained brain section. The section is 1 mm. in front of the anterior commissure. The electrode protruded through the lateral ventricle and its stimulating tip was in the septal area.

Animals were scored on the percentage of time which they spent bar pressing regularly during acquisition. In order to find how much time the animal would spend in the absence of reward or punishment, a similar score was computed for periods of extinction. This extinction score provided a base line. When the acquisition score is above the extinction score, we have reward; when it is below the extinction score, we have punishment.

In order to determine percentage scores, periods when the animal was responding regularly (at least one response every 30 sec.) were counted as periods of responding; i.e., *intervals of 30 sec. or longer without a response were counted as periods of no responding.* The percentage scores were computed as the proportion of total acquisition or extinction time given to periods of responding.

Determination of Locus

On completion of testing, animals were perfused with physiological saline, followed by 10 per cent formalin. The brains were removed, and after further fixation in formalin for about a week, frozen sections 40 microns thick were cut through the region of the electrode track. These were stained with cresyl violet and the position of the electrode tip determined. Figure 3 is a photomicrograph showing the appearance of the electrode track in a stained and mounted brain section.

RESULTS

Locus

In Table 1, acquisition and extinction scores are correlated with electrode placements.

TABLE 1.   ACQUISITION AND EXTINCTION SCORES FOR ALL ANIMALS TOGETHER WITH ELECTRODE PLACEMENTS AND THRESHOLD VOLTAGES USED DURING ACQUISITION TESTS

Animal's No.	Locus of Electrode	Stimulation Voltage r.m.s.	Percentage of Acquisition Time Spent Responding	Percentage of Extinction Time Spent Responding
32	septal	2.2–2.8	75	18
34	septal	1.4	92	6
M-1	septal	1.7–4.8	85	21
M-4	septal	2.3–4.8	88	13
40	c.c.	.7–1.1	6	3
41	caudate	.9–1.2	4	4
31	cingulate	1.8	37	9
82	cingulate	.5–1.8	36	10
36	hip.	.8–2.8	11	14
3	m.l.	.5	0	4
A-5	m.t.	1.4	71	9
6	m.g.	.5	0	31
11	m.g.	.5	0	21
17	teg.	.7	2	1
9	teg.	.5	77	81

KEY: *c.c., corpus callosum; hip.,* hippocampus; *m.l.,* medial lemniscus; *m.t.,* Mammillothalamic tract; *m.g.,* medial geniculate; *teg.,* tegmentum.

Figure 4 presents the acquisition scores again, this time on three cross-sectional maps of the rat brain, one at the forebrain level, one at the thalamic level, and one at the mid-brain level. The position of a score on the map indicates the electrode placement from which this acquisition score was obtained.

The highest scores are found together in the central portion of the forebrain. Beneath the *corpus callosum* and between the two lateral ventricles in section I of Figure 4, we find four acquisition scores ranging from 75 to 92 per cent. This is the septal area. The Ss which produced these scores are numbered 32, 34, M-1, and M-4 in Table 1. It will be noticed that while all of them spent more than 75 per cent of their acquisition time re-

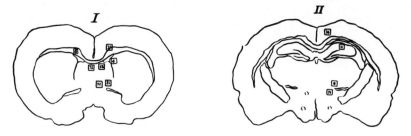

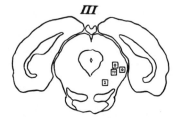

Fig. 4. Maps of three sections, (I) through the forebrain, (II) through the thalamus, (III) through the midbrain of the rat. Boxed numbers give acquisition percentage scores produced by animals with electrodes stimulating at these points. On section I the acquisition scores 75, 88, 92, 85 fall in the septal forebrain area. On the same section there is a score of 4 in the caudate nucleus, a score of 6 in the white matter below the cortex, and a score of 37 in the medial (cingulate) cortex. On section II the acquisition score of 36 is in the medial (cingulate) cortex, 11 is in the hippocampus, 71 is in the mammillothalamic tract, and 0 is in the medial lemniscus. On section III the two zeroes are in the medial geniculate, 2 is in the tegmental reticular substance, 77 falls 2 mm. anterior to the section shown—it is between the posterior commissure and the red nucleus.

sponding, they all spent less than 22 per cent of their extinction time responding. Thus the electrical stimulus in the septal area has an effect which is apparently equivalent to that of a conventional primary reward as far as the maintenance of a lever-pressing response is concerned.

If we move outside the septal area, either in the direction of the caudate nucleus (across the lateral ventricle) or in the direction of the *corpus callosum,* we find acquisition scores drop abruptly to levels of from 4 to 6 per cent. These are definitely indications of neutral (neither rewarding nor punishing) effects.

However, above the *corpus callosum* in the cingulate cortex we find an acquisition score of 37 per cent. As the extinction

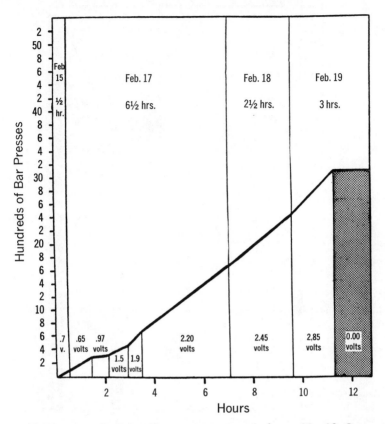

Fig. 5. Smoothed cumulative response curve for rat No. 32. Cumulative response totals are given along the ordinate, and hours along the abscissa. The steepness of the slope indicates the response rate. Stimulating voltages are given between black lines. Cross-hatching indicates extinction.

score in this case was 9 per cent, we may say that stimulation was rewarding.

At the thalamic level (section II of Fig. 4) we find a 36 per cent acquisition score produced by an electrode placed again in the cingulate cortex, an 11 per cent score produced by an electrode placed in the hippocampus, a 71 per cent score produced by an electrode placed exactly in the mammillothalamic tract, and a zero per cent score produced by an electrode placed in the medial lemniscus. The zero denotes negative reinforcement.

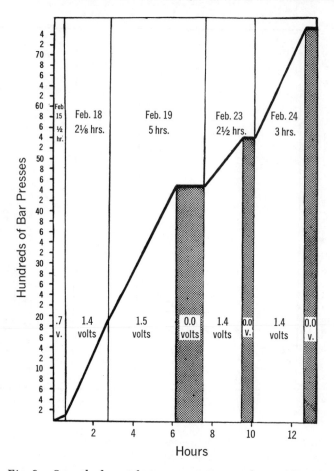

Fig. 6. Smoothed cumulative response curve for rat No. 34.

At the mid-brain level (section III of Fig. 4) there are two zero scores produced by electrodes which are in the posterior portion of the medial geniculate bodies; here again, the scores indicate a negative effect, as the corresponding extinction scores are 31 and 21 per cent. There is an electrode deep in the medial, posterior tegmentum which produces a 2 per cent score; this seems quite neutral, as the extinction score in this case is 1 per cent. Finally, there is an electrode shown on this section which actually stands 1½ mm. anterior to the point where it is shown; it was between the red nucleus and the posterior commissure. It produced an acquisition score of 77 per cent, but an extinction

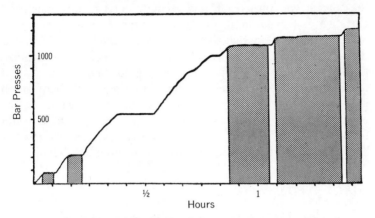

Fig. 7. Unsmoothed cumulative response curve showing about ¾ hr. of acquisition and ¾ hr. extinction for rat No. A-5. Shading indicates extinction.

score of 81 per cent. This must be a rewarding placement, but the high extinction score makes it difficult to interpret.

Behavior

We turn our attention briefly to the behavioral data produced by the more rewarding electrode placements.

The graph in Figure 5 is a smoothed cumulative response curve illustrating the rate of responding of rat No. 32 (the lowest-scoring septal area rat) during acquisition and extinction. The animal gave a total of slightly over 3000 responses in the 12 hr. of acquisition. When the current was turned on, the animal responded at a rate of 285 responses an hour; when the current was turned off, the rate fell close to zero.

The graph in Figure 6 gives similar data on rat No. 34 (the highest-scoring septal rat). The animal stimulated itself over 7500 times in 12 hr. Its average response rate during acquisition was 742 responses an hour; during extinction, practically zero.

Figure 7 presents an unsmoothed cumulative response curve for one day of responding for rat No. A-5. This is to illustrate in detail the degree of control exercised by the electrical reward stimulus. While this rat was actually bar pressing, it did so at 1920 responses an hour; that is, about one response for every 2 sec. During the first period of the day it responded regularly while on acquisition, extinguished very rapidly when the current was turned off, and reconditioned readily when the current was turned on again. At reconditioning points, E gave S one stimulus to show that the current was turned on again, but E did not place S on the lever. During longer periods of acquisition, S occasionally stopped responding for short periods, but in the long run S spent almost three-quarters of its acquisition time responding. During the long period of extinction at the end of the day, there was very little responding, but S could be brought back to the lever quite quickly if a stimulus was delivered to show that the current had been turned on again.

DISCUSSION

It is clear that electrical stimulation in certain parts of the brain, particularly the septal area, produces acquisition and extinction curves which compare favorably with those produced by a conventional primary reward. With other electrode placements, the stimulation appears to be neutral or punishing.

Because the rewarding effect has been produced maximally by electrical stimulation in the septal area, but also in lesser degrees in the mammillothalamic tract and cingulate cortex, we are led to speculate that a system of structures previously attributed to the rhinencephalon may provide the locus for the reward phenomenon. However, as localization studies which will map the whole brain with respect to the reward and punishment dimension are continuing, we will not discuss in detail the problem of locus. We will use the term "reinforcing structures" in further discussion as a general name for the septal area and other structures which produce the reward phenomenon.

To provide an adequate canvass of the possible explanations for the rewarding effect would require considerably more argument than could possibly fit within the confines of a research paper. We have decided, therefore, to rule out briefly the possibility that the implantation produces pain which is reduced by electrical stimulation of reinforcing structures, and to confine further discussion to suggestions of ways the phenomenon may provide a methodological basis for study of physiological mechanisms of reward.

The possibility that the implantation produces some painful "drive stimulus" which is alleviated by electrical stimulation of reinforcing structures does not comport with the facts which we have observed. If there were some chronic, painful drive state, it would be indicated by emotional signs in the animal's daily behavior. Our Ss, from the first day after the operation, are normally quiet, nonaggressive; they eat regularly, sleep regularly, gain weight. There is no evidence in their behavior to support the postulation of chronic pain. Septal preparations which have lived healthy and normal lives for months after the operation have given excellent response rates.

As there is no evidence of a painful condition preceding the electrical stimulation, and as the animals are given free access to food and water at all times except while actually in the Skinner boxes, there is no explicitly manipulated drive to be reduced by electrical stimulation. Barring the possibility that stimulation of a reinforcing structure specifically inhibits the "residual drive" state of the animal, or the alternative possibility that the first electrical stimulus has noxious aftereffects which are reduced by a second one, we have some evidence here for a primary rewarding effect which is not associated with the reduction of a primary drive state. It is perhaps fair in a discussion to report the "clinical impression" of the Es that the phenomenon represents strong pursuit of a positive stimulus rather than escape from some negative condition.

Should the latter interpretation prove correct, we have perhaps located a system within the brain whose peculiar function is to produce a rewarding effect on behavior. The location of such a system puts us in a position to collect information that may lead to a decision among conflicting theories of reward. By physiological studies, for example, we may find that the reinforcing structures act selectively on sensory or motor areas of the cortex. This would have relevance to current S-S versus S-R controversies (8, 9, 13, 16).

Similarly, extirpation studies may show whether reinforcing structures have primarily a quieting or an activating effect on behavior; this would be relevant to activation versus negative feedback theories of reward (6, 13, 15, 17). A recent study by Brady and Nauta (1) already suggests that the septal area is a quieting system, for its surgical removal produced an extremely active animal.

Such examples, we believe, make it reasonable to hope that the methodology reported here should have important consequences for physiological studies of mechanisms of reward.

SUMMARY

A preliminary study was made of rewarding effects produced by electrical stimulation of certain areas of the brain. In all cases rats were used and stimulation was by 60-cycle alternating current with voltages ranging from ½ to 5 v. Bipolar needle electrodes were permanently implanted at various points in the brain. Animals were tested in Skinner boxes where they could stimulate themselves by pressing a lever. They received no other reward than the electrical stimulus in the course of the experiments. The primary findings may be listed as follows: (*a*) There are numerous places in the lower centers of the brain where electrical stimulation is rewarding in the sense that the experimental animal will stimulate itself in these places frequently and regularly for long periods of time if permitted to do so. (*b*) It is possible to obtain these results from as far back as the tegmentum; and as far forward as the septal area; from as far down as the subthalamus, and as far up as the cingulate gyrus of the cortex. (*c*) There are also sites in the lower centers where the effect is just the opposite: animals do everything possible to avoid stimulation. And there are neutral sites: animals do nothing to obtain or to avoid stimulation. (*d*) The reward results are obtained more dependably with electrode placements in some areas than others, the septal area being the most dependable to date. (*e*) In septal area preparations, the control exercised over the animal's behavior by means of this reward is extreme, possibly exceeding that exercised by any other reward previously used in animal experimentation.

The possibility that the reward results depended on some chronic painful consequences of the implantation operation was ruled out on the evidence that no physiological or behavioral signs of such pain could be found. The phenomenon was discussed as possibly laying a methodological foundation for a physiological study of the mechanisms of reward.

REFERENCES

1. Brady, J. V., & Nauta, W. J. H. Subcortical mechanisms in emotional behavior: Affective changes following septal forebrain lesions in the albino rat. *J. comp. physiol. Psychol.*, 1953, **46,** 339-346.

2. Delgado, J. M. R. Permanent implantation of multilead electrodes in the brain. *Yale J. Biol. Med.*, 1952, **24**, 351-358.

3. Delgado, J. M. R. Responses evoked in waking cat by electrical stimulation of motor cortex. *Amer. J. Physiol.*, 1952, **171**, 436-446.

4. Delgado, J. M. R., & Anand, B. K. Increase of food intake induced by electrical stimulation of the lateral hypothalamus. *Amer. J. Physiol.*, 1953, **172**, 162-168.

5. Dell, P. Correlations entre le système vegetatif et le système de la vie relation: Mesencephale, diencephale, et cortex cerebral. *J. Physiol.* (Paris), 1952, **44**, 471-557.

6. Deutsch, J. A. A new type of behavior theory. *Brit. J. Psychol.*, 1953, **44**, 304-317.

7. Gastaut, H. Correlations entre le système nerveux vegetatif et le système de la relation dans le rhinencephale. *J. Physiol.* (Paris), 1952, **44**, 431-470.

8. Hebb, D. O. *The organization of behavior.* New York: Wiley, 1949.

9. Hull, C. L. *Principles of behavior.* New York: Appleton-Century, 1943.

10. Hunter, J., & Jasper, H. H. Effects of thalamic stimulation in unanaesthetized animals. *EEG clin. Neurophysiol.*, 1949, **1**, 305-324.

11. Krieg, W. J. S. Accurate placement of minute lesions in the brain of the albino rat. *Quart. Bull. Northwestern Univer. med. School.*, 1946, **20**, 199-208.

12. MacLean, P. D., & Delgado, J. M. R. Electrical and chemical stimulation of frontotemporal portion of limbic system in the waking animal. *EEG clin. Neurophysiol.*, 1953, **5**, 91-100.

13. Olds, J. A neural model for sign-gestalt theory. *Psychol. Rev.*, 1954, **61**, 59-72.

14. Rosvold, H. E., & Delgado, J. M. R. The effect on the behavior of monkeys of electrically stimulating or destroying small areas within the frontal lobes. *Amer. Psychologist*, 1953, **8**, 425-426 (abstract).

15. Seward, J. P. Introduction to a theory of motivation in learning. *Psychol. Rev.*, 1952, **59**, 405-413.

16. Skinner, B. F. *The behavior of organisms.* New York: Appleton-Century, 1938.

17. Wiener, N. *Cybernetics.* New York: Wiley, 1949.

[ADDENDA FROM THE ORIGINAL PRINTING OF THIS ARTICLE: IN REFERENCE TO THE AUTHORS: *McGill University. The research reported here was made possible by grants from the Rockefeller Foundation and the National Institute of Mental Health of the U.S. Public Health Service. The authors particularly wish to express their thanks to Professor D. O. Hebb, who provided germinal ideas for the research and who backed it with facilities and funds. The authors are also grateful to Miss Joann Feindel, who performed the histological reconstructions reported here.* IN REFERENCE TO OLDS: *National Institute of Mental Health Postdoctorate Fellow of the U.S. Public Health Service. Received July 15, 1954. The present preliminary paper deals mainly with methods and behavioral results. A detailed report of the locus of positive, negative, and neutral reinforcing effects of electrical brain stimulation is being prepared by the first author.* (Editor's note: The detailed report of anatomical locations concerned with reinforcing effects produced by electrical stimulation appeared in the following article: Olds, J. A preliminary mapping of electrical reinforcing effects in the rat brain. *J. comp. physiol. Psychol.,* 1956, **49,** 281-285. More complete mappings of the reinforcing effects of brain stimulation can be found in: Olds, J., Travis, R. P., and Schwing, R. C. Topographic organization of hypothalamic self-stimulation functions. *J. comp. physiol. Psychol.,* 1960, **53,** 23-32; Olds, M. E. and Olds, J. Approach-avoidance analysis of rat diencephalon. *J. comp. Neurol.,* 1963, **120,** 259-295)].

ELECTROPHYSIOLOGICAL CORRELATES OF AVOIDANCE CONDITIONING IN THE CAT

※ E. R. John and K. F. Killam

AT PRESENT much information has been accumulated concerning the electrical activity of the central nervous system and an equally large amount relative to learned behavior. Yet relatively little is known about the relationships between the electrical activity of the brain and the adaptive behavior which it presumably directs. From studies of animals with brain lesions, much knowledge has been gathered concerning the central neural structures necessary for the acquisition or retention of certain responses. Less well understood is the manner in which activity in these structures modifies and interacts with incoming information to generate adaptive behavior. Some indication of these processes should be obtainable, however, by direct observation of the electrical activity from brain structures during the acquisition and performance of behavioral responses. Reviews of the extensive literature in this field have been published recently by

REPRINTED FROM *Journal of Pharmacology and Experimental Therapeutics*, **125**:252-274. COPYRIGHT © 1959, THE WILLIAMS & WILKINS CO., BALTIMORE 2, MARYLAND, U.S.A.

Yoshii, Matsumoto, and Hori (1957) and Rusinov and Rabinovich (1958).

A major difficulty in this approach has been the identification
of relevant signals in the midst of generalized brain activity.
This paper reports an attempt to solve this problem by the use
of a "frequency-tagged" condition stimulus in experiments in
which frequency discrimination formed a requirement of the
conditioning procedure. The recurrent conditioned stimulus has
been termed a "tracer conditioned stimulus" (TCS) because the
neural signals evoked may be followed through the brain somewhat as a radioactive tracer can be followed through a chemical
process. Correlates of learning were identified by searching the
records of electrical activity, obtained from several parts of the
brain during the acqustion of the conditioned response, for
brain potentials whose frequency was correlated with that of the
TCS.

Since the appearance of electrical potentials at the TCS frequency was to be used to identify structures that were handling
the information at any given stage of training, it was necessary
to avoid changes which might be associated with the animal's
adaptation to the TCS alone. Therefore, before avoidance training
was initiated, the animals went through a period of familiarization during which the TCS was repeatedly presented, un-
paired with any consequence. When no further changes in the
recorded electrical responses were observed in a series of presentations of the TCS, avoidance training was was begun.

During the acquisition of a conditioned avoidance response
(CAR) a progression of changes in electrical responses was noted,
terminating in an electrical response pattern specific for the performance of the CAR, once it had been acquired. Despite the fact
that these electrical changes developed in parallel with behavioral
changes, suggesting that they were related to learning, additional exploration of the coincidence of the behavioral responses
with the appearance of the electrical pattern was undertaken by
manipulating the animals' behavior with psychological or pharmacological techniques. The former included tests of *generalization* of the CAR to stimuli of the same modality but other
frequencies, as well as to stimuli of the same frequency but another modality; *transfer* of the CAR to a TCS of the same frequency
but another modality, but now associated with reinforcement;
and *extinction* of the CAR. The pharmacological manipulation to

be reported here consisted of the administration of reserpine in sufficient dosage to block the CAR.

METHODS. Recording electrodes were implanted in 6 cats under pentobarbital anesthesia. All animals were subjected to CAR training and 4 also received conditioned approach training. In all 6 essentially the same progression of electrical changes was observed during CAR training. This report will be restricted to the detailed analysis of the electrical changes observed with the 2 animals subjected only to CAR training. In both animals, stainless steel screws resting lightly on the dura were placed over the cortical visual and auditory areas, while bipolar electrodes were oriented stereotaxically into the lateral geniculate body, the superior colliculus and the mesencephalic reticular formation. In one animal, additional electrodes were implanted in anterior and posterior hippocampus and in the lateral portion of the amygdaloid complex; in the other, electrodes were placed in fornix, septum and nucleus ventralis anterior of the thalamus.

These placements were chosen to monitor electrical activity in the classical afferent system: cortical placements, superior colliculus and lateral geniculate; in the extralemniscal system: midbrain tegmentum and ventralis anterior of the thalamus; and in the rhinencephalic forebrain: fornix, septum, hippocampus and amygdala.

In both cats, all electrode placements were confirmed by histologic examination at the conclusion of the experiments. The maximum variation in placements common to the 2 animals was 0.5 mm in geniculate and superior colliculus. The electrodes implanted in the deep structures of the brain consisted of two 32-gauge insulated stainless steel wires laminated to a coated 22-gauge steel strut. The electrodes were trimmed off at the tip of the strut, so that recordings were taken from the cross section of the 2 wires separated by the width of the strut.

Procedures were carried out in a sound-resistant, shielded, two-compartment hurdle box, one wall of which consisted of a one-way vision mirror which enabled observation of the animal. The tracer visual stimulus was provided by a fluorescent tube in the rear wall of the apparatus which flickered at 10 flashes per sec. The same tube provided steady light of identical intensity between periods of flicker. Other flicker frequencies were used as indicated for generalization studies. The light intensity was moderate but sufficient to illuminate the entire interior of the hurdle box. The presence of a mirror as one wall and the use of glossy white paint on the others minimized variations in intensity inside the box. The auditory tracer stimulus, used in transfer studies, consisted of 10/sec clicks from an 8 inch speaker driven by 9 V, 0.5 millisec pulses from a Grass stimulator.

Following an initial healing period after surgery of 10 days to 2 weeks, electrical recordings were taken, using a Grass model 111B electroencephalograph, at all daily sessions throughout the experimental procedures which are described below. Throughout the various procedures, periodic attempts were made to assure that the responses observed were not due to artifacts introduced by the equipment used. The fluorescent tube was covered, masking the light but not shielding electric radiations into the box or blocking out any possible auditory cues. No sound accompanied the on-off of the tube. The photocell used to monitor the flashing light was also removed to avoid radiation of signals when it was energized. The leads were moved to other terminals on the input terminal box. Records were taken with the apparatus as normal except that a 10,000 ohm resistance was substituted for the animal. Finally the experimenter would cover the animals' eyes with his hands. Under all the conditions described, no evidence of artifacts could be discerned.

Experimental procedures. A. Familiarization: Twenty 15-second periods of flicker (10/sec) were presented daily for 20 days. The time interval between flicker periods randomly varied from 15 to 75 seconds so that on the average there occurred 1 flicker period per minute over a total time of 20 minutes.

B. Training: After familiarization, a conditioned avoidance response (CAR) was established to 10-second flicker using 20 randomly spaced flicker periods daily. Fifteen seconds after onset of each flicker period, intermittent shocks at an intensity of 0.2 to 0.4 mA were delivered to the feet of the animal once every 5 seconds until it crossed the hurdle (escape), at which time shock was terminated and the flicker replaced by steady light. If crossing occurred within 15 seconds after the onset of flicker (CAR), the flicker was replaced by steady light and no shock was delivered. The time interval between the onset of the flicker (TCS) and CAR was recorded as the "response latency." This training procedure was continued daily until crossing occurred in 15 seconds or less in all 20 TCS presentations on a single day, that is, until no shock was delivered to the animal throughout an entire day's training session (100% CAR).

C. Generalization: After criterion was reached (100% CAR) to 10-second flicker, other flicker frequencies ranging from 6.8 to 13/sec were presented. If crossing of the hurdle occurred in 15 seconds or less, flicker was terminated and replaced by steady light. If crossing did not take place, the flicker was terminated at 15 seconds and replaced by steady light. *In no case was shock administered.* Thus, while CAR was reinforced by termination of the presumably aversive stimulus, failure was not punished. Crossing responses to flicker frequencies other than 10 per second therefore constitute evidence of generalization rather than of new learning.

Following completion of tests for generalization to other flicker frequencies, 10/sec clicks were presented for 20 15-sec periods in the presence of steady flourescent light. Failure to cross the hurdle within 15 seconds was not punished by shock; the clicks were terminated either on performance of the CAR or at the end of 15 seconds without CAR.

D. Transfer training: After (C) was completed, training was initiated to transfer the CAR to 10/sec clicks which were now paired with shock. The procedure was completely analogous to that used in (B) except that silence rather than steady sound replaced the clicks at the termination of each stimulus period.

E. Effects of reserpine: After transfer was achieved, 70 μg/kg of reserpine was injected intramuscularly. Recording of the electrical activity and behavioral performance, both to the original and transferred TCS, was taken every other hour for 8 hours and then periodically until the behavioral response returned to criterion (100% CAR).

F. Experimental extinction: One of the animals suffered an accidental injury and died at this stage. In the remaining animal, after the above procedures were concluded, the CAR to 10/sec flicker was experimentally extinguished. The extinction procedure on each day was as follows: (1) Twenty flicker periods were presented and the latency of crossing was measured. If the crossing did not occur within 15 seconds after the onset of the flicker, the flicker was terminated and no shock was delivered. (2) Fifteen minutes of continuous flicker was presented and the number of crosses of the hurdle were recorded. Crossing was not reinforced by the termination of the TCS, nor were shocks delivered. (3)

Twenty flicker periods were delivered as in (1) above. This extinction procedure was continued until no CAR's were obtained during the 2 sessions of 20 15-second flicker periods on a single day and until no evidence of autonomic response to the TCS could be observed, *e.g.*, pupillary dilation and alteration in respiration. Electrical recordings were taken during the 15/sec flicker sessions.

G. Effect of extinction on a transferred response: After extinction of the CAR to 10/sec flicker was achieved, 10/sec clicks were presented to see whether the CAR to the auditory stimulus had also been extinguished. The latency of the CAR's was measured as usual. Flicker periods were then interspersed with click periods to see whether the extinguished CAR to flicker would rebound if the CAR was elicited by clicks.

Analysis of data. During the procedures outlined above, a sequence of changes was observed in the electrical activity associated with the learning of the CAR. Of necessity only discrete points in this continuum can be illustrated. In order to analyze the data 4 procedures were carried out. First, various stages in the learning curve were designated from the behavioral protocols. Second, a section of record was selected that was typical of the series of TCS presentations at each stage. Third, the selected records were characterized for the dominant electrical patterns and the patterns for successive stages were compared. Since electronic frequency analysis equipment was not available, frequency measurements were made with calipers and overlays. Finally, in an effort to inject more continuity into this method of presentation, the recordings obtained on the day before and the day after each illustration were scored for similarity or dissimilarity to the example. For each figure presented to illustrate changes during conditioning, the percentage of "similar" recordings is indicated on the day from which the example was selected and a comparison is made with the preceding and succeeding days.

RESULTS. Observations during the long period of familiarization, training generalization, transfer and subsequent stabilization consisted for each animal of 45 to 60 minutes of electroencephalographic recordings at each of 48 daily sessions. Further studies during psychological and pharmacological manipulation of the learned behavior involving an additional 79 hours of recording over 45 days for one animal and 32 hours over 5 days for the other. The mass of data accumulated revealed a complex sequence of changes in the electrical activity of various brain structures emitted spontaneously and in response to the repeated presentations of the TCS. Since similar acquired responses appeared at approximately the same stages of learning in both animals, the figures presented are composites which depict typical changes in electrical activity in structures common to both animals as well as electrical activity recorded from other electrodes in each animal.

Familiarization. The familiarization period for each animal lasted for 21 days. Upon repeated presentations of the same 10/sec flicker a diminution of the central electrical response was observed, not only within a given daily session of 20 trials but also progressively from day to day. On initial presentation of the flickering light, high-voltage, frequency-specific responses[1] were observed in visual cortex (IPSI and CON),[2] lateral geniculate body (GEN), superior colliculus (S. COLL.) and hippocampus (HIPP). Occasional labeled potentials might also be seen in the tegmentum (RF), septum (SEPT) and amygdala (AMYG) (Fig. 1A). The labeled responses disappeared first from the amygdala and then from the hippocampus.

The pattern of disappearance of frequency-specific responses in the visual pathway was of particular interest. After 6 days (120 repeated presentations of the flickering light), an intermediate stage was observed in which the lateral geniculate responses waxed and waned during the flicker rather than maintaining their earlier constant amplitude (Fig. 1B). During the periods when no geniculate response was apparent, labeled potentials were still recorded in the reticular formation and in the visual cortical derivations. As the familiarization period was continued, the cyclical diminution of geniculate responses became more frequent and more marked (Fig. 1C) until, after 19 to 21 days of flicker presentation, the high-amplitude, frequency-specific responses dropped out completely. When the final vestige of this response was no longer evoked by flicker, avoidance training was initiated.

---

[1] The term "evoked potentials" is used to denote electrical activity induced by the presentation of the TCS. Evoked potentials at the same frequency as the TCS, or at multiples or submultiples thereof, are referred to as "labeled responses," "frequency-specific responses" or "following."

[2] "IPSI" refers to records between 2 electrodes on the same hemisphere, and "CON" to transcortical records.

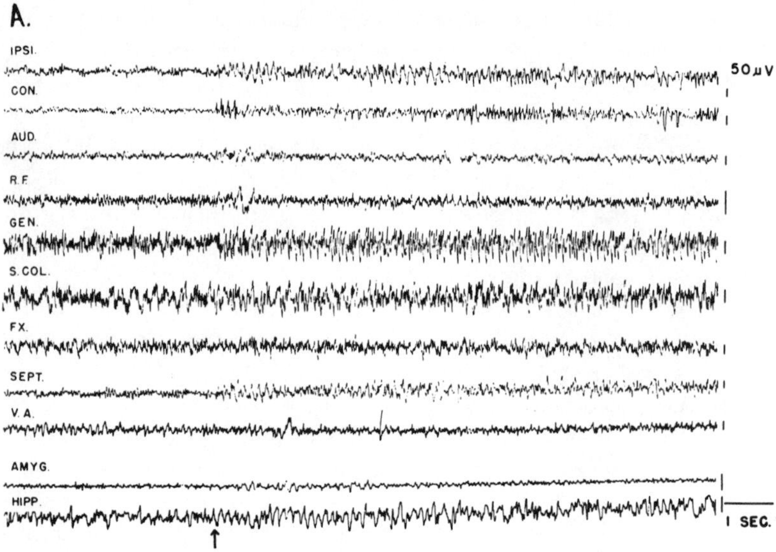

A.

Fig. 1A. Electrical response to the TCS recorded at the beginning of the familiarization period. IPSI (100%)—bipolar derivation from the same optic gyrus; CON (100%)—bipolar transcortical (visual) derivation; AUD (73%+)—auditory cortex; RF (65%+)—midbrain tegmentum (reticular formation); GEN (50%−)—lateral geniculate body; COLL (95%)—superior colliculus; FX (100%)—fornix; SEPT (100%)—septum; VA (100%)—nucleus ventralis anterior of the thalamus; AMYG (67%)—lateral amygdaloid complex; HIPP (100%) —hippocampus. Records obtained on the day after the illustrated responses showed a generalized slight diminution in labeled responses, with the decrement most marked in SEPT, AMYG, and HIPP.

(*Note for Figs. 1A, 1B, and 1C.* Percentages refer to all responses for both animals, recorded on the day the illustrated records were obtained, which displayed the essential characteristics of the example. Plus or minus denotes whether the records which differed from the example were characterized consistently by more or less pronouncd labeled responses. The annotation "a" indicates that due to either sudden, quick movements of the animal or the appearance of shorting artifact from a broken cable the records were too obscured to allow analysis.)

Training. The conditioned avoidance response was established in the 2 animals in 19 and 21 days of training, respectively. This learning was accompanied by a sequence of changes in electrical activity, the salient features of which will be presented in terms of the stages of the learning process with which they coincided.

B

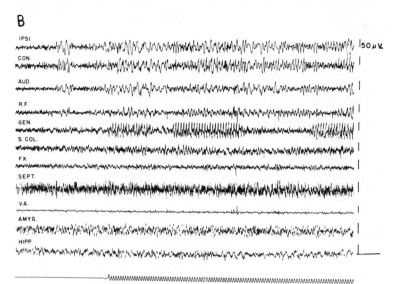

Fig. 1B. Electrical responses to the TCS recorded in the middle of the familiarization procedure. Note the prounced waxing and waning in the lateral geniculate response (GEN) and the presence of labeled responses in various structures, including RF, during the waning phase: IPSI (95%), CON (95%), AUD (90%), RF (95%), GEN (50%—), COLL (95%), FX (95%), SEPT (95%), VA (95%), AMYG (100%), HIPP (100%). Recordings obtained the day before those illustrated were essentially comparable to the figure with somewhat more labeled responses visible in SEPT, AMYG, and HIPP and with less prounced waxing and waning in GEN. Little change was observed the next day except for more pronounced GEN fluctuations.

A. Initial effects of shock: At the initiation of training, the association of shock with the TCS led to an over-all increase in background activity and to the return or increase of labeled electrical responses (Fig. 2). High-voltage, frequency-specific waves were recorded from optic cortex, lateral geniculate, superior colliculus, fornix and septum. The potentials from the fornix and septum became similar, in contrast to earlier and later stages. Occasional bursts of frequency-specific potentials were seen in records from the auditory cortex. The hippocampus, however, did not exhibit "following" of the TCS until 80 shock trials had been presented.

B. Discrimination of the TCS: As pairing of TCS and shock continued, animals gave evidence of discrimination of the TCS by

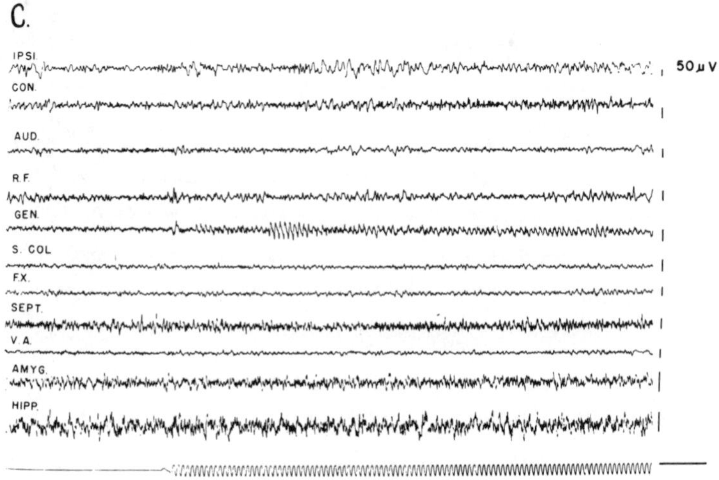

C.

Fig. 1C. Electrical responses to the TCS recorded at the end of the familiarization procedure. Note the general absence of labeled responses. During some trials, even the low-amplitude labeled responses visible in GEN were not apparent: IPSI (73%+), CON (93%+), AUD (97%), RF (90%+), GEN (80%−), COLL (93%a), FX (100%), SEPT (70%+), VA (100%), AMYG (80%a), HIPP (90%a). Recordings obtained on the previous day showed somewhat more pronounced labeled responses in cortical derivations and GEN, and appreciably more in RF. An exceedingly marked increase in labeled responses was observed in all leads except VA, AMYG, and HIPP on the next day, when avoidance training began.

exhibiting behavior reminiscent of the "conditioned emotional response," i.e., at the onset of flicker, the animals cringed, growled and defecated. This behavior was well established by the fifth day of training when no avoidance responses had yet been made.

During this period marked changes occurred in electrical recordings from various brain structures (Fig. 3). First, the generalized, high-amplitude responses seen after the first shock experiences diminished, and then were replaced by marked and persistent frequency-specific responses in visual cortex, reticular formation and hippocampus. There was a striking absence of evoked potentials in superior colliculus and auditory cortex. The similarity of the potentials recorded from the fornix and septum persisted.

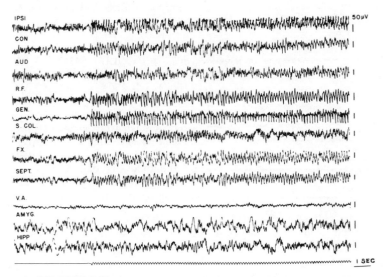

Fig. 2. Electrical responses to the TCS recorded on the initial day of avoidance training. IPSI (93%−), CON (93%−), AUD (90%−), RF (83%−), GEN (100%), COLL (100%), FX (100%), SEPT (100%), VA (90%+), AMYG (100%), HIPP (100%). The marked labeled responses were absent from recordings obtained the previous day. Recordings obtained on the next day, as training continued, showed a generalized decrease in labeled responses. This decrease was most apparent in the cortical derivations. VA showed an increase in labeled responses.

The labeled potentials recorded from the lateral geniculate body were markedly reduced over those seen during the early pairing of TCS with shock. The most extreme example, characteristic of one animal, is depicted in Fig. 3. In both animals, as well as in subsequent animals, this decrement in response approximated that seen in the terminal stages of the familiarization period before CAR training began. In many instances there was even a decrease in the responses beyond that obtained during the familiarization period. This pattern became evident with the appearance of behavior resembling the conditioned emotional response and persisted in the recordings from the geniculate body until a significant number of CAR's were elicited. At this time a decrease was observed in frequency-specific potentials

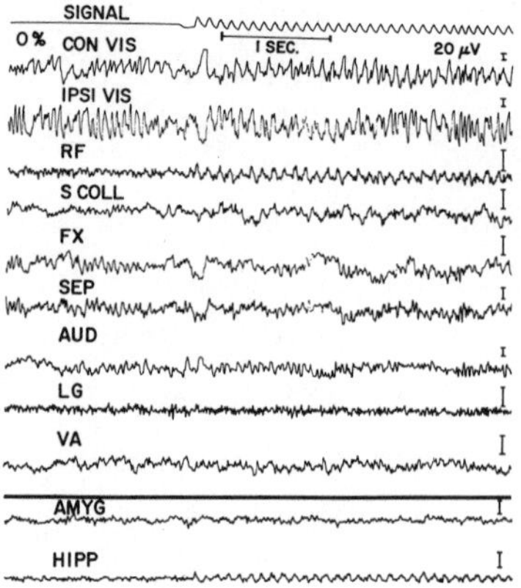

Fig. 3. Electrical responses to the TCS obtained on the fifth day of training; CAR performance 0%. CON (100%), IPSI (100%), RF (80%−), COLL (93%−), RX (100%), SEPT (93%+), AUD (100%), LG (50%+; see text), VA (85%+), AMYG (93%), HIPP (100%). Recordings on the previous day showed somewhat less labeled responses in cortical derivations. The major changes observed on the following day were a decrease in labeled responses in RF and an increase in COLL.

recorded from the midbrain tegmentum and hippocampus as the labeled potentials returned to the recordings from the lateral geniculate body (discussed below).

C. Early conditioned avoidance responses: The earliest avoidance responses to the TCS occurred at a stage when there was an increased incidence of spontaneous hurdle crossing. At this point only relatively minor alterations were observed in the electrophysiological recordings during TCS (Fig. 4). An evoked response in the auditory cortex appeared and amygdaloid activity showed an increase in amplitude. Frequency-specific responses remained in the optic cortex and hippocampus and began to appear sporadically in superior colliculus, although they were still not recorded from the lateral geniculate body. The response of the reticular formation, however, became less discrete and regular, while the apparent synchronization between fornix and septum was accentuated during the TCS.

In contrast to these small quantitative changes in the responses to TCS observed during the first avoidance responses, a number of important qualitative changes appeared when a significant level of CAR performance had been reached (Fig. 5). By the 24% performance level, stable, high-voltage potentials appeared in the lateral geniculate body at the TCS frequency, while high-voltage slow waves were observed in superior colliculus with superimposed low-voltage, TCS-frequency activity. The frequency-specific potentials were no longer marked from visual cortical recordings taken transcortically (*con vis*), although they remained present in records taken from electrodes on the same

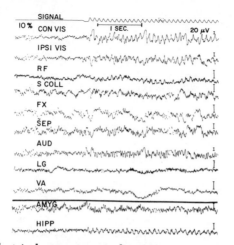

Fig. 4. Electrical responses to the TCS; CAR performance 10%.
CON (100%), IPSI (75%—), RF (100%), COLL (100%), FX (100%),
SEPT (100%), AUD (100%), LG (50%+; see text), VA, (100%),
AMYG (100%), HIPP (100%). Recordings obtained on the previous
day were essentially similar except for more pronounced labeled response in RF and less in COLL. On the following day, both animals
showed sharp improvement in CAR performance, accompanied by a
decrease in labeled responses in CON, RF, COLL, and HIPP and an
increase in LG.

hemisphere (*ipsi vis*). Outside of the visual system, changes
were also observed. Following of the TCS lessened in the auditory
cortex and the reticular formation. Fornix and septal recordings
became disassociated and some indications of frequency-specific
responses appeared in fornix. These subsequently became more
marked and then diminished again by the time 65% CAR was
reached. No tracings were obtained from the hippocampus or
amygdala at the 24% CAR level of performance.

D. Well-established CAR: When performance reached 65% correct responses (Fig. 6), electrical responses to the TCS became
stable in many brain structures and appeared to be characteristic
of the fully trained animal. In the visual system, high-voltage,
frequency-specific responses consistently appeared in the lateral
geniculate body and high-voltage, slow activity was even more
evident in the superior colliculus. The visual cortex, however,
showed a markedly different response from that obtained earlier;
evoked responses appeared at a multiple of the TCS frequency, at
20 or 30/sec. Auditory cortex showed TCS following only sporad-

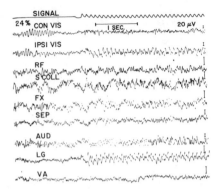

Fig. 5. Electrical response to the TCS; CAR performance 24%.
These tracings and the percentages below refer only to one of the
animals, since the other showed an abrupt large increment in performance at this time: CON (100%), IPSI (100%), RF (85%−), COLL
(100%), FX (100%), SEPT (100%), AUD (95%), LG (100%), VA
(100%). On the previous day, the same general configuration was observed, except that there was appreciably more labeled response in
CON and appreciably less in LG. On the following day, a further improvement in CAR performance occurred, accompanied by a general
increase in labeled responses except in RF, LG, and COLL which
showed some diminution.

ically. Activity in the reticular formation was decreased in amplitude relative to that seen at earlier stages and included little
labeled response. Again, as during the 24% CAR stage, fornix and
septum showed no relationship although some frequency-specific
response to the TCS, most marked in fornix, was visible in the
recordings from both structures. Somewhat higher amplitude
activity was seen in the amygdala than in previous recordings.
Frequency-specific responses no longer appeared in the tracings
obtained from the hippocampus, although the amplitude of activity was higher.

When criterion was reached (100% CAR), the most marked
changes noted were in the activity of the amygdala, which displayed bursts of 40/sec waves during the TCS, and in nucleus
ventralis anterior of the thalamus, which for the first time acquired a marked frequency-specific response to the TCS (Fig. 7).
Electrical patterns from visual cortex were only slightly altered.
The evoked cortical responses tended to appear more often at
20/sec than at 30/sec and tracings from the 2 visual derivations
were more often different than alike, with respect to TCS follow-

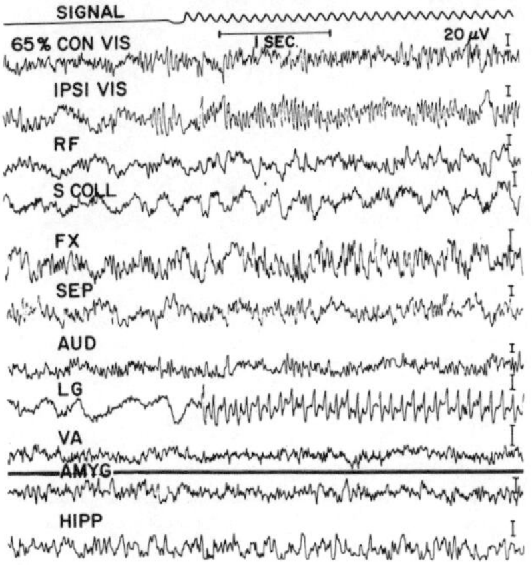

Fig. 6. Electrical responses to the TCS; CAR performance 65%. The 30/sec potentials illustrated in the recordings from CON and IPSI were the dominant form of labeled responses in those structures, although intervals of 10/sec and 20/sec responses were observed: CON (93%−), IPSI (87%−), RF (70%+), COLL (83%+), FX (70%+), SEPT (68%+), AUD (78%+), LG (90%−), VA (85%+), AMYG (75%+), HIPP (80%+). The salient differences in the recordings obtained on the previous day were less pronounced 30/sec responses in IPSI and CON, less marked slow waves in COLL and more labeled responses in SEPT and HIPP. On the following day there was a decrease in 30/sec responses in IPSI and CON, with an increase in 20/sec responses, a further decrease in the amplitude of HIPP, a marked decrease in the labeled responses in FX, and 40/sec waves appeared in AMYG.

ing. Frequency-specific responses showed increased amplitude in the lateral geniculate body and the slow waves from the superior colliculus were also enhanced.

Responses at the TCS frequency were further decreased in reticular formation and were no longer recorded from the auditory cortex, fornix, septum and hippocampus. The over-all amplitude of background activity in these structures also decreased markedly.

Figure 8 is a graphic summary of the electrical changes during the familiarization and CAR training periods. The ordinate represents the incidence of labeled responses in the various structures monitored, expressed as a percentage of the responses on each day of recording. The abscissa represents experimental days, and the points at which figures were selected are appropriately indicated.

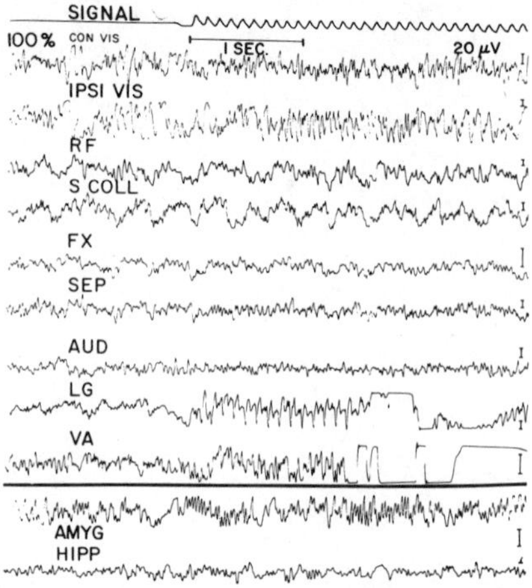

Fig. 7. Electrical responses to the TCS; CAR performance 100%.
CON (100%), IPSI (83%+), RF (83%+), COLL (90%), FX
(80%+), SEPT (100%), AUD (100%), LG (100%), VA (63%−),
AMYG (67%− less 40/sec), HIPP (100%). On the previous day more
30/sec labeled responses were observed in CON and IPSI; more
labeled responses were observed in AUD; and the amplitude of HIPP
was somewhat greater. Labeled responses appeared in VA but were
less consistent than on the day illustrated. On the following day,
various psychological manipulations were initiated (see text).

E. Changes in spontaneous electrical activity during training:
During the training period spontaneous activity in many brain
structures, recorded in the absence of the TCS, became strikingly
modified to include features of the acquired electrical response
to the TCS characteristic of the particular stage of learning (Fig.
9). These rhythms dominated the spontaneous activity recorded
during early stages of acquisition of the CAR, but became less
evident as training progressed. When the CAR was established at
the 100% criterion, spontaneous activity was very different from
that recorded at 0%, but activity resembling responses evoked by
the TCS occurred primarily in the amygdala (40/sec bursts of
high-voltage waves), in the superior colliculus (slow wave activity) and in visual cortex (20 to 30/sec potentials).

During intervals between conditioning trials, animals in the
conditioning apparatus demonstrated a set of behavioral changes
parallel to the alterations in spontaneous electrical activity of the
brain just described. During initial training, affective responses
were shown throughout the experimental period including almost

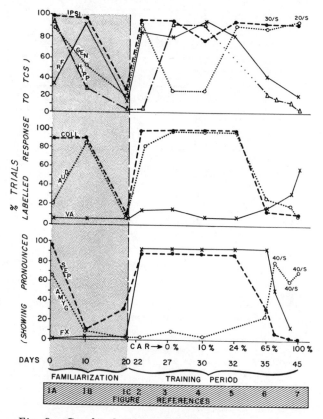

Fig. 8. Graphical representation of the distribution of labeled responses through familiarization and conditioning (for details see text).

continuous growling and vocalizing and frequent defecation. As training continued, these responses diminished but the level of motor activity was increased and the incidence of spontaneous crossings of the hurdle rose sharply. When the CAR was well established, the incidence of spontaneous hurdle crossing became very low and few signs of affective response were present. Of particular interest was the high correlation of spontaneous electrical activity patterns reminiscent of acquired responses to the TCS, particularly in amygdala and visual cortex, with spontaneous crossing of the hurdle at this stage.

The patterns of electrical changes occurring during the acquisition of the CAR and the patterns preceding the performance of

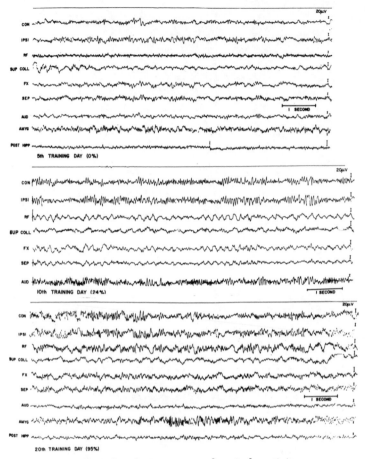

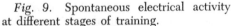

Fig. 9. Spontaneous electrical activity
at different stages of training.

the CAR in the fully trained animals were not seen in untrained
animals or in animals being subjected to the familiarization procedure. Labeled electrical responses to the flashing light were
observed in the untrained animals as the animals crossed the
barrier in the course of the random motor activity associated
with exploratory behavior as well as when the animals were not
moving about. Occasionally there would appear in a recording
from a single area a fleeting response that in comparison to the
electrical changes described as occurring during training would
be considered similar, *e.g.*, a short burst of multiple-frequency

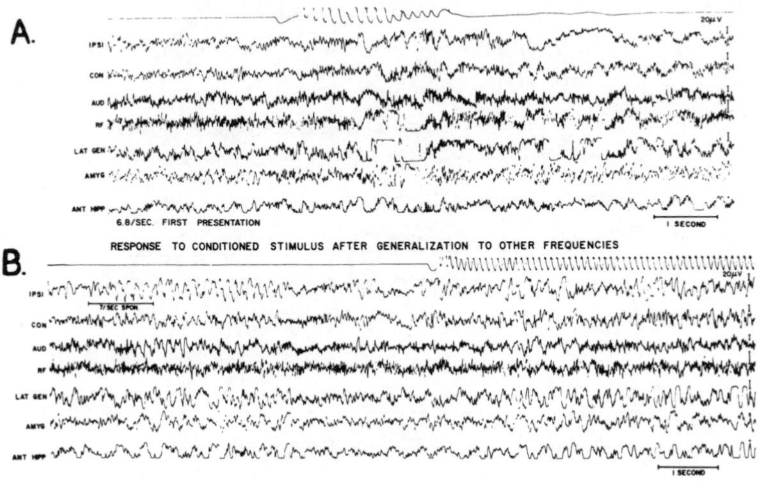

Fig. 10. A. Electrical responses during generalization of the CAR to a different flicker frequency from that of the original TCS. B. Electrical responses to the original TCS after a series of presentations of a different flicker frequency.

responses in the visual cortical leads. However, during such activity the records from the other central nervous system structures were dissimilar to the records obtained during the training procedure.

It has not been possible from these studies to delineate any particular structure that could be considered to generate the conditioned avoidance behavior. Rather it has been observed that, associated with the generation of the behavior, electrical activity appears in many structures. Undoubtedly there are additional structures involved in the performance of the conditioned behavior that were not monitored in this study. Whether activity in the structures monitored in this study is common to the generation of other types of conditioned behavior will need to be ascertained.

Generalization. After 100% performance of the CAR had been established to light flickering at 10/sec, initial presentation of flicker at a frequency of 6.8/sec elicited the CAR. However, central electrical responses to the new stimulus remained bound to the original TCS frequency; for example, 20 to 30/sec in visual cortex (Fig. 10A). After repeated presentations of the 6.8/sec stimulus without reinforcement, however, electrical activity of

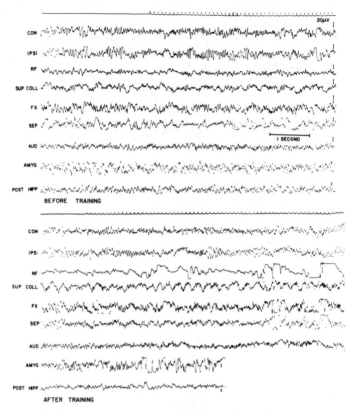

Fig. 11. Electrical responses to clicks at the same frequency as the original visual TCS: A, before training; B,
after transfer of training.

the brain showed a 7/sec basic frequency, and avoidance responses were no longer elicited. At this stage, re-presentation of
the original TCS (10/sec flicker) elicited 7/sec potential responses
in the brain and no behavioral avoidance response was obtained
(Fig. 10B). After further presentation of the 10/sec TCS, the electrical responses characteristic of a trained animal returned to the
electrical records and the animals again performed conditioned
avoidance responses. Similar data were obtained during the tests
of generalization to 13/sec flicker.

Transfer. In both animals trained to 100% CAR with 10/sec
flickering light, presentation of 10/sec clicks did not evoke frequency-specific potentials in the electrical records nor was the

CAR elicited (Fig. 11A). Shock was then paired with the clicks, using a procedure parallel to that used in earlier training to flicker. Only 2 reinforced presentations of the 10/sec clicks in 1 animal and 4 reinforced presentations in the other were required to establish fully the CAR to 10/sec clicks. In both cases, the electrical activity evoked at central sites by 10/sec clicks then bore a remarkable resemblance to that evoked by 10/sec flicker (Fig. 11B), particularly with respect to the incidence of 20 and 30/sec activity in visual cortex, the high-voltage slow waves in the superior colliculus and the 40/sec bursts in the amygdala.

The effects of reserpine. Six hours after reserpine (70 μg/kg, i.m.) the animals evidenced no avoidance responses, and 8 hours after reserpine, no escape responses. Reduction of spontaneous crossings of the hurdle, together with the characteristic decay of the behavioral response and its subsequent return in 3 days, are shown in Figure 12. Following administration of reserpine, the alterations in the behavioral responses paralleled alterations in the acquired electrical responses; and the electrical responses returned with the return of the CAR.

The EEG recordings after the disappearance of the CAR are typified by Figure 13. The frequency of the evoked potentials recorded from the visual cortex is that of the TCS, 10/sec, rather than 20 to 30/sec as just before the test. Marked labeled potentials reappear in the reticular formation and fornix. The high-voltage, slow waves disappeared from the superior colliculus and there was a decay in the responses in the lateral geniculate recordings. The 40/sec burst activity in the amygdala was no longer present. These findings resemble a regression to records obtained around the 25% performance level of the CAR during training. The alteration of electrical changes after reserpine approximated a reversal of the training progression in a telescoped fashion.

Furthermore, after reserpine, at any given behavioral performance level the electrical recordings were similar to those seen at the same level of performance during the acquisition of the CAR. Three to 4 hours after administration of the drug, the behavioral performance level was 70 to 80% correct responses. At this time, frequency-specific responses were no longer present in the records obtained from the nucleus ventralis anterior of the thalamus, and the 40/sec burst activity was not observed in the records from the amygdala. Six to 8 hours after the drug was ad-

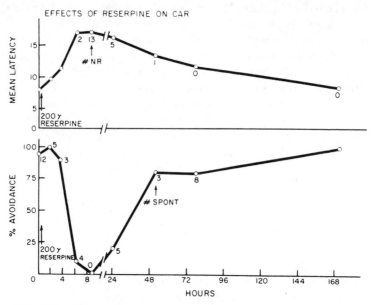

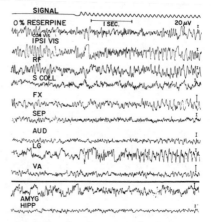

Fig. 12. Effects of reserpine on per cent performance and latency of CAR.

Fig. 13. Electrical responses to the TCS during suppression of CAR following reserpine.

ministered, when the CAR was completely suppressed, the transcortical visual records were relatively isopotential, whereas records obtained from the 2 electrodes on the same optic gyrus exhibited frequency-specific following. The high-voltage slow activity disappeared from the superior colliculus records.

With the disappearance of escape behavior, approximately 8 hours after the drug was administered, frequency-specific potentials appeared in the records from the reticular formation and

in both visual cortical leads. The responses in the lateral geniculate became more irregular but frequency-specificity was observed over short periods of time. Of interest is the fact that
evoked potentials did not return in the hippocampal leads, although they could be seen in records from the fornix. As the
drug action waned, the electrical patterns characteristic of the
trained animal reappeared in approximately the reverse order.
An additional phenomenon of interest, observed after reserpine,
was a marked hypersynchrony in the visual system which could
be evoked or could appear spontaneously. This hypersynchrony,
which was not associated with seizure discharge in the rhinencephalic structures, will be described in detail in a forthcoming
paper.

Throughout the period in which the CAR was blocked by
reserpine the animals reacted to the presentation of the TCS by
growling, crouching, defecating and by vigorously attempting
various routes of anticipatory evasion other than the appropriate
one of crossing the hurdle. Between presentations of the TCS,
the reserpinized animals displayed the behavior usually described as "tranquilized." Throughout the duration of action of
reserpine, they exhibited side effects characteristic of the drug
action.

Experimental extinction. After the extinction procedure was
initiated, the first electrical response to wane from the pattern
characteristic of the trained animal was the 40/sec burst activity
in the amygdala. This response was quite labile, in that it would
occasionally reappear during the extinction period, sometimes
for no apparent reason, but usually in association with a CAR. At
a later stage, flinching and growling were once more seen in response to the TCS and marked multiple-frequency responses in
the visual cortical recordings persisted as long as the animal exhibited these overt responses. Interestingly, some indication of
frequency-specific responses could again be observed in the
hippocampus during this phase. As the extinction procedure continued, visual cortical following at 10/sec first appeared for short
periods, during the typical multiple-frequency responses, and
then gradually occupied more and more of the visual cortical
records. Frequency-specific responses gradually diminished in
the lateral geniculate. The amplitude of activity recorded from
the amygdala decreased, the slight following previously seen
in the hippocampus diminished, and occasional brief periods of

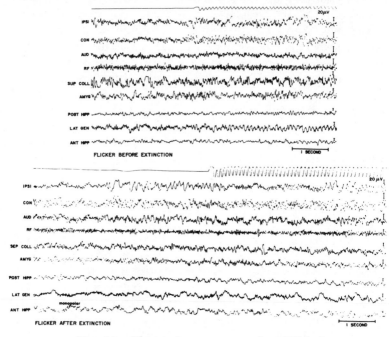

Fig. 14. Electrical responses to the TCS before and after extinction of CAR.

following appeared in the reticular formation. As the behavioral extinction criterion was reached, the electrical activity recorded from all structures became essentially identical with that which had been observed earlier in the advanced stages of the familiarization procedure. While frequency-specific responses could still be observed occasionally in various structures, they persisted only briefly and did not resemble those of the trained animal before extinction (Fig. 14).

After the CAR to 10/sec *flicker* was completely extinguished, presentation of the nonextinguished TCS, 10/sec *clicks*, still evoked conditioned avoidance responses. Accompanying the CAR to 10/sec clicks, evoked potentials similar to those seen before extinction of the CAR to the flicker stimulus appeared in the visual cortical tracings. When a balanced, randomly mixed series of 10/sec flicker and click stimuli was presented to the animal, performance of the CAR to flicker returned to a performance level of 30%. The accompanying electrical responses were comparable to those seen at corresponding performance levels during training. On the following day a series of only the visual stimulus was repeated and neither conditioned avoidance nor associated electrical responses were elicited.

DISCUSSION. These experiments were designed to enable the identification of electrical events in the brain which were correlated with the acquisition and retention of an overt conditioned response. A series of changes was observed in both the form and central distribution of electrical responses to a "tracer," repetitive conditioned stimulus, during the acquisition of a conditioned avoidance response. Since the alterations in electrical responses developed as a continuous process, the attempt to present discrete features so as to categorize the responses at different stages of learning inevitably oversimplifies the observations. Stages of the learning process have been selected, however, at which marked changes in activity could be seen to occur in certain brain areas, although in other regions changes were only gradual. However, it is urged that this description be considered at best as providing only a preliminary outline of central events taking place during avoidance learning.

It was our assumption that the appearance of evoked potentials, particularly at the frequency of the tracer conditioned stimulus or a multiple thereof, indicated the arrival of information about the peripheral event at a central structure. We have termed such responses as "labeled" for the purpose of this discussion.

The data revealed that presentation of a novel TCS, in the form of flickering light, resulted in labeled electrical responses not simply in the classical visual system (lateral geniculate, superior colliculus and optic cortex), but in the extralemniscal sensory pathway (reticular formation) and in the rhinencephalon (hippocampus and amygdala) as well. As the familiarization procedure progressed, labeled electrical responses gradually disappeared and it became exceedingly difficult to tell from the recorded activity when the flashing light was turned on or off. The phenomena are reminiscent of the process of "habituation" described by other workers (Hernandez-Peon and Scherrer, 1955; Galambos, Sheatz, & Vernier, 1956; Sharpless & Jasper, 1956) and considered to be an active function of the reticular formation. Whereas prior workers have observed this phenomenon after the continued presentation of periodic stimuli for long intervals, the present results show that marked diminution of responses can take place in a cumulative fashion, over a number of weeks with relatively brief periods of irregularly spaced stimulus presentations separated by 24 hours. The order of disappearance of central responses (rhinencephalon, reticular formation and superior colliculus, visual cortex and finally thalamic relay nucleus) suggests that, if the process is an active one, the several participating systems display a differential susceptibility, with the classical afferent path being the most resistant.

When avoidance training was initiated and the TCS paired with shock, an increased degree of arousal in the animals was associated with an immediate return of the previously diminished labeled electrical responses in some, but not all, of the monitored structures. Of particular interest, however, is the fact that responses did not reappear in the hippocampus, which furnishes evidence that reversal of the whole familiarization process did not occur with this increased arousal. Furthermore, subsequent changes in recorded electrical responses in the various structures during training appeared independent of the simple consequences of arousal since certain labeled responses which reappeared after initial shock again diminished despite continued pairings of the TCS and shock during training. The findings (Hagbarth & Kerr, 1954; Killam & Killam, 1957) indicating that increased reticular outflow causes active blockade in sensory relays further support the view that increased reticular formation activity leading to arousal would not *per se* cause a reappearance of electrical responses previously diminished during familiarization.

As the animals began to associate onset of flicker with the imminence of shock (when shock had been paired with the TCS about 80 times), behavioral evidence of discrimination of the TCS was observed without appropriate avoidance behavior. This coincided with an abundance of labeled potentials in relay nuclei of the visual pathway while cortical receiving areas showed clear labeled responses to the TCS. It is not yet possible to decide whether, at this discrimination phase of learning, signals were being transmitted to the cortex by extralemniscal pathways, though the impressive responses then recorded in the reticular formation support this view. While there is considerable evidence for corticopetal projections from the reticular formation (Moruzzi & Magoun, 1949; Lindsley, Bowden, & Magoun, 1949), their distribution is usually inferred to be more generalized than in the present instance. It is conceivable, alternatively, that elements of the relay nuclei responded so massively that no potential difference occurred between the bipolar recording electrodes. At the same stage, labeled responses appeared in the hippocampus.

After a surprisingly long "stimulus discrimination phase," perhaps related to the familiarization of the animals to the TCS prior to training, the CAR gradually became established. As the animals began to manifest CAR and moved into what might be called the "stimulus-response association phase" of learning, a new pattern of electrical responses emerged and those most characteristic of the stimulus discrimination phase diminished. As the activity waned in the reticular formation and hippocampus, labeled electrical responses appeared in the lateral geniculate body and superior colliculus. It is possible that the frequency-specific response in the reticular formation was previously instrumental in the suppression of similar frequency-specific responses in the visual pathways. Whatever the mechanism, the stimulus-response association phase began with the apparent establishment of a previously nonoperative afferent pathway for the signal. As the CAR performance improved from 25 through 65%, the gradual shift in labeled responses from reticular formation to specific relay nuclei of the visual system continued and the rhinencephalic system ceased to respond to the TCS. The latter change might be related to a diminution of affective reaction to the TCS as the incidence of failure and consequent shock decreased. Further experiments will be necessary to establish whether this inverse relationship between reticular formation and hippocampus on the one hand and relay nuclei on the other is functional or fortuitous.

Another major alteration in electrical activity during this part of the learning process was the departure from frequency-specificity in the evoked responses of the visual system. The slow wave in the colliculus, first observed in the stimulus-discrimination phase, became more pronounced while visual cortical responses became double or triple the TCS frequency. The precise frequency observed in the cortex suggested that 2 or 3 events occurred at each flash of light. Whether the first event is evoked by activity in the primary afferent pathway and later events by activity in more circuitous routes, or whether the presentation of the TCS evoked a repetitive cortical discharge, still remains to be determined. Whatever the explanation, this alteration in response appeared closely associated with final stages of learning.

Throughout these stages of discrimination and association, spontaneous electrical activity was observed similar to or even identical with the labeled responses evoked by the TCS. These changes, also reported by Livanov, Korolikova, & Frenkeli (1951) and Yoshii et al. (1956), were described as "assimilation of rhythm." The fact that, at later stages of training, spontaneous performance of the CAR frequently followed the appearance of such spontaneously emitted, acquired patterns of central activity suggests their possible relation to "memory." One must certainly consider the possibility that such spontaneous repetition of the acquired electrical response to the TCS might serve in the formation of stable new associations and enable them to be carried over from session to session. Most speculations on the neural mechanisms underlying learning have in fact postulated some mechanism which enabled the central representation of a transient event to persist for a period of time while a more permanent "trace" was developed.

During the final stages of conditioning, the animal perfected motor aspects of the CAR and reduced its latency. The new central events recorded during this period were the appearance of 40/sec bursts of high-voltage activity in the amygdala and the occurrence of labeled responses to the TCS in the nucleus ventralis anterior of the thalamus. Similar amygdala burst activity has been previously described by Lesse (1957) as recorded from the lateral portion of the amygdala. Histological examination of electrode placements in the current study revealed that electrode tips were in the lateral portions of the amgydaloid complex. The bursts of activity in the amygdala were almost invariant preludes to performance of the CAR, whether evoked by the TCS or spontaneously emitted. Their relevance to the final, stable, 100% performance level was further attested by their disappearance during abolition of the CAR by reserpine or experimental extinction.

Confirming evidence for the significance of the electrical response observed after the final establishment of the CAR was obtained by studies of generalization. Essentially, a test for generalization asks whether 2 different stimuli are equivalent in their ability to elicit some common response. The data presented sug-

gest that when an animal responds with similar conditioned behavior to 2 different frequencies of flickering light, the central
electrical responses to the 2 stimuli are basically the same. Thus,
in the generalization trials, the initial presentation of 7/sec
flicker evoked both the CAR and electrical responses comparable
to those evoked by 10/sec flicker admixed with electrical responses related to the frequency of the presented stimulus. When
generalization no longer occurred, evoked central responses reflected only the frequency of the new stimulus. Similarly, when
subsequent 10/sec flicker was at first represented centrally with
predominantly a 7/sec electrical response, no CAR occurred. After
several trials, the central responses again corresponded to the
frequency of the TCS, and the CAR returned. Throughout the generalization procedure, neither 7 nor 10/sec flicker was reinforced
by shock.

On the presentation of 10/sec clicks, neither the criterion of
conditioned response nor that of central electrical response indicated the existence of any stimulus equivalence across sensory
modalities. The transfer of training, however, occurred at a remarkable rate; the CAR to the pulsed auditory stimulus was fully
established after only 2 to 4 reinforcements. Further, following
this transfer of training, the *auditory* TCS evoked potentials in the
visual system similar to those elicited by the *visual* TCS.

These data suggest that transfer of training resulted in the
establishment of central stimulus equivalence. However, after
experimental extinction of the CAR to the visual TCS, when it was
no longer effective in eliciting either the CAR or its acquired
electrical correlates, an interesting phenomenon was observed.
The auditory TCS still retained the capacity to elicit the CAR and
part, but not all, of the acquired electrical correlates were manifested. A subsequent temporary restitution of the ability of the
visual TCS to elicit both the CAR and labeled electrical responses
was observed. This suggests that all of the electrical correlates
evoked in the visual system by the auditory TCS after transfer
are not essential to the performance of the CAR, and also indicates
that the "extinguished" responses to a particular stimulus can be
reactivated by another stimulus with appropriate characteristics.

The primary purpose of the various psychological procedures
which have been described was to evaluate the significance of
the observed labeled responses in mediating the conditioned behavior. In the course of carrying out these procedures, a num-

ber of phenomena were observed which may be considered to provide evidence about mechanisms underlying the organization of afferent input to the central nervous system. During the process of familiarization, it was observed that central electrical responses to a stimulus were suppressed. Generalization tests indicated that under certain circumstances the electrical responses evoked by a particular stimulus may have the characteristic form of responses acquired to a prior different stimulus of the same modality. The phenomena observed during transfer of training indicate that a stimulus in one modality, with the appropriate characteristics, may come to evoke the electrical responses previously established to a similar stimulus over a different modality.

A single mechanism can be postulated which might account for these 3 phenomena. During repeated experience with a stimulus, an extralemniscal system may be organized which is in some fashion "tuned" to the characteristics of the stimulus in such a manner that this system can interact with classical afferent systems and exert an inhibitory or facilitatory influence. Interaction of this tuned system with a specific afferent system in an inhibitory fashion could result in the selective suppression of afferent input with certain characteristics, as observed in familiarization. Conversely, interaction in a facilitatory fashion, stabilized during conditioning, could result in the producton of electrical responses in the specific system which bore the characteristics imposed by the tuned system rather than those related to the afferent input, as observed in generalization. Presentation of a new stimulus in a different modality, but with the appropriate characteristics and in the proper context, might result in the activation of the tuned system. Subsequent facilitatory action of the tuned system might result in the production of electrical responses in an afferent system different from that of the new stimulus, as observed in transfer and in the resurgence of response in the visual system after extinction when the auditory TCS was presented.

To some extent, this hypothesis is supported by the data obtained by Chow, Dement, & John (1957) who showed that functional equivalence is not achieved by a procedure which only establishes stimulus equivalence with respect to *cortical* electrical responses.

The relationship between the acquired central electrical responses and the CAR was investigated further by observing the consequences on both of the administration of reserpine. As the performance of the CAR deteriorated after reserpine, the acquired electrical responses disappeared in essentially the reverse order to that seen during acquisition of the CAR. As drug effects wore off, the sequence of changes in electrical response to the TCS basically recapitulated those seen during initial acquisition of the CAR. Finally, experimental extinction of the learned behavioral response resulted in a parallel gradual disappearance of the acquired electrical activity.

These various observations support the conclusion that the acquired electrical responses are neurophysiological correlates of avoidance conditioning. Perhaps more important, these experiments present a novel method of investigating the neurophysiological mechanisms mediating learning and the effects of drugs on the central nervous system.

SUMMARY

Central electrical responses to a flickering light (TCS) have been recorded from cats having electrodes chronically implanted in cortical and subcortical areas during (a) initial presentation of the stimulus, (b) familiarization, (c) acquisition and performance of a conditioned avoidance response (CAR), (d) generalization to other frequencies of flickering light, (e) transfer to pulsed auditory stimulation, (f) blockade of the CAR by reserpine and (g) extinction of the CAR.

Frequency-specific responses (labeled responses) recorded from visual cortex, auditory cortex, lateral geniculate, superior colliculus, amygdala and hippocampus upon first presentation of the TCS waned and disappeared during the familiarization process.

With the initial pairing of shock with TCS, labeled responses reappeared in all structures except the amygdala and hippocampus. The responses were modified in form and amplitude in the different areas of the brain in different phases of learning. Of particular interest was the shift in location of labeled responses from the classical visual pathway to the extralemniscal ascending system and then back to the major visual path again during successive stages of avoidance training.

At 100% CAR 40/sec burst activity in the amygdala and mul-

378   E. R. JOHN AND K. F. KILLAM

tiples of the TCS frequency in the cortical responses were characteristic features.

Evidence of the functional relevance of the electrical responses observed in certain central structures was obtained by studies of generalization, of transfer and of the effects of reserpine.

REFERENCES

Chow, K. L., Dement, W. C., & John, E. R. *J. Neurophysiol.*, 1957, **20**, 482.

Galambos, R, Sheatz, G., & Vernier, V. G. *Science*, 1956, **123**, 376.

Hagberth, K. E., & Kerr, D. I. B. *J. Neurophysiol.*, 1954, **17**, 295.

Hernández-Peón, R., & Scherrer, H. *Fed. Proc.*, 1955, **14**, 71.

Killam, K. F., & Killam, E. K. *Reticular formation of the brain.* Boston: Little, Brown, 1958.

Lesse, H. *Fed. Proc.*, 1957, **16**, 79.

Lindsley, D. B., Bowden, J. W., & Magoun, H. W. *EEG clin. Neurophysiol.*, 1949, **1**, 475.

Livanov, M. N., Korolikova, T. A., & Frenkeli, G. M. *Jur. Vysh. Nervn. Deyat.* (Russ.), 1951, **1**, 251.

Moruzzi, G., & Magoun, H. W. *EEG clin. Neurophysiol.*, 1949, 1, 455.

Rusinov, V. S., & Rabinovich, M. Y. *EEG clin. Neurophysiol.*, 1958, Suppl. 8.

Sharpless, S., & Jasper, H. H. *Brain*, 1956, **79**, 655.

Yoshii, N., Gastaut, H., & Pruvot, P. *Communications, XX int. physiol. Congr., Brussels*, 1956, 985.

Yoshii, N., Matsumoto, J., & Hori, Y. *Communications, First int. Congr. neurol. Sci., Brussels*, 1957.

[ADDENDA FROM THE ORIGINAL PRINTING OF THIS ARTICLE: IN REFERENCE TO THE AUTHORS: *Departments of Physiology, Pharmacology and Anatomy, University of California Medical Center, Los Angeles, California. Received for publication October 6, 1958. Part of this material was presented before the American Society for Pharmacology and Experimental Therapeutics, Baltimore, Maryland, September, 1957.* IN REFERENCE TO JOHN: *Present address: Department of Psychology, River Campus, University of Rochester, Rochester 20, New York.* IN REFERENCE TO KILLAM: *This investigation was supported in part by a Senior Research Fellowship (Keith F. Killam) from the United States Public Health Service and by grant G-3354 from the National Science Foundation.*]

ELECTROGRAPHIC STUDIES OF THE FORMATION OF TEMPORARY CONNECTIONS IN THE BRAIN ⚜ *Frank Morrell and Herbert H. Jasper*

PAVLOV (1920) described the establishment of conditioned salivary secretion to a non-specific stimulus as a "temporary connection" between the center responding to the conditioned stimulus and that responding to the unconditioned stimulus. When sound was used as the conditioned stimulus for salivation the "temporary connection" would be between the auditory "center" and the "food center." Such a connection is truly conditional. It is formed by chance or deliberate experimental juxtaposition in time of two stimuli, one of which always (innately) results in a given response.

The physiological basis for nature of such temporary connections remains one of the most important unsolved problems of neurophysiology. Important hypotheses have been proposed by Hebb (1949), Eccles (1953), and Walter (1953) and problems

REPRINTED FROM *Electroencephalography and Clinical Neurophysiology*, 8:201-215. COPYRIGHT © 1956 BY ELSEVIER PUBLISHING COMPANY.

of their anatomical location have been reviewed by Hilgard and
Marquis (1940) and Lashley (1950). Our approach has been to
use the electrical activity of the cortex itself as a means of making a more direct study of neurophysiological mechanisms underlying the formation of temporary connections in the brain.

In the human electroencephalogram the arrest or "blocking"
of the occipital alpha rhythm in response to visual stimulation or
attention might be considered as a kind of "unconditioned response." Many early workers noted incidentally that this EEG
response was readily conditioned to an auditory stimulus (Durup
& Fessard 1935; Loomis, Harvey, & Hobart 1936-1937; Jasper &
Cruikshank 1937, and Cruikshank 1937). Travis and Egan (1938)
and Knott and Henry (1941) made quantitative studies of this
apparent conditioning process; the latter authors attempted to
control the factor of "sensitization" of "pseudo-conditioning" by
presenting the sound 4 sec. before the light stimulus.[1]

Using the alpha blocking reaction to a visual stimulus in man
as the unconditioned response, Jasper and Shagass (1941) were
able to establish nearly all forms of Pavlovian conditioning, including simple, differential, delayed, cyclic, trace, and backward
"reflexes." Such temporary connections were quite readily extinguished without reinforcement. Responses to delay intervals,
such as occurred in delay, trace, and cyclic conditioning, were
remarkably consistent in their time of incidence, more accurate
in fact than was the subject's voluntary estimate of the time
interval. Comparison of subjective estimates of time intervals, in
a subsequent study (Jasper & Shagass 1941b), was the conditioned alpha blocking response to time intervals showed that
the two phenomena were apparently independent, which argues
against the suggestion of Loomis, Harvey, and Hobart (1937)
that the conditioned alpha blocking was related directly to an
"attempt to see" or to a conscious anticipatory set.

More recent studies by Motokawa and Huzimori (1949) and
Iwama (1950), using the alpha blocking reaction in man as a
"conditioned response," have attempted to show a relationship
between the degree of "inhibition" in the conditioning process

[1] Pseudo-conditioning occurs when a subliminal stimulus, used as CS,
is made liminal by an increase of general cortical excitability induced by
simultaneous presentation of an effective UCS. Therefore, the presumed
CR is actually a direct or unconditioned response to the conditioned stimulus.

and an increase in the alpha rhythm. Morrell and Ross (1953) showed that there was an increase in visuo-motor reaction time during "inhibitory" processes involved in extinction, delayed and differential conditioning.

Attempts to condition the electrical activity of the cortex in animals have met with technical difficulties, due principally to the problem of establishing sufficiently constant experimental conditions in unanaesthetized animals to obtain consistent changes in cortical electrical activity. Shagass (1941) succeeded in conditioning occipital strychnine spike responses to a complex tone in anaesthetized cats. However, since spiking occurred spontaneously as well, statistical treatment was necessary and thousands of trials were required to establish some effect of conditioning upon the frequency of these strychnine spikes.

In the present report we shall describe a technique which has been reasonably successful in studies of conditioning the electrical activity of the cortex in unanaesthetized monkeys. We shall present preliminary results which formed the basis for a subsequent study of the effects of experimental epileptogenic lesions upon the process of temporary connection formation in the brain, to be presented in a later report.

TECHNIQUE

Eight normal adult monkeys (Macaca Mulatta) were used in this study. The animals were immobilized with a minimum of discomfort, lying prone on a table, with their heads clamped in a cushioned head holder and their extremities tied loosely. After a few moments of struggling they remained relatively quiet during the experiment. They would occasionally become drowsy and go to sleep, though an attempt was made to keep them alert during the conditioning procedures.

The animals were placed in a relatively sound-proof room, with all signal controls and recording apparatus outside. In preliminary experiments in an open laboratory setting conditioning was extremely difficult due to adventitious sounds.

Electroencephalographic records were taken by means of either insulated phonograph needles inserted through the skull to the dura, or by steel hooks inserted through the scalp into the galea. Standard electrode placements were measured with reference to skull landmarks. Bipolar leads were used from frontal, central, parietal occipital, and from anterior and posterior temporal regions. Since the brain was not exposed, localization would be only approximate.

Several EEG records were taken prior to conditioning in order to accustom the animals to the experimental situation and to obtain "normal" EEG records for comparison of those obtained during conditioning sequences. Experiments were not begun until the animals were relaxed and adjusted to the situation as judged by absence of muscle action potentials in the electromyogram and a normal heart rate as recorded with an electrocardiogram.

EEG records were taken with the Offner Dynagraph (type D). Stimuli were controlled by a manual switch which also signalled the incidence of each stimulus on the recording paper with the EEG record.

The unconditioned stimulus was a stroboscopic flicker of red light (the Epiphote) placed 18 inches in front of the eyes so that the entire visual field was illuminated. There was no sound associated with the flash of light in this apparatus. Flicker frequencies between 6 and 500 f/sec. were used in different experiments. The "blocking" reaction or photic "driving" evoked in occipital cortex was considered the "unconditioned response."

Conditioning stimuli were as follows:

1. *Auditory stimuli* composed of pure tones of sufficient intensity to produce a minimal "startle" response when first presented were used. This initial response dissapeared rapidly after several repetitions of the stimulus until no detectable response was seen in the EEG.
2. *Electrical stimuli* of minimal intensity were administered to the skin of the ankle by means of intradermal electrodes. Intensity was adjusted to cause a minimal evoked potential response in somato-sensory cortex (1-2 V.) without causing leg withdrawal or any other evidence of pain. This will be referred to as a "tactile" or "touch" stimulus.
3. *Visual stimulation,* as a conditioning stimulus, was made possible by variation in the background illumination of the room.

The conditioning stimulus always preceded the unconditioned stimulus by a variable interval of about 2 or 3 sec. The unconditioned stimulus (flicker) was then turned on and both stimuli

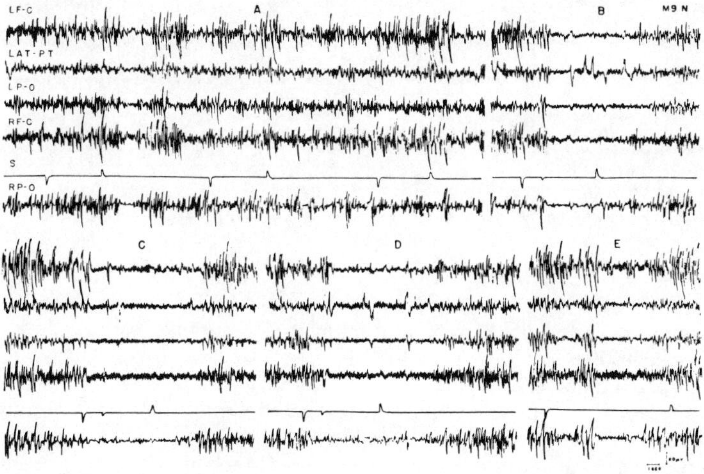

Fig. 1. Examples of EEG records of conditioning in monkey M9, relaxed, slightly drowsy, but not asleep. The records were from the left fronto-central (LF-C), left ant.-post. temporal (LAT-PT), left parieto-occipital (LP-O), right front-central (RF-C), and right parieto-occipital areas (RP-O). S is the signal indicating the occurence of stimuli. In A is shown the absence of response to a 500 c/sec. tone, the conditioned stimulus, following its repetition for adaptation prior to conditioning. In B is shown the first conditioning trial with a generalized activation response to the UCS flicker at 500 f/sec. (second pip on signal line). A generalized activation response has been conditioned to the tone (first pip) in C, but only appears in occipital regions after further conditioning in D. When the tone was presented alone, after conditioning, a biphasic activation response was obtained as shown in E, the first being the simple conditioned response to the tone, the second a response to the previous time interval between tone and light.

continued for 3 or 4 sec. together. They were both turned off simultaneously. The intertrial interval was intentionally varied widely in the attempt to avoid cyclic conditioning.

Conditioning to a given type of stimulus was carried out on one day and 3 to 7 days allowed to elapse before conditioning to another modality of stimulus. Simple conditioning to sound, touch, or light was completed in a two-week period; then a two week rest period was allowed before undertaking differential conditioning. This made a minimum of six sessions for each animal in this control series.

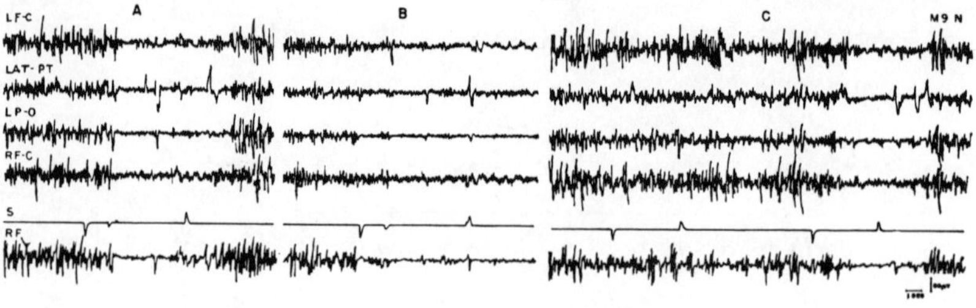

Fig. 2. Examples of conditioning to a weak electric shock to the skin ("touch") in monkey M9. EEG records followed same order as shown in Fig. 1. A. First conditioning trial showing response to UCS (flicker 500/sec.) but none to CS (touch to right leg). B. Fully developed CR to touch with blocking localized to occipital regions. C. Differential response to touch after conditioning. The first stimulus (touch to left leg) had been negatively conditioned, i.e., never paired with flicker, while the second stimulus (touch to right leg) is that used in B and had been reinforced.

RESULTS

A. Blocking or "Desynchronizing" Conditioned Response

On presentation of a photic stimulus at 500 c/sec. a clear blocking or desynchronization of the parieto-occipital alpha rhythm was seen.

The minimal intensity of stimuli used for conditioning (tone, touch, or change in background illumination) when presented alone initially caused a blocking reaction of all cerebral rhythms which was most pronounced in central regions. On repetition, however, this response completely disappeared (Fig. 1A). At the beginning of the paired trials, therefore, the CS caused no change in cerebral activity while the UCS produced a clear blocking (Fig. 1B). The first stage in conditioning was identified by the fact that the blocking response began before onset of the flicker and in response to the CS. Most important is the fact that this initial evidence of a temporary connection appears in all leads more or less equally and simultaneously (Fig. 1C).

If the conditioning process is continued, a gradual contraction of the blocking reaction occurs, limiting it to the occipital region (Fig. 1D). This sharply localized blocking response to the conditioned stimulus is the final form of the CR. Such a response is quite selective and can be made to distinguish between tones, for example, of 200 and 500 cycles by constantly reinforcing one tone and presenting the other without reinforcement. Differential responses to positively and negatively conditioned stimuli are illustrated in Figure 2C.

The lack of EEG response to the CS before conditioning is shown in A, while a conditioned blocking response to touch, which was localized to occipital leads, and did not appear in the frontal derivations on either side, is shown in B.

Generally, similar responses were obtained to each sense modality, although the number of trials required to establish a temporary connection to light (change in background illumination) as CS was slightly greater than that to tone or touch. (Mean 13.2 trials for light as compared to 8.2 for tone.)

The criterion taken for the number of trials necessary for the establishment of simple conditioning was the first of a series of 4 successive unreinforced responses to the conditioned stimulus. The criterion for differential conditioning was the first trial in a series of 9 correct responses in 10 trials. The number of trials to reach these criteria for both simple and differential conditioning are present in Table I. It will be noted that the degree of consistency is quite high with the exception of animal M8. This animal was frightened and weak, ate poorly, and died before the experiments were completed. The number of trials necessary to produce a clear conditioned response were considerably greater in this animal than in all of the others. The mean for the normal group in the above table includes this sick animal but an additional figure, in parenthesis, is given excluding this animal in order to give a more "normal" mean.

The number of trials required for differential conditioning was about three times that required for simple conditioning. The same relative "difficulty" between conditioning to sound, touch, or light, obtains for differential as well as simple conditioning.

There seems to be little effect of "sophistication," i.e., alteration of results produced solely by repeated exposure to the test situation. In some animals there was evidence for spontaneous recovery of conditioned response two weeks after an experimental series which had been terminated by extinction of the response by repeated unreinforced trials.

The number of trials necessary to extinguish a conditioned response, once established, was also recorded. This was compared with the number of trials which were required for adaptation to the conditioned stimulus at the beginning of the session. The

TABLE I. NORMAL CONTROLS: NUMBER OF TRIALS
TO CONDITION

	SIMPLE			DIFFERENTIAL		
Animal	Auditory	Somatic	Visual	Auditory	Somatic	Visual
M8	31	25				
B9	9	7	12	28	26	39
M10	7	8	12	25	21	36
M11	6	5	11	19	21	31
M12	7	11	15	21	20	32
M13	9	5	11	22	14	38
M14	14	10	17	30	19	34
M15	6	5	15	21	20	34
Mean	11.1	9.5	13.2	23.7	20.1	34.8
Normal	(8.2)	(7.2)				

conditioned stimulus produced a generalized blocking or
"arousal" response when first presented which rapidly disappeared with repetition. The criterion for both adaptation and
extinction was the number of trials before the first of a series of
four successive stimuli which produced no response. If it took
a larger number of trials to extinguish the response after conditioning than it had taken to adapt to the same stimulus prior to
conditioning, this should represent a measure of "strength" of the
conditioned connection established.

The per cent difference between adaptation and extinction was
calculated by the following formula:

$$\frac{N \text{ Ext. trials} - N \text{ Adapt. trials}}{N \text{ Adapt. trials}} \times 100 = \text{per cent difference}$$

This gave the percentage increase of trials required to extinguish
the conditioned response as compared to simple adaptation to
repetition of the same stimulus before conditioning. The results
are summarized in Table II. It will be noted that simple adaptation to the conditioning stimulus required only about 5 to 8
stimuli (with the exception of the sick animal, M8). Extinction
after conditioning required about 3 times as many trials following
a simple conditioning series, and about 4 times as many to produce extinction following the differential series of trials. The
per cent difference between adaptation and extinction varied
widely with different animals, with a minimum of 160 as the

TABLE II. NORMAL CONTROLS: TRIALS TO ADAPTATION, EXTINCTION, AND PER CENT DIFFERENCE*

| | SIMPLE CONDITIONING | | | | | | | | | DIFFERENTIAL CONDITIONING | | | | | | | | |
| | Auditory | | | Somatic | | | Visual | | | Auditory | | | Somatic | | | Visual | | |
Animal	A	E	%D	A	E	%D	A	E	%D	A	E	%D	A	E	%D	A	E	%D
8	18	33	83	29	41	41												
9	6	20	233	10	20	100	5	16	220	8	34	325	11	39	254	6	28	366
10	5	18	260	7	18	157	4	15	275	8	30	275	10	29	190	6	21	250
11	5	17	240	7	22	214	5	16	220	8	26	225	8	28	250	6	19	216
12	7	19	271	8	23	187	5	20	300	8	29	262	10	31	210	6	26	333
13	5	16	220	7	19	171	5	12	140	4	28	600	7	29	314	8	22	275
14	5	28	460	12	39	225	4	29	625	8	40	400	12	37	208	7	29	314
15	6	19	216	9	26	188	4	17	325	7	29	314	8	28	250	6	21	250
Mean**																		
Normal	7	21	248	11	26	160	5	18	300	7	31	343	9	32	239	6	24	286

* To nearest whole number

** %D = $\dfrac{\text{Extinction (E)} - \text{Adaptation (A)}}{\text{Adaptation (A)}} \times 100$

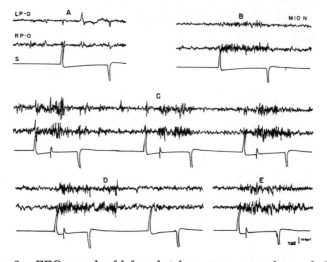

Fig. 3.   EEG records of left and right parieto-occipital areas before and during conditioning of a tone to flicker (UCS) at 50 f/sec. *A.* Tone (500 c/sec.) before conditioning. *B.* Effect of flicker (50/sec.) alone. Response is at 12-14 c/sec. which may be subharmonic. *C.* A series of consecutive conditioned responses showing the "faciliatory" response to the tone (CS). *D.* Differential CR. Positive tone (reinforced) is 50 c/sec.; the negative tone is 1000 c/sec. *E.* Simple CR as in *C.* But with a particularly long-lasting faciliatory effect continuing considerably past the end of stimulation.

mean for simple conditioning to touch and a maximum of 343 as the mean for differential conditioning to sound (tone).

It may be significant that the number of trials required for adaption to sound, touch, or light, show the reverse, relative order from that for trials to condition, e.g., light shows quickest adaptation and requires greatest number of trials to condition; touch shows slowest adaptation and most rapid conditioning. The relative order of number of extinction trials, however, parallels the order of number of trials required in initial conditioning.

B. Facilitatory Conditioned Response

When the flicker frequency was reduced from 500 f/sec. to 50 f/sec., a sudden change was noted in the response from the occipital cortex. The moderate voltage background activity, instead of "blocking" with the onset of the flicker showed an abrupt augmentation and regularization at a rhythm of 12-14 c/sec. This was quite consistent and occurred with every presentation of the flicker.

It was possible to condition this augmented or facilitatory cortical response by the same means as that used for the "blocking" CR. An example of the simple facilitatory conditioned response is shown and a differential response in Figure 3D. The second stimulus was a tone of 1000 c/sec. which had never been reinforced. The cortical response to this tone was quite different. If one examines the tracing carefully, a faint response can be seen to the 1000 c/sec. tone. This is a residual generalization phenomenon and disappears with continued reinforcement of the differentiation.

In some instances the facilitatory response outlasted both conditioned and unconditioned stimuli, as shown in Figures 3D and 3E. This is an important argument against the notion that any of these responses (UCR or CR) are simple evoked potentials rather than centrally organized reactions.

In most instances the repetitive response was at a subharmonic of the flicker frequency. It is very likely, therefore, essentially the same response as that to be described below as "photic driving."

C. Repetitive or "Photic Driving" Conditioned Response

The characteristic unconditioned response of the occipital cortex to intermittent photic stimulation at lower frequencies is a series of potential waves which "follow" the flicker frequency. These responses are of greatest amplitude and regularity when the flicker frequency approaches that of the spontaneous electrical rhythms of the occipital cortex, namely, about 6 or 12 per sec. It is commonly called "photic driving." This provides a positive, frequency specific, unconditioned response which can be used with the various conditioned stimuli, in the attempt to form responses of a different character than the alpha blocking described above.

It was found that when a low frequency flicker was the UCS the establishment of a localized (occipital) blocking response to tone, touch, or light was somewhat easier than with a 500 c/sec. flicker, judged by extinction trials and per cent extinction-adaptation difference, and the response was more persistent when established.

Accordingly, the low frequency flicker (6-12 sec.) was then

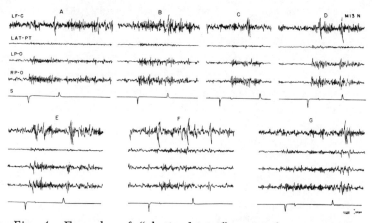

Fig. 4. Examples of "photic driving" occipital response when flicker was reduced to within the range of normal rhythms, 6-12/sec. *A-B*. Simple photic responses to flicker at 6/sec. Note the variation in form and regularity of these two successive responses to the same stimulus. *C*. First conditioning trial showing response to UCS (flicker at 6/sec.) but no response to CS (tone 500 c/sec.). *D-G*. Varieties of conditioned "photic driving." In *D* and *E* the response is rather irregular (as in *B*). Note that the latency is less in *E* than in *D* and that an eyeblink artifact can be seen in *D* at the time the flicker appears, and well after the repetitive cortical response has begun. *F* is a frequency specific (to the UCS) response at a lower voltage, gradually building up to onset of flicker. *G* is a regular frequency specific CR fully established. Note in all tracings that this response, unlike the early blocking CR, is always localized to parieto-occipital regions, with some lower voltage response in posterior temporal regions.

used as the UCS on all animals. However, in the course of establishing such CR's a different kind of response was also noted. This latter was a frequency specific (to the UCS) occipital discharge beginning in the CS-UCS interval, i.e., preceding the onset of intermittent photic stimulation. It always occurred after the early phase of conditioning when the CS elicited a general blocking reaction and before the localized blocking CR had been established. In fact it was sometimes mixed with the latter, the CS-UCS interval containing both blocking and photic driving components (Fig. 5F).

The photic driving CR differed in several respects from the blocking CR. It was not always uniform or frequency specific throughout and varied considerably in form and latency. Unlike the blocking reaction it did not usually begin with the onset of

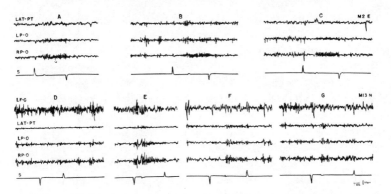

Fig. 5. Other experiments showing further varieties of conditioned "photic driving." *A-B.* Frequency specific (flicker 6/sec. in *A* and 8/sec. in *B*) repetitive discharge beginning before onset of flicker and gradually increasing in voltage to point when flicker appears. Tone of 500 c/sec. in CS. *C.* This is the localized desynchronization, limited to occipital regions, which is the most stable form of the conditioned electrographic complex. *D.* Another experiment. Background light (CS) alone before conditioning. There was no cortical response. *E.* Conditioned repetitive response to background light. Flicker at 6/sec. is UCS. *F.* A mixed response showing a low voltage frequency specific component and a brief localized desynchronization. *G.* As in *C*, a typical conditioned desynchronization of the localized variety but with background light rather than tone as the CS.

the CS but appeared later in the CS-UCS interval. With continued reinforcement it "crept" closer to the onset of the CS. It also showed increasing regularization and more closely approximated the flicker frequency as reinforcement was continued. Furthermore this repetitive discharge appeared first and was only present in the occipital leads. It showed no tendency to generalization at any time.

The photic driving conditioned response was much less stable than the blocking response, and showed considerable irregularity from time to time during conditioning. Some variation was also observed in the unconditioned response, as illustrated by two examples in Figure 4A-C.

After conditioning, a series of rhythmic waves appeared, following the conditioning (e.g., a 500 c/sec. tone), before the photic stimulus was turned on, as shown in Figure 4D-G. In spite of the variability in these conditioned responses, they were not much more variable than were the unconditioned photic driving responses. Most remarkable was the fact that the frequency of the conditioned occipital response appeared to be the same as that of the intermittent photic stimulus used as the unconditioned stimulus. It was necessary, of course, to examine this conclusion very critically because the flicker frequency was very close to that of the spontaneous electrical rhythms in the resting record.

With further conditioning the positive "photic driving" conditioned response tended to disappear and be replaced by the local occipital blocking response, even with continued reinforcement. This is illustrated in records from another experiment shown in Figure 5. In this example a frequency specific response to a flicker of 6 f/sec. is shown in A and at 8 f/sec. from another series in the same animal in B. The conditioned stimulus in this example was a 500 c/sec. tone. It seemed that when the 6 f/sec. flicker was the unconditioned stimulus the conditioned response assumed this same frequency, while it changed to 8/sec. in another series when the higher frequency was used as the unconditioned stimulus. In each case, as conditioning trials were continued, this "positive" response was replaced by what seemed to be a simple local blocking response, as illustrated in Figure 5C. A similar sequence was shown when using a visual or tactile conditioning stimulus, as illustrated in Figure 5D-G.

Usually the frequency specific repetitive conditioned response appeared between the sixth and fifteenth trial, and disappeared between the thirteenth and twenty-eighth trial. It was more readily established with auditory or visual conditioning stimuli than with the tactile stimulus, though the form of the electrical response, as recorded from the occipital cortex, was independent of the type of conditioning stimulus used. However, once the response was established, it occurred only to the stimulus to which it had been conditioned, not to a different tone than that which had been conditioned, and not to other forms of stimuli (touch or light) to which the response had not been conditioned. This suggests that the occipital response was a truly specific conditioned response, and not an unspecific "sensitization" or "setting" of a rhythmic response in the occipital cortex which might be then "triggered" by any unspecific stimulus.

Since this response only occurred at flicker frequencies close to the natural rhythms, it was important to determine whether it was merely a non-specific augmentation of rhythms already present or was truly related to the frequency of the UCS.

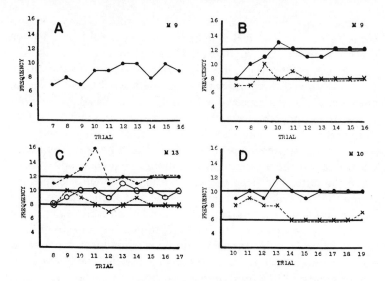

Fig. 6. Chart of frequency changes in occipital electrical activity in the course of conditioning of repetitive responses. Counts are plotted for 10 consecutive trials, beginning with the trial on which the CR first appears. Horizontal black lines in *B, C,* and *D* are flicker frequencies used as UCS in the several experiments. Filled circles, open circles, and ✕'s indicate the frequency counts in the CS-UCS interval (for 1 sec.). *A.* One second counts of the alpha frequency during presentation of the adapted tone to which this animal will later be conditioned. *B.* Frequency counts in CS-UCS interval during conditioning of same tone as in *A* to flicker of 12/sec. and 8/sec. *C.* Similar counts in another animal conditioned with flicker at 8, 10, and 12/sec. *D.* A third animal conditioned with flicker at 6 and 10/sec. The same CS is used in all the recorded experiments for each animal. Each flicker frequency represents a separate experiment.

Several animals had been conditioned with a variety of frequencies as UCS (within the 6-12 c/sec. range) in different experiments. In 3 of these animals the frequency of the UCR was plotted against the frequency of the CR for 10 successive trials beginning with the trial at which the photic driving CR first was noted. As a control, frequency counts were made of the alpha rhythm, in one second epochs, during 10 successive presentations of the adapted tone to which the animal was later conditioned. In addition each animal served as his own control because the responses were plotted against 2 or 3 flicker frequencies in each case. These results are plotted in Figure 6.

It was apparent from these results that the auditory stimulus alone (a pure tone at 500 c/sec.) had no appreciable effect upon the frequency of the rhythmical electrical activity from the occipital region after the initial trials necessary for adaptation. In the same animal this tone was paired with an 8 f/sec. flicker in one conditioning series and with a 12 f/sec. flicker in another series. It is apparent from the curve shown in Figure 6B, that the conditioned response tended to stabilize gradually with repeated trials, approaching more closely the 8 per sec. frequency when this was the unconditioned stimulus frequency, and 12/sec. when the latter had been the unconditioned stimulus frequency. In another animal flicker frequencies of 8, 10, and 12/sec. were used in different conditioning series, and the results (Fig. 6 C) show a definite tendency for the conditioned response frequency to be determined by the unconditioned stimulus frequency in each case. Likewise a similar frequency specific conditioned response appeared in a third animal, as shown in Figure 6D.

DISCUSSION

Two distinct forms of conditioned response have been obtained. The first is a repetitive discharge at the flicker frequency and the second is a more stable, well localized desynchronization or "activation pattern." Both responses are limited to occipital and para-occipital areas. Moreover, under these experimental conditions there is a characteristic and consistently reproducible pattern of events which seems to provide objective and more coherent evidence for certain aspects of the mechanism of formation of temporary connections between one sensory system and another.

Before conditioning begins the unconditioned stimulus evokes a "photic driving" response from posterior head regions which shows no systematic change with repeated presentation. The conditioned stimulus (tone, touch, or light) elicits on first presentation a general alerting response characterized by an increase in muscle tension, increase in heart rate, widening of palpebral fissures, and searching eye movements and a generalized cortical "desynchronization" or "activation" of the EEG which is most prominent in the rolandic area. All the components of this response show adaptation: that is, they diminish and finally disappear with repeated presentation of the stimulus. Any alteration in the stimulus or of any variable in the experimental situation will restore the response in full.

It seems probable that this general alerting reaction is identical with what Pavlov (1928) described as the "orienting reflex." The diffuse desynchronization is the cortical component of this reflex and represents a general "arousal" or increase in excitability (Jasper 1936, Motokawa 1949) of the entire cortex preparatory to dealing with a new situation. It may be distinguished from the localized desynchronization seen in the occipital alpha rhythm on presentation of a light stimulus or the equally well localized blocking of rolandic beta activity noted with continuous hand movement (Jasper & Penfield 1949). Both the occipital and rolandic rhythms may be unilaterally affected if the stimulus is adequately lateralized (Adrian 1947). Bremer (1953) has demonstrated similar discrete desynchronization in the auditory cortex when it is appropriately stimulated. In the normal animal, the generalized alerting reaction is never unilateral nor is it confined to any specific sensory representation.

After several paired trials, the CS again elicits a generalized "blocking" response identical in all respects to the original alerting reaction. The reappearance of this reaction is not surprising. It has been shown by Sokolov (1954) that the orienting reflex, after being extinguished in relation to a particular stimulus, is restored when that same stimulus is made the signal for a conditioned response. The fact that this restored general cortical activation also gradually disappears, despite continued reinforcement, is additional evidence of its "orienting" nature. As paired trials are continued, the diffuse activation pattern gives way to a precise, frequency specific (to the flicker frequency) discharge limited to the occipital regions. Finally, with present recording techniques, the repetitive discharge, even with continued reinforcement, appears to be replaced by focal low voltage fast activity which is also sharply limited to occipital (to a lesser degree, parietal and posterior temporal) areas. There is an intervening stage when the repetitive response and the localized asynchronous response are mixed, both occurring in the same CS-UCS interval (Fig. 5F). Differentiation may begin during the phase of generalized activation but is usually not well established until either the repetitive or the localized activation phase.

These stages of development are very similar to those described by Livanov (1945) as stages in the cortical desynchronization which characterizes a motor conditioned reflex. He describes a stage of pregeneralization during which desynchronization is present only in the cortical projection area stimulated by the unconditioned stimulus; a stage of generalization during which the desynchronization spreads throughout the entire cortex; a stage of concentration during which the desynchronization localizes in the cortical projection areas of the efferent system responsible for the reflexly conditioned activity.

Such findings suggest that the alpha blocking or desynchronization corresponds to a definite functional state of the cortical area involved, an activation or excitation of the neuronal units therein. It has been argued (Sokolov 1954) that this is the specific cortical expression of orienting or alerting behavior and that the circumscribed activations of direct projection systems are merely smaller components of the generalized orienting reflex. Interpreting the data in this manner one can recapitulate the pattern as follows:

The conditioning stimulus when first presented causes a generalized orienting response, expressed as a diffuse desynchronization of cortical rhythms. On repeated presentation this rapidly adapts until there is no evident cortical response. Then, when paired trials are begun, the conditioned stimulus becomes a signal for the flicker (UCS) which is to follow. The general orienting reflex is restored. As paired trials are continued, again the orienting reflex begins to disappear as it is replaced by the repetitive discharge at the flicker frequency. This latter is the specific conditioned response. The orienting response disappears unevenly, however. Frontal and central rhythms return to a "resting" stage while activation persists in the occipital, parietal, and posterior temporal regions, i.e., those areas required for the perception and elaboration of the stimulus and the mediation of the response.

The disappearance of the repetitive, frequency specific discharge, despite continued reinforcement, is somewhat surprising. It may be, however, that this is an artifact of the electrical recording system used in this study. There is evidence that during the establishment of conditioning the localized desynchronization and the repetitive discharge compete (Fig. 5F) for predominance. It is likely that both responses actually persist in the final electrographic complex, the positive discharge being obscured (reduced to below the amplifier noise level) by the lower voltages generated (Adrian 1949) when many of the nerve cells are firing asynchronously. We suspect that an auto-correlation (Brazier 1954) or frequency analysis of the CS-UCS interval in the final complex might reveal a clear persistent rhythm at the flicker frequency.

On the other hand, the lack of disappearance (extinction) of the final localized desynchronization is unusual if the latter is considered a component of orienting behavior. It was Pavlov's contention that an orienting reflex could not be conditioned precisely because it was extinguished by the same repetition of the stimulus that was necessary to condition it.

There are at least two interpretations of this phenomenon. If the localized blocking *is* a fraction of the orienting reflex, then one must conclude that a portion of the orienting reflex remains within the conditioned reflex as a requisite for the adequate perception of the signal stimulus. However, EEG desynchronization may not always be a component of the orienting reflex, but rather a non-specific sign of cortical activation which reflects a variety of unrelated neural events. The localized blocking may be a new positive conditioned activation entirely separate from the orienting response. There is, in fact, some evidence supporting a real distinction between generalized and local "arousal" patterns.

The diffuse EEG "arousal" produced by electrical stimulation of the brain stem reticular system (Moruzzi & Magoun 1949; Lindsley, Bowden, & Magoun 1949) is in sharp contrast to the localized desynchronization incident upon activity in a circumscribed area. Moreover, it shows the same anterior and central predominance (Adrian, Bremer, & Jasper 1954) exhibited in the general EEG "arousal" induced by sudden or forceful peripheral stimuli. On the other hand, Jasper (1949) and many co-workers have demonstrated, in the intralaminar and related nuclei of the thalamus, a more highly specialized portion of the reticular formation. The thalamic system appears to be closely related by both ascending and cortico-fugal fibers to specific cortical regions, overlapping those of the direct projection systems, and permitting local effects upon specific cortical areas (Penfield & Jasper 1954). Electrical stimulation of these nuclei at low frequency (within range of normal background rhythms) produces the recruiting response of Morison and Dempsey (1942), while high frequency stimulation may induce discrete blocking. Furthermore, in a recent study Jasper, Naquet, and King (1955) have demonstrated that recruiting responses in direct sensory projection areas may be arrested by simultaneous sensory stimulation as well as by simultaneous activation of the ascending reticular formation. However, the blocking induced by discrete sensory stimulation may under certain conditions exert its effect only on the recruiting response in the given sensory representation while ascending reticular activation disrupts recruiting responses from all areas. It is possible that the repetitive conditioned response and the localized desynchronization utilize these same or overlapping thalamic pathways, thus resulting in a similar occlusion effect in the final complex. With these recording techniques, we cannot of course distinguish between real occlusion at single units and the algebraic result of the loss of field effects by desynchronization.

The thalamic reticular system provides a physiologic and anatomic basis for local facilitation or "alerting" of a given cortical area without necessarily involving the entire cortex. These findings parallel behavioral observations which clearly distinguish general alerting or arousal response from those sharply delimited reactions involved in focussing attention on a single object. It seems likely that two kinds of temporary connection have been established under the same experimental conditions—a repetitive, frequency specific discharge and a focal activation pattern limited to a specific sensory system.

The localized occipital frequency specific, repetitive discharge which, following paired trials, is elicited by a previously ineffective stimulus and is subject to differentiation, we regard as an objective trace in cortical activity of a conditioned temporary connection.

SUMMARY

A technique has been developed which makes possible the establishment and recording of conditioned cortical electrical responses in the normal unanaesthetized monkey. These responses were of two forms; a repetitive discharge specific to the frequency of the unconditioned stimulus, and a localized activation pattern limited to the sensory receiving area of the unconditioned stimulus. These responses appear in a relatively constant sequence with the first evidence of conditioning being a generalized activation followed by the repetitive response and then the localized activation of the sensory receiving area.

REFERENCES

Adrian, E. D. The development of nerve cell rhythms. *Arch. Psychiat. u. Z. Neurol*, 1949, **183**, 197.

Adrian, E. D. *The physical background of perception.* Oxford: Clarendon, 1947.

Adrian, E. D., Bremer, F., & Jasper, H. H. *Brain mechanisms and consciousness.* Oxford and Springfield, Mass.: Blackwell and Charles Thomas, 1954.

Bagchi, B. K. The adaptation and variability of response of the human brain rhythm. *J. Psychol.*, 1936, **3**, 463-485.

Bailey, P., & von Bonin, G. *The isocortex of man.* Urbana, Ill.: Univer. of Illinois, 1951.

Barlow, J. S., & Brazier, M. A. B. A note on a correlator for electroencephalographic work. *EEG clin. Neurophysiol.*, 1954, **6**, 321-325.

Brazier, M. A. B., & Casby, J. U. Cross-correlation and autocorrelation studies of electroencephalographic potentials. *EEG clin. Neurophysiol.*, 1952, **4**, 201-211.

Bremer, F. *Some problems in neurophysiology.* London: Athlone, 1953.

Bohm, M. Tvorba Docasnych Spojov U Cloveka Za Pathologickych Stavov Kory. (Formation of temporary connections in man during pathologic states of the cerebral cortex.) *Neurol. Psychiat. Cesk.*, 1953, **16**, 275-292.

Cruikshank, R. M. Human occipital brain potentials as affected by intensity-duration variables of visual stimulation. *J. exp. Psychol.*, 1937, **21**, 625-641.

Durup, G., & Fessard, A. E'électroencéphalogramme de l'homme. *Année psychol.*, 1935, **36**, 1-32.

Eccles, J. C. *The neurophysiological basis of mind.* London: Oxford, 1953.

Gastaut, H. *The epilepsies, electro-clinical correlations.* Springfield, Ill.: Charles C Thomas, 1954.

Gastaut, H. *Introduction à l'étude electroencéphalographique du comportement.* Marseille: Saint Leon, 1954.

Hebb, D. O. *The organization of behavior.* New York: Wiley, 1949.

Helfrich, Dorothy L. Preliminary investigation of the conditioning of the flicker response of the human electroencephalogram. Unpublished master's thesis, State Univer. of Iowa, 1948.

Hilgard, E. R., & Marquis, D. G. *Conditioning and learning.* New York: Appleton-Century, 1940.

Iwama, K. Delayed conditioned reflex in man and brain waves. *Tohoku J. exp. Med.,* 1950, **52,** 53-63.

Jasper, H. H. Cortical excitatory state and synchronization in the control of bioelectric autonomous rhythms. *Cold Spring Harb. Symp. Quant. Biol.,* 1936, **4,** 320.

Jasper, H. H. Diffuse projection systems: The integrative action of the thalamic reticular system. *EEG clin. Neurophysiol.,* 1949, **4,** 405-419.

Jasper, H. H., & Cruikshank. R. M. Electroencephalography. II. Visual stimulation and the after image as affecting the occipital alpha rhythm. *J. gen. Psychol.,* 1937, **17,** 29-48.

Jasper, H. H., Cruikshank, R. M., & Howard, H. Action currents from the occipital region of the brain in man as affected by variables of attention and external stimulation. *Psychol. Bull.,* 1935, **32,** 565.

Jasper, H. H., Naquet, R., & King, E. E. Thalamocortical recruiting responses in sensory receiving areas in the cat. *EEG clin. Neurophysiol.,* 1955, **7,** 99-114.

Jasper, H. H., & Penfield, W. Electrocorticograms in man: Effect of voluntary movement upon the electrical activity of the precentral gyrus. *Arch. Psychiat. Nervnkr.,* 1949, **183,** 162-174.

Jasper, H. H., & Shagass, C. Conditioning the occipital alpha rhythm in man. *J. exp. Psychol.,* 1941, **26,** 373-388. (a)

Jasper, H. H., & Shagass, C. Conscious time judgments related to conditioned time intervals and voluntary control of the alpha rhythm. *J. exp. Psychol.,* 1941, **28,** 503-508. (b)

Knott, J. R., & Henry, C. E. The conditioning of the blocking of the alpha rhythm of the human electroencephalogram. *J. exp. Psychol.,* 1941, **28,** 134-144.

Kopeloff, L. M., Barrera, S. E., & Kopeloff, N. Recurrent convulsive seizures in animals produced by immunologic and chemical means. *Amer. J. Psychiat.,* 1942, **98,** 881.

Kopeloff, L. M., & Kopeloff, N. Anaphylaxis in the rhesus monkey. *J. Immunol.,* 1936, **36,** 83.

Kopeloff, N., Davidoff, C. M., & Kopeloff, L. M. General and cerebral anaphylaxis in the monkey (Macacus Rheusus). *J. Immunol.,* 1936, **30,** 477.

Laufberger, V. La réponse conditionée par imagination dans l'encéphalogramme. *C. R. Soc. Biol., Paris,* 1950, **144,** 467-468.

Liberson, W. T., & Cadhilac, J. G. Hippocampal responses to sensory stimulation in the guinea pig. *EEG clin. Neurophysiol.,* 1954, **6,** 710-711.

Lindsley, D. B., Bowden, J., & Magoun, H. W. Effect upon EEG of acute injury to the brain stem activating system. *EEG clin. Neurophysiol.,* 1949, **1,** 475-486.

Lindsley, D. B., Schreiner, L. H., Knowles, W.B., & Magoun, H. W.

Behavioral and EEG changes following chronic brain stem lesions in the cat. *EEG clin. Neurophysiol.*, 1950, **2**, 483-498.

Livanov, M. N. Les processes des fréquences dans l'électrocérébro-gramme *Bull. Biol. Med. exp.*, 1938, **5**, 248.

Livanov, M. N. The relation between rhythmic stimulation and the electrical response of the cortex. *J. Physiol., U.S.S.R.*, 1940, **28**, 172.

Livanov, M. N., & Poliakov, K. L. The electrical reactions of the cerebral cortex of a rabbit during the formation of a conditioned defense reflex by means of rhythmic stimulation. *Bull. Acad. Sci., U.S.S.R.*, 1945, **3**, 286.

Loomis, A. L., Harvey, E. N., & Hobart, G. A. Cerebral states during sleep as studied by human brain potentials. *J. exp. Psychol.*, 1937, **21**, 127-144.

Loomis, A. L., Harvey, E. N., & Hobart, G. Electrical potentials of the human brain. *J. exp. Psychol.*, 1936, **19**, 249-279.

Morison, R. S., & Dempsey, E. W. A study of thalamo-cortical relations. *Amer. J. Physiol.*, 1942, **135**, 281.

Morrell, F., & Ross, M. Central inhibition in cortical conditioned reflexes. *Arch. Neurol. Psychiat., Chicago*, 1953, **70**, 611-616.

Moruzzi, G., & Magoun, H. W. Brain stem reticular formation and activation of the EEG. *EEG clin. Neurophysiol.*, 1949, **1**, 455-473.

Motokawa, K. Electroencephalograms of man in the generalization and differentiation of conditioned reflexes. *Tohoku J. exp. Med.*, 1949, **50**, 225-234.

Motokawa, K., & Huzimori, B. Electroencephalograms and conditioned reflexes. *Tohuku J. exp. Med.*, 1949, **50**, 215-223.

Pacella, B. L., Kopeloff, N., Barrera, S. E., & Kopeloff, L. M. Experimental production of focal epilepsy. *Arch. Neurol. Psychiat., Chicago*, 1944, **52**, 189.

Pampiglione, G. Phenomenon of adaptation in human EEG. *Rev. Neurol.*, 1952, **87**, 197-198.

Pavlov, I. P. *Lectures on conditioned reflexes.* New York: International Publishers, 1928. 2 vols.

Penfield, W., & Jasper, H. H. *Epilepsy and the functional anatomy of the human brain.* Boston: Little, Brown, 1954.

Popov, N. A. Contribution à l'étude de la réaction d'arrêt du rhythme alpha chez l'homme. *C. R. Soc. Biol., Paris*, 1950, **144**, 1667-1669.

Popov, N. A. Contribution à l'étude de l'inhibition interne des réflexes conditionnés electrocorticaux. *C. R. Soc. Biol., Paris*, 1950, **144**, 906, 908.

Popov, N. A. Du rôle exclusif de l'ecorce cérébrale dans la formation des réflexes conditionnés électrocorticaux. *C. R. Soc. Biol., Paris*, 1949, **143**, 765-766.

Popov, N. A. Observations électroencéphaliques sur les reactions corticales chez l'homme. *Année psychol.*, 1953, **53**, 415-429.

Rusinov, V. S. An electrophysiological analysis of the connecting function in the cerebral cortex in the presence of a dominant area. *Communications, XIX int. physiol. Congr., Montreal,* 1953.

Shagass, C. Unpublished master's thesis, Univer. of Rochester, 1941.

Shagass, C., & Johnson, E. P. The course of acquisition of a conditioned response of the occipital alpha rhythm. *J. exp. Psychol.,* 1943, **33**, 201-209.

Sokolov, E. Higher nervous activity and the problem of perception. *Communications, XIV int. psychol. Congr.,* 1954.

Toman, J. E. P. Flicker potentials and the alpha rhythm in man. *J. Neurophysiol.,* 1941, **4**, 51-61.

Travis, L. E., & Egan, J. B. Conditioning of the electrical response of the cortex. *J. exp. Psychol.,* 1938, **22**, 524-531.

Travis, L. E., & Knott, J. R. Brain potential studies of perseveration. I. Perseveration time to light. *J. Psychol.,* 1936, **3**, 97-100.

Walter, W. G. *The living brain.* London and New York: Norton, 1953.

[ADDENDA FROM THE ORIGINAL PRINTING OF THIS ARTICLE: IN REFERENCE TO THE AUTHORS: *Department of Neurology and Neurosurgery, McGill University and the Montreal Neurological Institute, Montreal, and the Division of Neurology, University of Minnesota Medical School, Minneapolis, Min. Received for publication: October 15, 1955. Supported in part by a grant from the Teagle Foundation.*]

NEUROLOGY AND THE
MIND-BRAIN PROBLEM

❁ *R. W. Sperry*

THE DISCREPANCY between physiological processes in the brain and the correlated psychic experiences to which they give rise in consciousness has ever posed a baffling puzzle to students of psychology, neurology, and the related sciences. Despite steady advancement in our knowledge of the brain, the intrinsic nature of mind and its relation to cerebral excitation remains as much an enigma today as it was a hundred years ago.

Interest in the problem of the mind-brain relationship extends far beyond the immediate concerns of neurology and psychology. Inability to comprehend the essence of mind has been a major obstacle to the progress of philosophy throughout its history. Questions such as those concerning scientific truth, the nature of reality, and the place of man in the cosmos require for their study some knowledge of the constitution, quality, capacities, and limitations of the human mind, through which medium all such problems must be handled. Much of man's religious dogma and his moral and even legal codes is deeply influenced in the final analysis by mind-matter concepts. In fact, all the ultimate aims and values of mankind could be profoundly affected by a thor-

REPRINTED FROM *American Scientist,* 40:291-312. COPYRIGHT © 1952 BY THE SOCIETY OF THE SIGMA XI.

oughgoing rational insight into the mind-body relationship. It was the broad significance of the problem as much as the difficulty of reaching a solution that prompted William James (1) to declare that the attainment of a genuine glimpse into the mind-brain relation would constitute "*the* scientific achievement before which all past achievements would pale."

The struggles of philosophy with psychophysical problems, although carried on over centuries and by some of the greatest thinkers in history, have as yet failed to produce anything of much satisfaction to the tough-minded scientist. Further progress from philosophical synthesis can be expected only after science has succeeded in furnishing philosophy additional data with which to work. For example, we shall be in a much better position to study mind-brain relations after we have attained some conception of the neural patterning involved even in such simple mental activities as the perception of color, time, pattern, size, and the like. Eventually it should be possible to list the special features which distinguish those brain excitations that are accompanied by consciousness from those that are not. Once this latter objective is achieved, it may be feasible, at last, to attack the mind-body problem with some effectiveness.

It is really the "brain" part of the mind-brain relation that most urgently needs clarification. Neurological science thus far has been quite unable to furnish an adequate description of the neural processes involved in even the very simplest forms of mental activity. Once the unknown neural events become sufficiently understood, it may be found that the mind-brain problem will tend to resolve itself. In any case, hope for progress now seems to lie entirely in this direction.

Accordingly we may by-pass many blind alleys of philosophical controversy, and turn immediately to the neural correlates of conscious experience. In the following discussion we shall be concerned principally with the nature of the neural processes themselves, keeping in mind questions such as the following: How do the brain patterns of visual sensation, for example, differ essentially from those of auditory or other modes of sensation? How does the pattern of brain excitation in the visual perception of a triangle differ from the excitation involved in perceiving a square or a circle? And so on. Thus, we propose to deal primarily with definite scientific questions subject to objective scientific answers in neurological terms.

CURRENT STATUS OF THE PSYCHO-
NEURAL DILEMMA

Any immediate attempt to relate brain processes to psychic experience appears rather discouraging. To provide the colorful richness and infinite variation of quality and meaning in mental experience we find only a mass of brain tissue consisting essentially of closely packed nerve fibers and cell units roughly similar to one another in constitution, in structure, and in the physiological functions they perform. Such variation in size, shape, chemistry, conduction speed, excitation threshold, and the like, as has been demonstrated in nerve cells remains negligible in significance for any possible correlation with the manifold dimensions of mental experience.

Near the turn of the century it was suggested by Hering (2) that different qualities of sensation, such as pain, taste, and color, along with other mental attributes, might be correlated with the discharge of specific modes of nervous energy. Electronic methods of recording and analyzing nerve potentials, developed subsequently, have however failed to reveal any such qualitative diversity. It has been possible to demonstrate by other methods a refined constitutional specificity among neuron types (3, 4). However, proof is lacking that this specificity influences in any manner the quality of impulse conduction. It seems rather to be operative primarily in the developmental patterning of the neural circuits. Although qualitative variance among nerve energies has never been rigidly disproved, the doctrine has been generally abandoned on a number of grounds in favor of the opposing view, namely, that nerve impulses are essentially homogeneous in quality and are transmitted as "common currency" throughout the nervous system.

Impulses traveling in the optic, auditory, proprioceptive, and other sensory pathways are, accordingly, believed to be similar in nature. "It is not the quality of the sensory nerve impulses that determines their diverse conscious properties but rather the different areas of the brain into which they discharge." This is the current point of view, and it seems to be warranted. When an electric stimulus is applied to a given sensory field of the cerebral cortex in a conscious human subject, it produces a sensation of the appropriate modality for that particular locus, that is, a visual sensation from the visual cortex, an auditory sensation from the auditory cortex, and so on (5). When one looks for intrinsic differences in the matrix of these sensory fields that might account for qualitative psychic differences, there is disappointingly little to be found. Slight variations in the size, number, arrangement, and interconnections of the nerve cells have been demonstrated, but as far as psychoneural correlations are concerned, the more obvious similarities of these sensory fields to each other and to all other cortical fields, including the association and motor areas, seem much more remarkable than are any of the minute differences. Furthermore, sensations as diverse as those of red, black, green, and white, or of touch, cold, warmth, movement, pain, posture, and pressure apparently may arise through activation of the same cortical areas. For these and other reasons the reference of subjective quality to cortical locus, in itself, has little explanatory value. What seems to remain is some kind of differential patterning effects in the brain excitation. We may state, rather vaguely, that it is the difference in the central distribution of impulses that counts.

In short, current brain theory encourages us to try to correlate our subjective psychic experience with the activity of relatively homogeneous nerve-cell units conducting essentially homogeneous impulses through roughly homogeneous cerebral tissue. To match the multiple dimensions of mental experience we can only point to a limitless variation in the spatiotemporal patterning of nerve impulses. The difference between one mental state and another is accordingly believed to depend upon variance in the timing and distribution of nerve excitations, not upon differences in quality among the individual impulses.

On the foregoing points there is comparative agreement (6, 7, 8). When we proceed to the question of exactly how conscious meaning is related to the spatiotemporal patterning of brain excitation, all certainty is lost and we enter an area of free speculation. The oldest, simplest, and still the most common notion on this matter holds that brain patterns resemble in form, and in a sense copy in miniature, outside objects and those of consciousness. For example, in the visual perception of a simple geometric figure like a triangle, the brain pattern is considered to be, at least roughly and with certain qualifications, triangular in form. This doctrine, formally called *psychoneural isomorphism* (9), has been extended to correlations in intensity, and in temporal organization as well as in spatial patterning. It appears to receive some direct support in the anatomical evidence that the sensory surfaces, such as the retina, skin, cochlea, and so on, are in fact projected onto the brain centers according to an orderly topographic plan.

In a corollary of this hypothesis adopted particularly by the Gestalt school of psychology (9, 10, 11, 12) it is contended that subjective experience is not correlated with the orthodox neural excitations traveling along fiber pathways, as commonly supposed, but rather with secondary electrical fields and currents which these excitations create in the brain tissue. The secondary electrical patterns, with their "field forces," are conceived to be massive and to spread through and between the nerve cells and fibers, pervading the cerebral tissue as a volume conductor. Unlike the scattered array of separated impulses from which they are generated, these mass patterns are unified and continuous in nature and therefore more like the patterns of subjective experience. This added correspondence in continuity and unity, along with the postulated similarities in form, intensity, and temporal patterning already mentioned, is believed to alleviate the discrepancy between neural and psychic processes.

Isomorphism, as has been stated by Boring (6), represents the most natural and naive way of dealing with mind-brain relations. It is implied unintentionally in a great deal of scientific as well as lay thinking about brain function, especially where perception, imagery, or memory is involved. For example, the neuro-anatomist unwittingly works on this premise when he searches the brain for fiber pathways to unite the two halves of the visual field, which—inconveniently for the concept of isomorphism—are projected separately to opposite hemispheres of the cerebral cortex.

When the philosophic and logical basis of isomorphism is examined, its seeming metaphysical solace tends to dissolve, and it becomes difficult to see how anything is gained by having the neural processes copy the contents of consciousness. Furthermore, recent experiments designed specifically to test the importance of the postulated field forces in cerebral organization have failed to disclose any significant influence of such factors (13, 14). Finally, it seems to me that our general knowledge of brain structure and physiology has for many years been quite sufficient to rule out any possibility that cerebral processes duplicate, even remotely, the patterns of subjective experience. This point is amplified in some detail below.

Other current theories of perception based more closely on the classical concepts of brain physiology ignore or deny any need for psychoneural isomorphism. In an effort to account for the retention of perceptual habits following destruction of major portions of the brain areas involved in learning, Lashley (15) has suggested that incoming sensory excitations may spread outwardly in waves that travel along the homogeneous fiber feltwork of the cortex. These spreading waves are presumed to set up widespread interference patterns such that any visual figure—a triangle, for example—becomes translated in the brain into a multi-reduplicated "scotch-plaid" type of pattern extending over the entire cortical area. All correspondence in shape with the original figure is lost in the reduplicated brain patterns.

Another hypothesis which has been proposed to account for our knowledge of universals and the perception of auditory and visual forms (16) postulates a scanning function to the alpha brain rhythm, which, as it passes up and down through the successive layers of the cortex, is supposed to bring about an enlargement and reduction inversely of the incoming sensory patterns. The authors of this theory expressly deny that the spatiotemporal distribution of brain excitations representing a given figure need resemble the actual figure in any simple way.

A third, rather different picture of the perceptual process is proposed by Hebb (17). Convinced that visual perception occurs beyond the sensory receiving area of the cortex, he has attempted to follow the sensory pattern deeper into the brain. The type of excitation process arrived at, although vague in actual detail, retains even less resemblance to the original stimulus pattern than in the two foregoing theories.

In these and other hypotheses of perception it is assumed, in opposition to the tenets of isomorphism, that sensory stimuli become transformed in the brain into patterns of excitation that need not resemble in any way either the original stimulus or the contents of consciousness. The brain is presumed to work with a kind of code of its own, in which the symbols bear no direct correspondence to the mental experiences they represent.

With the doctrine of psychoneural isomorphism rejected along with that of specific nerve energies, some such codal scheme has seemed to be the only remaining alternative. The problem is thereby reduced to that of discovering the correct nature of a brain code based on the patterning of homogeneous nerve impulses. Even these restrictions have continued to leave a wide range for speculation. Advancements in neurology and psychology in the past several decades have tended progressively to limit this range, but its boundaries have again been widened of late by contributions from the field of computing-machine and signal engineering. Again one can find estimations of the contents of consciousness based on the total number of possible combinations and permutations of neuron elements. Other writers would code mental information into individual neurons, and still others into their protein molecules. The scope and diversity of opinion to be found in the current literature reflect our general confusion and almost complete lack of guiding principles.

Whereas the doctrine of psychoneural isomorphism has purported to bridge the mind-brain gap through principles of similarity and correspondence, the various "coding" schemes leave one with no basis whatever for resolving the problem. Even the most neurologically sophisticated of these latter hypotheses, as now stated, seem only to exaggerate rather than to minimize the mind-brain dichotomy. Perhaps as a hangover from early behaviorism, many investigators have continued to pride themselves on a deliberate policy of ignoring entirely any questions that touch upon the relation of subjective experience and neural activity.

The following comment of Charles Sherrington (18) remains as valid today as when he wrote it more than eighteen years ago: "We have to regard the relation of mind to brain as still not merely unsolved, but still devoid of a basis for its very beginning." It is not a solution we aspire to but only a basis on which to begin.

A DIFFERENT APPROACH TO THE PROBLEM

A tentative attempt is made in the following discussion to point out and to justify another approach to the interpretation and understanding of mental activity. So far, only the vague outlines of the scheme are discernible. Even these outlines, however, if they could be verified, would help considerably to orient our efforts and would automatically eliminate much misguided speculation.

The proposed scheme rests on a view of brain function which was most nearly approximated in the old motor theory of thought, now largely abandoned. Despite its recognized shortcomings and errors, this forsaken offspring of behaviorism taken in combination with the pragmatism of C. S. Pierce (19) possibly holds the key to a comprehension of brain function far advanced beyond anything developed subsequently. An analysis of our current thinking will show that it tends to suffer generally from a failure to view mental activities in their proper relation, or even in any relation, to motor behavior. The remedy lies in further insight into the relationship between the sensori-associative functions of the brain on the one hand and its motor activity on the other. In order to achieve this insight, our present one-sided preoccupation with the sensory avenues to the study of mental processes will need to be supplemented by increased attention to the motor patterns, and especially to what can be inferred from these regarding the nature of the associative and sensory functions. In a machine, the output is usually more revealing of the internal organization that is the input. Similarly in the case of our thinking apparatus an examination of its terminal operations and finished products may be more enlightening than any amount of analysis of the transport of raw materials into it.

Only after we have attained some understanding of the way in which the sensory and thought processes become transformed into motor activity, can we hope to comprehend their meaning and plan of organization. Only then can valid working principles be found to curb and to guide future theorizing.

Utilization of this motor approach immediately helps us to view the brain objectively for what it is, namely, a mechanism for governing motor activity. Its primary function is essentially the transforming of sensory patterns into patterns of motor coordination. Herein lies a fundamental basis for the interpretation, direct or indirect, of all higher brain processes including the mental functions. At first thought such statements will probably seem most short-sighted and unsatisfactory. Nevertheless, for purposes of scientific analysis, a perspective of this kind seems necessary, and we may turn now to an attempt to justify it.

Partial support is found in phylogenetic considerations which indicate that the vertebrate brain was designed primitively for the regulation of overt behavior rather than for mental performance. As one descends the vertebrate scale, purely mental activity becomes increasingly insignificant compared with overt response. Among the salamanders and lower fishes, where thought processes are presumably negligible, the bulk of the nervous apparatus is clearly concerned with the management of motor activity. To the extent that sensation and perception are evident, these would appear to serve directly for the guidance of response. From the fishes to man there is apparent only a gradual refinement and elaboration of brain mechanisms with nowhere any radical alteration of the fundamental operating principles. In man as in the salamander the primary business of the brain continues to be the governing, directly or indirectly, of overt behavior.

Overt behavior, upon analysis, we find to be constituted almost entirely of patterns of muscular contraction. It follows that the principal function of the nervous system is the coordinated innervation of the musculature. Its fundamental anatomical plan and working principles are understandable only on these terms.

Further support for this point of view may be found in the study of brain architecture. One searches the cerebrum in vain for any structures that seem to be designed for the purpose of forming, cataloguing, storing, or emanating copies or representations of the outside world (see p. 418). If any scheme or plan at all is evident in the complicated fiber associations and nuclear interconnections of the brain, it is a design patterned throughout for governing excitation of the "final common (motor) pathways." Such information as is now available regarding physiological functions of the various brain centers correlates with the anatomical data to support the same thesis.

To the neurologist, regarding the brain from an objective, analytical standpoint, it is readily apparent that the sole product of brain function is motor coordination. To repeat: *the entire output of our thinking machine consists of nothing but patterns of motor coordination.* The neurohumoral and glandular components may be disregarded in this discussion. We may also disregard the various by-products of brain activity such as heat, electric potentials, carbon dioxide, and other metabolites released into the blood stream, cerebrospinal fluid, and surrounding tissues.

This classification of the electric potentials as an irrelevant by-product rather than an important end-product of brain activity requires some comment, inasmuch as certain authors have considered these to be the essential correlates of consciousness. It is well established that brain activity generates electrical currents and potential changes which vary greatly in rate and amplitude. These phenomena extend well beyond the confines of the brain and may be recorded readily at the surface of the scalp. It would be difficult or impossible at this point to furnish irrefutable proof that the manufacture of these electrical changes is not a major object of cerebral activity. However, many reasons for doubting it, both direct and implied, will be found throughout the present discussion.

In our scheme these stray mass potentials have no more special function or meaning than have the similar electrical currents that pervade the entire body whenever the hearts beats, muscles contract, and so on. There is no evidence that they react back upon the processes that produce them nor otherwise influence these processes in any significant fashion. Brain organization, we suspect, is maintained in spite of these secondary electrical effects, not because of them. In a conscious patient with brain exposed under local anaesthesia it should not be difficult to pass electric currents through a sensory field of the cortex during perceptual tests. We would anticipate no functional disturbance provided the currents were maintained within the normal physiological limits. In so far as electrical changes do operate directly in the conduction of nerve impulses, synaptic transmission, maintenance of excitatory thresholds, and so forth, they constitute an essential part of the brain function itself and are not to be classed as one of its end-products.

The layman naturally assumes the major work of the brain to be the manufacture of ideas, sensations, images, and feelings, the storage of memories, and the like, and often expects the physical correlates of these to be some kind of aural end-product phosphorescing within the cortex or emanating from its convolutions. These subjective phenomena may, however, be regarded as phases of brain function itself, not products of it. Scientific analysis has failed to disclose any output at the cerebral level other than the miscellaneous by-products mentioned above. Excepting these, the entire activity of the brain, so far as science can determine, yields nothing but motor adjustment. The only significant energy outlet and the only means of expression are over the motor pathways.

Thus, whether accompanied by consciousness or not, all brain excitation has ultimately but one end, to aid in the regulation of motor coordination. Its patterning is determined throughout on this principle. It follows that efforts to discover the neural correlates of consciousness will be more successful when directed on this basis than when guided by arbitrary correlations with psychic experience, stimulus patterns, or outside reality, or by analogies with various types of thinking machines.

The above approach to mental functions may require some shift in our customary perspective on the interrelation of cerebral and motor processes. Instead of regarding motor activity as being subsidiary, that is, something to carry out, serve, and satisfy the demands of the higher centers, we reverse this tendency and look upon the mental activity as only a means to an end, where the end is better regulation of overt response. Cerebration, essentially, serves to bring into motor behavior additional refinement, increased direction toward distant, future goals, and greater overall adaptiveness and survival value. The evolutionary increase in man's capacity for perception, feeling, ideation, imagination, and the like, may be regarded, not so much as an end in itself, as something that has enabled us to behave, to act, more wisely and efficiently.

Perceptions and ideas are found, upon analysis, to have their factual significance and meaning in terms ultimately of overt operation. Their meaning derives from the potential effect, that is, the difference they make or may make in behavior. In both its phylogenetic and ontogenetic histories, mental activity develops out of, and in reference to, overt action.

Actually the interrelation of motor and mental activity is one of cyclic and reciprocal interdependence. However, the nature of the problem and current trends in our thinking make it necessary at this time to emphasize particularly the dependence of the mental upon motor activity.

Any separation of mental and motor processes in the brain would seem to be arbitrary and indefinite. Mental processes are intimately associated with other integrative mechanisms which we are accustomed to recognize as serving for the regulation of motor adjustment. Sensory and associative processes, conscious and unconscious alike, are obliged to merge and interlace in the brain with the motor patterns. There are no boundary planes in the cerebrum to keep the two apart. In many or most situations overt response is guided closely and directly by the excitation patterns of thought and perception. Temporally, therefore, as well as spatially, the mental and the motor patterns must integrate, mesh, and interlock.

The same relationship is indicated in more specific anatomical and physiological observations. The great pyramidal motor pathway from the cerebral cortex is constituted of fibers which arise from many cortical areas, sensory as well as motor. Motor responses may be elicited directly by electrical stimulation of sensory areas, as, for example, the visual and the somesthetic cortex. The extrapyramidal motor outflow from the cerebral cortex likewise arises from associative and sensory cortical fields as well as from those traditionally designated as motor. Excitation patterns in the sensory and associative areas, therefore, have to integrate with patterns in the subcortical motor systems as well as with those in neighboring motor fields.

In brief, we conclude that the unknown cerebral events in psychic experience must necessarily involve excitation patterns so designed that they intermesh in intimate fashion with the motor and premotor patterns. Once this relationship is recognized as a necessary feature of the neural correlates of psychic experience, we can automatically exclude numerous forms of brain code which otherwise might seem reasonable but which fail to meet this criterion.

It follows further that the more we learn about the motor and premotor mechanisms, the more restrictions we add to our working picture of the unknown mental patterns and hence the closer our speculation will be forced to converge toward an accurate description of their true nature.

IMPLICATIONS FOR A THEORY OF PERCEPTION

Past theory and speculation concerning the neural correlates of subjective experience have been based to a large extent upon phenomena of visual pattern perception. For the sake of comparison some further implications of the present thesis may also be illustrated most effectively with reference to the same material. Consider the cerebral excitations which take place, for example, during the visual perception of a simple geometric figure, say a triangle. Of what exactly does the brain process consist, and how is it patterned?

A satisfactory explanation of the neural events involved in this one simple example of visual perception would carry us a long way toward an understanding of cerebral organization and mind-brain relations in general. Several possible types of answer as suggested in isomorphic theory and in other recent theories of perception have already been mentioned above.

By comparison, one arrives at a quite different kind of picture by utilizing the approach advocated earlier in this paper (pp. 409-414). This approach does not lead us to expect in the cerebral process any kind of triangularity, linearity, nor even a unity corresponding to that of the perceived triangle. Nor are we led to seek any kind of codal representation of these. What we are prompted to search for, primarily, is an excitation process so patterned as to bring about a central adjustment that will put the premotor and motor systems into readiness for adaptive response to the given triangle. Reasoning on this principle from the motor mechanism backward, step by step, into the association and sensory centers, one is able to construct a working picture of the brain pattern which, although necessarily vague in the present state of our knowledge, differs significantly in principle from anything obtained by tracing the retinal triangle centralward or by attempts to translate the subjective triangle directly into neural patterns.

If there be any objectively demonstrable fact about perception that indicates the nature of the neural process involved, it is the following: In so far as an organism perceives a given object, it is prepared to respond with reference to it. This preparation-to-respond is absent in an organism that has failed to perceive. In the case of the triangle, a person who perceives it, is ready to point to it, to outline it with his finger, to show its location and orientation in space, to pick it up, describe it, etc. Animals lacking the verbal and symbolic capacities of man illustrate the principle more simply. The perceiving animal is able to avoid or to approach the triangle, to run under it or up one edge of it, to leap to a corner of it or to pick it up in its mouth by one of the points, etc. The presence or absence of adaptive reaction potentialities of this sort, ready to discharge into motor patterns, makes the difference between perceiving and not perceiving.

The preparation-to-respond in perception is a demonstrable fact. All that need be questioned is whether it may not be a consequence of, rather than a part of, the cerebral process which actually constitutes the perception itself. In this regard we may emphasize again that the structure of the brain, as well as what is known of its physiology, discourages any effort to separate the motor from the sensory and associative processes. To the best of our knowledge there is only a gradual merging and transformation of the one into the other, with nothing to suggest where perception might end and motor processes begin. That the preparation for response *is* the perception is suggested by further considerations.

Perception is not correlated with the immediate arrival of stimulus patterns in the sensory receiving areas of the cortex. Compare two persons gazing at the same visual field in which lies a triangle, with only one of them perceiving the triangle. (Failure to perceive elements of the visual field is common enough with respect to ordinary scenes or pictures but is more strikingly illustrated in the case of hidden figures in picture puzzles, *trompe-l'oeil* paintings, ink blots, etc.) In both persons the retinal pattern and its transmission into the visual receiving areas of the brain are essentially identical. Therefore, the mere transmission of sensory patterns into the visual cortex does not, in itself, constitute perception nor is it sufficient to bring it about. This is also suggested in the fact that many of our perceptions involve the combined influence of afferent patterns from more than one sense modality. In the case of vision, postural and kinesthetic factors are regularly involved along with the retinal cues in determining the spatial orientation and stability of "visual" perception. Since these different afferent influences are projected to separate cortical fields, the combined perceptual effect must lie deeper.

Perception is more than the mere passage of sensory patterns into passive brain protoplasm. In the nonperceiving subject the stimulus pattern of the hidden figure may pour into the brain for seconds or even minutes, producing widespread secondary and tertiary effects throughout the nervous system, without the figure's being seen. Something else is needed, something that approaches an active and specific adjustment on the part of the brain.

This fact is indicated in our ability to see the same stair

diagram as if from above or below, or a cube diagram with first one corner extending toward us and then another. The stimulus pattern during the perceptual shift remains constant, as does its projection into the brain. The perceptual shifts must therefore depend on active changes within the brain itself. It should be noted also that these perceptual shifts involve changes in the tendency to respond. When one corner of the cube is nearest, we are ready to react to the cube, to reach for it, handle it, deal with it in these terms. When the other corner seems nearest, our reaction tendencies shift accordingly.

Many other examples can be cited to illustrate the same fact, namely, that perception is basically an implicit preparation to respond. Its function is to prepare the organism for adaptive action. The problem of what occurs in the brain during perception can be attacked much more effectively once this basic principle is recognized.

It follows that it will be necessary to learn something about the nature of those central integrative mechanisms that lead into motor adjustment before we can picure in any detail the neural processes of perception or of other mental activities. Knowledge of the stimulus pattern and its projection into the cerebral cortex is not enough. The patterning of the perceptual process is determined as much by the organization of the central mechanisms as it is by the sensory influx. This is evident in the general tendency to perceive selectively what one is already looking for and expects to see. Carried further this may lead to visual illusions or, in the extreme, to hallucinations. In the latter case, almost the entire organization is determined centrally. Hallucinations constitute further evidence that the psychic experience is not correlated with the discharge of the retinal image into the visual cortex, but depends on subsequent and more complex operations.

It is common to think of visual hallucination and visual imagery as dependent on some kind of central rearousal of an essentially sensory pattern. In the case of the visual image of a triangle, for example, we might postulate a re-excitement in the visual cortex of a triangle or whatever coded pattern—according to our favored theory of perception—the sensory stimulus is presumed to establish there. This would demand the dispatch from somewhere in the centers of an array of discharges patterned somewhat like the original sensory influx. It is difficult to see how such a pattern could be dispatched from anywhere other than from the retina itself. This difficulty is not encountered when we conceive of perception as an incipient preparation for action, with the brain excitation taking the form of a central adjustment leading into response to the figure. Rearousal of this type of pattern from central sources is neurologically feasible.

ISOMORPHISM AND TOPOGRAPHIC PROJECTION IN SENSORY PATHWAYS

The rejection of isomorphism obliges us to find another explanation of the orderly topographic projection of sensory surfaces in the brain. Actually, further thought on the problem will reveal that an orderly anatomical projection fails anyway, under most conditions, to insure even a rough similarity between the brain pattern and that of the perceived figure. To illustrate, consider further the visual perception of a triangle. The brain pattern, in the first place, is split in two because the two halves of the visual field are projected to opposite hemispheres of the brain. The two halves are not neatly drawn apart with a gap between them, but instead the mid-plane of each is reflected laterally away from the other. This is the primitive condition; in man the mid-planes tend to be twisted posteriorly. Although fiber pathways that would serve to unify the visual areas of the two hemispheres have been sought, none has been found.

The triangular pattern is equally divided in the cortex only while the gaze is perfectly centered in the mid-plane of the figure. When the fixation point shifts to either side, the fragments of the triangle projected to each hemisphere change accordingly. As the eyes rove over the triangle from apex to base and from side to side, the shape and also the position of the cortical patterns change radically in each hemisphere. One can compare the effect photographically to a series of multiple exposures of various fragments of a triangle flashed successively with erratic shifting of the center of the figure in each hemisphere.

While this kaleidoscopic series of excitatory changes is taking place in the visual cortex of the brain, the figure of subjective experience remains constant, a unified whole, with a fixed orientation in space. If exactly the same retinal projection patterns were produced, not through eye and head movements but by actual movement of the figure itself while the gaze is kept fixed (as might be done with cinema projection methods), the subjective effect would, of course, be entirely different. With the projection to the visual cortex identical in each instance, the difference in "visual" sensation must be attributed to the difference in the proprioceptive influx from the eye muscles. The importance of proprioception in vision is only mentioned in passing because it illustrates further the impossibility of correlating perceptual experience with the immediate projection of the retinal image to the sensory cortex, as well as the lack of similarity between the form of the perceived triangle and that of the excitatory process in the brain.

Additional dissimilarity is caused by the enlarged cortical representation of the macula of the retina (20). The portion of the figure that falls on the macular area becomes magnified in the brain relative to the rest of the triangle. The resultant warping differs from moment to moment with each change of fixation. And, of course, the flat two-dimensional triangle becomes irregularly folded and twisted when projected upon the fissures and convolutions of the cortex. These latter spatial distortions also are subject to variation with each shift of fixation.

In summary, the topographic projection of the retina upon the cerebral cortex fails to insure any significant similarity in form between the figure of perceptual experience and that of the brain excitations. The possibility of psychoneural isomorphism is even more remote with respect to the other senses. Consider, for example, stereognosis and the perception of the three-dimensional form of a triangular block of wood placed in the hands. The cutaneous discharges projected to the cortex from the palms of the hands and the moving fingers as they explore the surface contours, already lacking any resemblance to triangularity, must further be integrated and interpreted at each instant with reference to the train of postural and kinesthetic cues entering from each of the many moving joints. The result is a brain process the configuration of which is hopelessly removed from that of the object perceived.

Topographic projection is explainable on other bases than that of mediating isomorphic representation. It is significant that the same type of fiber projection is found in the motor and associative parts of the brain and also in nonspatial sensory systems like that of smell and possibly taste. Certainly topographic projection is quite comprehensible as a reflection of the developmental processes of neurogenesis (3, 4) and would seem to be a simple framework on which to build more refined structural organization.

If topographic projection could be eliminated by random displacement of the nerve cell bodies, at the same time maintaining all the original synaptic connections and the conduction-time intervals, complete functional disorganization should follow according to isomorphic field theory. On the other hand, little or no disturbance would be expected from the standpoint of orthodox circuit theory.

IMPRESSED SENSORY PATTERNS VERSUS OPERATIONAL ADJUSTMENT

The major fluctuations in the excitation patterns of the visual cortex caused by ocular movements in perception are accompanied by simultaneous shifts in the nonvisual kinesthetic influx. These two inputs integrate with activity already going on in the brain centers to produce a relatively stable over-all adjustment to the perceived triangle. The constancy of the subjective experience derives, not from any constancy in the sensory patterns impressed on the cortex, but from the integrative effect of their more central resultant. This does not mean that the subjective constancy depends strictly upon the excitation of a final invariant group or pattern of central neurons. It is the functional, or operational, effect of the input patterns upon the dynamics of cerebral adjustment that counts. The over-all adjustment might have a constant functional or subjective value even though the particular neurons excited and the spatial and temporal patterning were to vary from experience to experience or to fluctuate radically during a single perceptual span. Waning in one part of the pattern, for example, might be compensated by increased intensity in another, or by the entry of new excitatory elements, to preserve the over-all effect.

It must be emphasized that the constancy and other subjective properties of the brain process are not to be evaluated in terms of sensory geometry or of even a closely related frame of reference as is our usual inclination. An entirely new frame of reference applies, one that is based ultimately on motor adjustment.

We may arrive at a better conception of the neural events in visual perception if we imagine our sample triangle as being constructed gradually in time out of dots and dashes that are passed successively into the brain to produce each its individual vertical effect. This may seem contradictory to demonstrated Gestalt principles in perception but actually it is contradictory only to some of the secondary inferences drawn therefrom regarding brain physiology. It is well established by tachistoscopic studies that a complicated pattern is not perceived in full detail with the initial projection of the pattern into the brain. The total picture comes gradually; at first the broader and bolder features are seen and then, by steps, further details. The perception of simultaneous *spatial* relations thus commonly depends upon *temporal* organization in the brain processes.

Consider the neural adjustments involved in perceiving a single dot on the wall before you. The stream of impulses entering the midbrain and cortex will first set up responses that tend to center the eye on the dot. This may involve head as well as eye movements and possibly the entire musculature. Immediately with perception of the dot comes readiness to locate it and to respond to it. Widespread facilitating and inhibiting effects are invoked in many parts of the brain. The cerebral mechanisms have become set for a certain class of reactions. This particular set will automatically exclude an infinite number of other reaction possibilities. Probably your eyes will not remain fixed upon the dot but will stay around the wall in its vicinity. As a result the stream of excitations in the brain will drift about the visual cortex. Nevertheless the dot appears to stay fixed meanwhile, and you remain oriented with reference to it.

Now suppose another dot is added in the neighborhood of the first. This sets up another stream of impulses which in turn arouses responses somewhat similar to those of the first dot. The adjustments from the first largely remain, however, and essentially the result is an additional adjustment superimposed upon the first.

The addition of a third dot sets up other reactions that further modify the adjustments already present. There are now three streams of impulses passing through the straite cortex. As the eyes move about from one dot to another and to neighboring points on the wall, the spatial patterning of the three streams of impulses through the cortex varies greatly. Not only do the three foci of excitation flash about in different positions in the cortical field, but the number projected in each hemisphere will fluctuate from none to three. The simultaneous spatial interrelationships thus undergo continuous variation in the cortex so that it is impossible to think of any type of horizontal "field" force binding these streams of impulses together in the constant pattern that is perceived.

To the three dots may be added two more, and so on. Then the dots can be closed gradually by dashes and more dots until the triangle is completed. The cerebral adjustment to a single dot meanwhile will have been built upon and modified into an adjustment to respond to a partial and finally a whole triangle. The sensory input must be pictured throughout as influencing and modifying premotor and motor patterns of excitation that are already present. One may say that the sensory input is perceived and acquires conscious meaning only in so far as it modifies preceding patterns of central activity. The foregoing approach to the perceptual process is suggested merely to aid in visualizing the neural events as an active meaningful adjustment, rather than as simply an impression or passive registration in brain tissue of a pattern of sensory excitation.

By the same procedure one might build a square or a hexagon. Although the first several dots in each case might be identical and arouse the same response, the final adjustment will differ according to the pattern completed. As emphasized by the Gestalt school, it is the over-all pattern that counts, both in the perceived figure and in the brain process; but this is no reasons for inferring isomorphic correspondence between the two, nor for assuming that it is the secondary mass electrical disturbances that constitute the important phase of the brain process.

UNITY, NUMBER, AND SIZE IN PSYCHONEURAL CORRELATION

When a visual figure is perceived as a unified whole, it is natural to suppose that the brain pattern also possesses a corresponding unity. In theories of the codal as well as of the isomorphic type a given unit in brain process is commonly supposed to represent a given unit of psychic experience.

We must, however, ask in what manner the brain process, as in the perception of a triangle, should be unified. Must the discharging neurons be side by side, unseparated by resting or inhibited cells? Or is it enough if their fiber processes link with one another? Or perhaps it is only the electric potentials they generate that must meet or overlap? Reference has been made above to the suggestion that conscious experience is correlated with secondary electrical changes that are massive, field-like, and continuous in nature. These very properties which would appear to preserve physiological unity, however, would at the same time seem to preclude any finely etched perceptual effects involving thin lines, abrupt contrasts, and sharp boundaries. The concept also fails to account for the unity of the visual scene, the projection of which is split in half in the cortex with the mid-lines directed outwardly and posteriorly. Discovery of duplicate projections of the retina via the pulvinar, colliculus, and so on, will hardly simplify matters. Actually we have yet to find any satisfactory criterion of unity in the neural processes that can account for the unity in psychic experience.

In the scheme proposed here it is contended that unity in subjective experience does not derive from any kind of parellel unity in the brain processes. Conscious unity is conceived rather as a functional or operational derivative. In perception it means only that the brain becomes adjusted to deal with the perceived object as a unit. There need be little or nothing of a unitary nature about the physiological processes themselves. The essential parts of the preparation-for-response may be rather widespread through the brain with nowhere a compact unified pattern of discharge that represents "triangle." The retention of perceptual and other habits following extensive brain lesions (15) and the seeming "equipotentiality" of cortical areas become less difficult to account for with such a concept of cerebral organization.

Closely related to the problem of unity is that of number. Consider the perception of two, three, or more triangles present in the visual field simultaneously. The brain process might be pictured as a corresponding number of excitation patterns each representing "triangle," in either isomorphic or signal-code terms. Actually, in the cerebral preparation for response to a number of items there is no need for a corresponding number of unitary excitation processes. Three triangles viewed simultaneously tend to be perceived together as one larger unit. The extent to which this unification occurs will vary, of course, with many factors, but in any case the brain process will not be found to be anything like a mere tripling of that which occurs in the perceiving of a single triangle. Consider the motor patterns involved in handling one tennis ball compared with those used in handling three tennis balls—or to be consistent, make it triangular blocks instead of spheres. A comparison of these motor processes at the cerebral level, even though vague, will be more suggestive of the principles of neural patterning involved in perceiving groups of items than will inferences based on attempts to trace the stimulus figures centralward.

The same principles apply to the perception of size. Compare the brain processes involved in preceiving a large and a small triangle. Are we to infer that the two are similar except that the former is larger? According to our present thesis there need be little or no correlation between the size of an object in perception and the size of the correlated brain pattern. The adjustment of the brain to deal with a large triangle will differ in certain respects, but it need not cover a larger volume of cerebral tissue. The nature of the differences is perhaps better indicated again by comparing the motor patterns involved in handling a small and a large triangular block. The motor-pool discharge in the two cases will differ with respect to timing and intensity in an extremely complex fashion but the size of the triangles is not reflected in any direct way in the extensity of the central excitations. This applies as well to the premotor firing and to all excitation following the initial sensory projection into the brain.

SENSORY EQUIVALENCE

Sensory equivalence is illustrated in the ability of an animal to recognize and to respond similarly to patterns of the same configuration even though these differ markedly in size from the one used in training. It has been almost universally inferred that some kind of brain mechanism is needed such that the equivalent sensory patterns, after filtering through the cerebral cortex, become funneled in one way or another into a given invariant central excitation regardless of their starting size and position at the sensory surface. Similar reasoning has been applied to problems of generalization and abstraction.

According to our present scheme, brain function is not organized on these principles at all. Psychic meaning is not so direct a reflection of corresponding properties in the brain mechanisms. Subjective meaning depends on the over-all *functional* effects of the physiological processes, not upon their copying or representing in code form the attributes of the stimulus. Further, the brain process must be viewed basically as an *adjustment to* a perceived or imagined item, not a reduplication or representation of it.

The "equivalent" responses of the rat to a large and to a smaller triangle, for example, whether it be jumping at doors or selecting alleys, may have little in common as far as the physiological details of the motor discharge are concerned. The same is true of the more central or perceptual part of the brain process. It is only in the over-all functional or operational effect that their essential similarity resides. In the centers as well as at the sensory surfaces the patterning counts. In the centers, however, it is not a copy-type or geometrical kind of pattern that is involved, but a much more intricate one fashioned in accordance with the complex web of brain pathways and designed to work through this medium into motor adjustment. The central excitation may vary considerably in its geometric, spatiotemporal, and other properties while maintaining invariant or equivalent functional value as measured with reference to motor adjustment. In other words the same functional effect and the same psychic meaning *may* be obtained from brain patterns the neuronal details of which differ considerably on different occasions. Not only may different neurons be involved, as many configurationists would agree, but more than this, the configuration of neurons may vary.

In the above examples, the visual perception of a triangle is assumed to be built up in the nervous system as an active operational adjustment that puts the brain in readiness to respond to the triangle. Although the general adjustment may involve actual motor changes, the core of the perceptual process in the higher centers is not itself a motor pattern. It is more premotor or better pre-premotor in nature, owing to the hierarchical plan of neural organization. This continued emphasis on the motor approach to mental activity should definitely not be taken to imply that subjective experience resides within any motor reaction or within the motor system. If obliged to localize the conscious experience, we could only suggest vaguely those brain centers midway functionally between the sensory input and motor output, where the coordinated action of the entire motor system may be governed as an integrated whole through the combined influences of most of the sensory excitations and mnemonic traces. This vital focus of neural organization might possibly be centered in the brain stem primarily, as suggested in the observations of Bailey (21), Penfield (5), and others, rather than in the cerebral cortex itself.

It has been indicated repeatedly that the brain excitation is neither a copy nor a codal representation of subjective experience. Psychic meaning is presumed to be intrinsic in the brain organization itself, such that once the brain patterns are fully understood, no additional "key" should be necessary to interpret the subjective meaning.

Much of what has been said above with reference to pattern perception applies to other forms of mental activity. Thinking itself may be regarded as a prolongation and elaboration of perception embodying additional factors such as insight, trial-and-error processes, reasoning, and especially the use of symbols. Essentially it is implicit, symbolic preparatory adjustment without commitment in overt action. The cerebral excitations are presumed to be patterned throughout with ultimate—but not necessarily direct—reference to the motor and premotor systems. This holds even where the thought process is entirely symbolic. In the person "thinking out loud," in whom we get some indication of the nature of the inner activity, it is noteworthy that the overflow into the motor periphery is clearly of such pattern as to effect coordinated innervation of the musculature.

Perhaps the mental experiences most difficult to account for in the terms proposed here are the immediate sensory qualities. We have no satisfactory explanation of these on any basis as yet, and it is not easy at present to see how the conscious qualities of sensation relate to their operational effects in the motor system. Of all psychic functions, the sensations are farthest removed from the motor side. They are genetically predetermined and involve a detector and discriminatory type of cerebral adjustment that has little direct commitment in motor activity.

Particularly in the case of sensory qualities it is tempting to have recourse to some form of specific nerve energies. For the present, however, it would seem more fruitful to assume that the difference between, for example, taste and tactile sensations does not derive from any difference in the quality of the individual impulses but rather from differences in the way in which the two afferent systems are linked into the central organization, and from the differential dynamic effects thereby secured. That the sensations have emerged in the course of evolution as attributes of mere complexity alone in neural organization seems less likely than that each sense modality depends upon a specific design the meaning of which may become apparent once the neurological analysis is carried far enough. Sensations certainly appear to function directly in the guidance and control of motor adjustment, and we can only hope that when the sensory regulation of motor coordination becomes more thoroughly understood, it will be possible to see where the sensory qualities fit into the rest of the scheme.

One need not feel distressed at the suggestion that all our noblest and most aesthetic psychic experiences may be found, on analysis, to consist merely of brain patterns designed, directly or indirectly, for the adjustment of muscular contraction and glandular secretion. This detracts nothing from their meaning and importance. In the same way our finest deeds consist only of patterns of muscle-fiber twitches, our greatest printed passages only of ink marks on paper, while our most ravishing music, as pointed out by William James, is but the rasping of hairs from a horse's tail on the intestines of a cat. Significance and meaning in brain function do not derive from the intrinsic protoplasmic or other analytic aspects of neural excitation, but rather from their higher-order functional and operational effects as these work upon successive brain states, upon the motor system, and thereby into the environment, and back into the brain. We should not expect to find that a single neuron or an isolated patch of neurons, or even a cortical center, could sense, feel, experience, or think anything in isolation. These psychic properties we envisage as depending upon a specific design and complexity in the vortex of neural activity, generally involving a reciprocal interplay of many parts.

It will be evident that our scheme leaves much unanswered. It is inevitable that the reader, like the writer, will find it wanting and unsatisfactory in many respects. At best it can only be offered tentatively as a possible basis on which to begin to describe the neural events of mental experience.

SUMMARY

At the core of all metaphysical problems stands the mind-brain relationship, real understanding of which could have vast influence on all the ultimate aims and values of mankind. The logical, philosophic, and semantic approaches to the question, though employed intensively by some of the greatest of human minds, have repeatedly failed to yield a satisfactory resolution of the problem. Hope for further progress is seen to lie in a scientific analysis of the neural correlates of psychic experience, and the present discussion has been restricted primarily to this essentially neurological problem.

Present-day science is quite at a loss even to begin to describe the neural events involved in the simplest forms of mental activity. Conjecture has been vague and varied, ranging from theories in which the brain patterns are supposed to parallel and to copy roughly the contents of consciousness, to a series of codal schemes in which psychic experience is represented by implication in various brain codes with no other meaningful psychoneural relation indicated.

An approach to the interpretation of higher brain functions is here suggested in which motor adjustment, rather than stimulus patterns or the contents of subjective experience, figures predominantly as a proper frame of reference for understanding the organization, meaning, and significance of brain excitation. Such an approach would seem to guarantee at least a better understanding of the brain processes themselves. Whether this in turn may help to resolve the baffling mind-brain enigma remains to be seen.

REFERENCES

1. James, W. *The principles of psychology.* New York: Holt, 1890..
2. Hering, E. *Memory: Lectures on the specific energies of the nervous system.* Chicago: Open Court, 1913.
3. Weiss, P. A. *Genetic Neurology.* Chicago: Univer. of Chicago, 1950.
4. Sperry, R. W. Mechanisms of neural maturation, in S. Stevens (Ed.), *Handbook of experimental psychology.* New York: Wiley, 1951.
5. Penfield, W. The cerebral cortex in man. I. The cerebral cortex and consciousness. *Arch. Neurol. Psychiat.*, 1938, **40**, 417-442.
6. Boring, E. G. *Sensation and perception in the history of experimental psychology.* New York: Appleton-Century, 1942.
7. Adrian, E. D. *The physical background of perception.* Oxford: Clarendon, 1946.
8. Clark, W. LeGros. *Anatomical pattern as the essential basis of sensory discrimination.* Springfield, Ill.: Charles C Thomas, 1947.
9. Kohler, W. *Gestalt psychology.* New York: Liveright, 1929.
10. Koffka, K. *Principles of Gestalt psychology.* New York: Harcourt, Brace, 1935.

11. Kohler, W., & Wallach, H. Figural after-effects: An investigation of visual responses. *Proc. Amer. phil. Soc.*, 1944, 88, 269-357.
12. Kohler, W., & Held, R. The cortical correlate of pattern vision. *Science*, 1949, 110, 414-419.
13. Sperry, R. W. Cerebral regulation of motor coordination in monkeys following multiple transection of sensorimotor cortex. *J. Neurophysiol.*, 1947, 10, 275-294.
14. Lashley, K. S., Chow, K, & Semmes, J. An examination of the electrical field theory of cerebral integration. *Psychol. Rev.*, 1951, 58, 123-136.
15. Lashley, K. S. The problem of cerebral organization in vision. In H. Klüver (Ed.), Visual mechanisms. *Biol. Symposia*, 1942, 7, 301-322.
16. Pitts, W., & McCulloch, W. S. How we know universals: The perception of auditory and visual forms. *Bull. Math. Biophysics*, 1947, 9, 127-147.
17. Hebb, D. O. *The organization of behavior: A neuropsychological theory*. New York: Wiley, 1949.
18. Sherrington, C. S. *The brain and its mechanism*. Cambridge, England: Cambridge Univer., 1933.
19. Pierce, C. Illustrations of the logic of science. II. How to make our ideas clear. *Pop. Sci. Monthly*, 1878, 12, 286-302.
20. Polyak, S. L. *The retina*. Chicago: Univer. of Chicago, 1941.
21. Bailey, P. Concerning the functions of the cerebral cortex. *J. nerv. ment. Dis.*, 1949, 110, 369-378.

[ADDENDA FROM THE ORIGINAL PRINTING OF THIS ARTICLE: IN REFERENCE TO THE AUTHOR: *Hull Anatomical Laboratory, University of Chicago.* ACKNOWLEDGEMENT: *For the basic concept developed in this discussion concerning the relation of mental processes to motor adjustment the author is indebted to the unpublished lectures and informal teachings of the late Professor R. H. Stetson, chairman of the department of psychology at Oberlin College, 1909-1939.*]